DATE DUE			

INVITATION
TO
CHEMICAL RESEARCH

E. Emmet Reid

INVITATION TO

CHEMICAL RESEARCH

E. EMMET REID, Ph.D., LL.D.

Professor of Chemistry, Emeritus, Johns Hopkins University

FRANKLIN

PUBLISHING COMPANY, INC.

Palisade, New Jersey

©
1961
FRANKLIN PUBLISHING COMPANY, INC.
Palisade   New Jersey

Second Printing, 1963
Third Printing, 1970

Printed in the United States of America

Foreword

The publication of Dr. Reid's *Invitation to Chemical Research* is timely. It appears at the start of a decade during which there will be a continuing upsurge in research and education in the sciences. The President's Science Advisory Committee has stated recently that American science must double and redouble, in size and strength, in the next generation. A larger fraction of the youth of America must select careers in science. Selection of a career is generally made during the high school or early college period of a student's education and is strongly influenced by the teacher. It is therefore imperative that those who teach science know their subject and receive appropriate reward and recognition. Research is an aid in the growth of the teacher. Research experience, at an early stage in a student's education, may be decisive in his selection of science as his life's work. Increased incentives and opportunities are being provided to young students to enable them to obtain experience in research. After a student has expressed the desire and demonstrated the capacity to become a scientist he should be ensured the opportunity to fulfill his promise. Furthermore, every scientist, qualified by training and experience to make significant scientific contributions, should be given the opportunity to do so.

Research is fundamental to graduate education. Research is creative. In the words of Dr. Vannevar Bush: "There is no greater satisfaction than comes from personal creation of new knowledge, from knowing by one's own efforts what no man has known before."

The author of this book loves research. He has demonstrated this love by the numerous contributions he has made to chemistry through research which he has conducted over a period of sixty years. Also, for two decades he made periodic visits to a number of selected colleges and universities in the southeast section of the country to promote the interest of faculty members and students in chemical research. This, too, was a work of love. His enthusiasm for research is contagious and many students have been stimulated to seek careers in chemistry as a result of their contacts with him.

It is hoped that many readers of this book will accept Dr. Reid's invitation so that they, too, can experience the satisfaction and realize the opportunities which result from creative research.

WALTER R. KIRNER

Program Director for Chemistry
National Science Foundation

TABLE OF CONTENTS

CHAPTER 3

INCENTIVES

CHAPTER 4

FINDING PROBLEMS

CHAPTER 9

MAKING NEW COMPOUNDS

CHAPTER 10

RESEARCH IN ORGANIC ANALYSIS

Preface

It has been great to have been living in this amazing half century and to have seen the explosive expansion of research and the consequent advances in science and technology, greater than all that have gone before, which have changed the material world so radically and have brought living conditions to such undreamed-of heights.

I am writing this book as a personal invitation to you and you and you to take part in the research which will show the way to advances beyond our present dreams. Some of you may be able to devote your total energies to it, some of you may take it as an avocation, but I hope that all will adopt the research attitude, relying on logical conclusions drawn from established facts, rather than on the assertions of others.

This book is largely a restatement of the ideas set forth in *Introduction to Organic Research*, which I published in 1924. By repetition I am trying to emphasize their importance. Emphasis is put on the fact that research is not magic but a combination of careful experimenting, close observing, and logical thinking, the result being proportional to the quality and quantity of these simple ingredients. I am paying particular attention to the development of research in chemistry in the United States since I am a chemist and happen to live here. No disparagement is intended of research in other sciences or in other countries. I have drawn illustrations from my own research, not because I think them important, but because I have inside information as to the thinking behind them.

My thanks are due to those whose names appear on sections in this book and also to other friends, too numerous to mention, who in one way or another have helped in the preparation of this volume.

Baltimore, Maryland
June 27, 1961

E. EMMET REID

INVITATION
TO
CHEMICAL RESEARCH

LOVE MAKES THE WORLD GO ROUND . . .
RESEARCH MAKES IT GO FORWARD.

1 ∎ Research the basis of progress

THE PARAMOUNT IMPORTANCE OF RESEARCH

The cave man did not have movies, automobiles, zippers, airplanes, juke boxes, or electric refrigerators. We have these and thousands of other things which contribute to our high standard of living. The cave man was surrounded by all the raw materials required for making all these things. The laws of mechanics and of chemistry were in full operation. Then, as now, electrons were dancing around ready to carry messages through the air or under the sea.

Why such a vast difference in the things we have when there is so slight a difference in what we are? The cave man was smart enough to make a living and raise a family under conditions under which a modern man would hardly last a week. He probably laughed at some of the same jokes that are now current. His daughter was just as skilful in landing her man as the modern debutante. For only a fraction of man's existence

3

on the earth do we have accurate history, but in this time the
smart men of any period have been about as smart as any before
or since, and the dumb have been just about as dumb. Demos-
thenes was as good an orator as William Jennings Bryan. Jacob
was as good a trader as any of his descendants. When I visited
the Louvre I saw artists copying Mona Lisa. If you go there
today you will probably find the same. Titian and Raphael still
rank high. Architects still copy the lines of the Parthenon. Moses
stands high as a lawgiver and leader.

To make anything you must know how to make it.
The cave man had everything that we have today except the
know-how. Our amazing industrial development has been made
possible by the vast accumulation of scientific knowledge and
technical know-how, every single item of which is the result of
someone's observing, thinking, and experimenting, that is, of
research. The term "research" is here used in its broadest sense
as applying to the efforts of any individual who is searching and
searching again, prying into the unknown, trying with the means
at his disposal to learn more about his environment or creating
new means to improve it. Kings strutted around and demanded
homage from their fellows, but it was the few individuals who,
by observation and experiments, discovered better ways of doing
things who led mankind to better living.

The desire for more seems to be universal with all
creatures, from the highest to the lowest of creation. The hunting
dog probably dreams of more foxes to chase; the lion goes in
search of more animals to kill. Men of all ages have wanted more
food, more clothing, more of everything. Some have been willing
to work harder to get more, but many have found it easier to
take it from others. So far as we know the dog does not dream of
superior foxes but only of more of the same kind, and it is the
same way with the lion. It appears to be an exclusively human
characteristic to imagine and want better things as well as more.
Now and then there has been an individual who had a vision
of a better way of obtaining things or even of better things that
might be made and, inspired by such a vision, he has set about
thinking and contriving to materialize his vision. Such indi-

viduals have added to human knowledge and made progress possible. Through the centuries, fortunately, there have been thousands of researchers, but relative to the billions of people who have benefitted by their research, they have been few. It is to these few that so many owe so much.

This book is concerned only with the material benefits of research because they are tangible and their direct relation to research can be traced. I have ridden in an oxcart, a horse-drawn buggy, a railroad train, a ship, and an airplane, and can compare their speed and comfort. Research has provided *"better* things for better living" and has made the living more comfortable, but what has it done for the one who lives? Some of the mental delights from research will be mentioned in chapter 3. "Ye shall know the truth and the truth will make you free." Knowledge gained by research has made us free from the blind terror of yellow-fever epidemics, as an example. Knowing the causes of other diseases has enabled us to combat them.

To us the crowning achievement of research is adding years to our lives. A child born in the United States in 1900 had a life expectancy of 47 years; one born this year may expect to live to 70. Counting the first 23 years as preparation for life, raising the expectancy from 47 to 70 doubles the productive period of life.

Research has given to the 180,000,000 of our citizens 4,000,000,000 years of life.

The real dates of history are those of scientific discoveries, not the accession of kings or the outbreak of revolutions. The discovery of the extraction of iron from the ore meant more for the human race than the founding of Rome, and the invention of Bessemer steel changed our manner of living more than the American Revolution. The advent of railroads, steamships, steel buildings, none of which would be possible without cheap and uniform steel, has altered the everyday life of our people more than a change of government could possibly do. The fruits of research are greater than the fruits of war. Pasteur was right when he said: "In our century, science is the soul of the prosperity of nations and the living source of all progress. Undoubtedly, the tiring daily discussions of politics seem to be our guide. Empty appearances!—What really lead us forward are a few scientific discoveries and their applications."

Professor Kraus stresses the importance of the application of research to our problems.[1]

The present age, our own, has only one outstanding achievement to its credit: It has learned how to apply research in the solution of man's everlasting problem, the problem of existence. Of all human activities, none is playing a more important role today than is research. Our continued well-being, indeed our very existence, may well depend on the effectiveness with which we are able to apply research in the solution of our ever-growing problems.

Maintaining that know-how is a prime requisite for a manufacturing operation is not to be understood as saying that it is the only thing necessary. Capital is required to provide the building and machinery and there must be men to operate it.

THE NATURE OF RESEARCH

But what is research? the achievement of the superman? the sport of kings? the privilege of the exalted few? It is all of these and more. Supermen may exhaust themselves in its pursuit, a king might pawn his crown to taste its joys, and the highest of earth may be made rich by its rewards, but it is like faith and love, which cannot be exhausted by the greatest yet may be partaken of by the humblest, provided they are pure in heart. There are no limitations as to age, wealth, or social position, yet the restrictions are severe enough to keep out the unworthy.

What then is research? It is not something portentous, something to be spoken of with bated breath as if pertaining to a higher sphere, but as Professor Remsen says:[2]

There is nothing mysterious about research. Every human being, in fact every animal, is by nature engaged in

---

[1] Charles A. Kraus, *Chem. Eng. News,* **28,** 3203 (1950).

[2] Written by request by the late President Ira Remsen, Johns Hopkins University.

research, that is to say, trying to find out something about its environment. Perhaps the word research is a rather large one to connote these elementary activities, but it is nevertheless true that they are in principle of the same kind as those which are commonly understood when the word is used. There have always been researchers, and the knowledge we have of the universe is due to them. Notwithstanding all that has been learned in the past, the problems that have been solved are almost insignificant compared with those that remain to be solved. Every important discovery, or perhaps it is safe to say every discovery, suggests new problems.

Closer examination shows that "research" is simple re-search, the ordinary word "search" with "re" prefixed, which means that if we search and do not find we must re-search—go back and search till we do find. There is no limit to the "re" as to time or trouble, the requirement being that the object of the search be located. This "re" means not simply again but again and again, not "until seven times; but until seventy times seven." Looking for a needle in a haystack has long been the popular idea of futility and it is unlikely that a superficial search would reveal the hiding place of the elusive needle, but *research* would examine every single straw, splitting it open if need be, and would inevitably locate the needle.

The quest may be the discovery of the chemistry of life or the determination of the sixth decimal place in the density of alcohol, and elaborate or simple resources may be required, but there must be thoroughness in either case and nothing must be left undone that might contribute to the certainty and accuracy of the result.

Research is an elastic term and may be applied to the greatest efforts of the mightiest intellects and also the slow, painful motions of small minds. Research may be comprehensive and colossal or it may be minute and even inconsequential.

Research is finding out something, adding something to the known. It is the reality and not the size of the addition that matters. A small advance in knowledge may be just as real as a large one, and a number of small gains make up progress. Columbus discovered the western continents, but it has required the labors of thousands of explorers, on a lesser scale, to chart the inlets and coves along their shores, and to explore the mountains and plains of their vast inland territory. It is all the same work, and the one explorer is as real a discoverer as the other. A gram, or even a milligram, of gold is as truly gold as all the gold in the crown jewels of the kingdoms of the world. Gold, if it be gold at all, is real gold: so it is with research. The smallest fact ascertained, provided it is new and is positively proved, is a real advance in knowledge, just as real as the greatest discovery. We do not speak of some gold as valuable and other gold as not. All gold is valuable. One nugget may be larger than another and thus bring more at the mint, but gold is gold, and whether it be nuggets panned in the Klondike or microscopic particles extracted by the cyanide mills of Africa, every grain of the shining dust adds that much to the wealth of the world. The determination of the melting point of a single new substance adds to the sum of human knowledge. This is research and is valuable. A number of such facts would be of greater, though not more real value. The door is open and whoever will, may enter the sacred company of discoverers and stand with Columbus, Newton, Lavoisier, Berzelius, Liebig, Perkin, and their like, as one of those who advance into the unknown and enlarge human knowledge, the benefactors of mankind.

In thus admitting to the exalted caste of discoverers those who offer small contributions as freely as those who come laden with rich treasures, we dare not make any discount on the quality. Brass and pyrites, however they may glitter, cannot pass the assayer; only twenty-four karat gold can be accepted. To be an advance in human knowledge the alleged discovery must be new and it must be true. To be a discovery, it must be an actual advance over what was previously known to any mortal on that subject and to be of any worth, it must be proved beyond any doubt. A piece of work to be of value must be so done and so recorded that it will never have to be done over. An accurate observation is true till the end of time. The interpretation of a fact may change, as theories come and go, but the fact itself, once established, is true for all time. A vast amount of chemical work goes for naught because it is not good enough for publication and permanent record and has to be done over in case anyone needs the information.

There are many who stand back for years waiting for the opportunity and facilities to undertake some big problem. One should be ambitious to attack the biggest possible problem, but meantime many small ones may be solved. Even a large problem may be handled on the installment plan.

It is doubtful if any man ever had a keener eye for research ability in others or did more to develop it than Daniel Coit Gilman. Of the research spirit he wrote:[3]

It is perpetually active. It is the search for the truth —questioning, doubting, verifying, sifting, testing, proving, that which has been handed down; observing, weighing, measuring, comparing the phenomena of Nature, open and recondite. In such researches, a degree of accuracy is nowadays reached which was impossible before the lens, the balance, and the meter, those marvelous instruments of precision, had attained their modern perfection.

With the growth of the scientific spirit grows the love of truth, and with the love of truth in the abstract comes the love of accuracy in the concrete.

QUALITIES OF RESEARCH

Newness

Research, as the word is here used, is a determined effort to discover something new, to extend human knowledge. It has much in common with detective work, but the element of newness is a distinctive difference. In finding out who robbed the bank, the detective is only discovering what the robber knew all along. Nothing has been added to the sum total of human knowledge. In science, the line is drawn sharply and the object discovered must not have been known before. Ethyl benzoate has been prepared by hundreds of chemists, but it was discovered by only one, the first one who made and *described* it. The proper description of it is as essential as the staking out and recording of a mining claim, which is invalidated if a prior

[3] D. C. Gilman, *Launching a University*, 1906, pp. 147-150.

discovery can be shown, and it is extremely embarrassing to a chemist to find that his discoveries have been anticipated by others.

While newness is an absolute quality in the sense that a thing is either new or not new, yet the newness may be limited in the extent of its application. A hatchet may have a new handle, in which case the newness applies only to the handle, and even then the new handle may have been fashioned from an old piece of wood—the newness being restricted to its form and present relation to the hatchet. The nine hundred and thirtieth person who prepares ethyl benzoate may find out something new about it, may determine its boiling point, or some other property, more accurately than had been done before, or may devise some easier or more economical way of making it, in either case adding to the sum of human knowledge and making a discovery.

There is no substance known about which something new may not yet be found out. New investigations are constantly appearing on the best-known substances, such as water and alcohol. In the index of *Chemical Abstracts* for 1920, there are 148 references to articles containing something new about ethyl alcohol. In the *Chemical Abstracts'* index for 1955, there are more than 600 entries on ethyl alcohol, showing that they are still finding out something new about it. If so much can yet be done on ethyl alcohol, with which Noah experimented disastrously, there is little difficulty in finding out something new about thousands of other substances which have been only superficially examined. Of course, only a part of these are references to research on ethyl alcohol, the majority being to more or less trivial information on production, uses, etc.

When planning a research program, the first thing is to ascertain just what has been done in that particular field so as to make sure that what is to be undertaken is really new and is a definite advance beyond what is already known. The density of ethyl alcohol has been determined with great accuracy and with most carefully prepared materials. It would not be worth while to redetermine the density of ethyl alcohol unless one had discovered some new means for purifying it or some more accurate method of finding the density.

Accuracy, Reliability, and Truth

These qualities may be grouped together, as they are closely related; in fact one need not try to differentiate between them, as no one of them is of any value without the other two.

Accuracy involves close observation and minute attention to all essential details. In the determination of physical constants, accuracy is required not only in making the observations themselves, but also in the instruments and apparatus employed. One might determine the density of a liquid to the fifth decimal place, but if the weights used are faulty, or the regulation of the thermostat unreliable, or the purity of the liquid questionable, the result will be worthless. False ideas of accuracy are often conveyed by calculating to four or five places of decimals results which are doubtful in the third or even in the second. It is much easier to read a thermometer to 0.01° than it is to be sure that it is correct to 0.1°, and it is obviously silly to record the hundredths unless one is certain of the tenths.

The standard of accuracy should be determined by the circumstances and the class of the investigation. Good judgment and common sense must decide the degree of accuracy that is needed in each part of an experiment. The only excuse for doing an atomic-weight determination is the possibility of excelling previous work in accuracy. The same statement holds for redetermining the physical constants of organic compounds. In determining the constants of a new compound, the standards accepted by the best investigators in that field should be considered.

It is common to speak of theories as evanescent and to regard facts as eternal, but how long the facts will endure depends on their accuracy, since, as Prins[4] has pointed out, future refinements in apparatus or methods may wipe out the facts as we now know them. A more precise determination super-

---

[4] *Chem. Weekbl.* **15**, 1381 (1918).

sedes a less accurate one, just as we discard an old telephone book when we receive the current directory. If we wish long life for our data, we must take the utmost care that they are so accurate that it will be difficult to improve upon them.

Reliability may be regarded as an addition compound of accuracy and truth for, if either of these is lacking, the result is untrustworthy, but it goes somewhat farther and includes also some other qualities. Measurements may be accurately and conscientiously made and yet lead to unreliable results if some source of error has been overlooked. An unsuspected impurity, perhaps an unknown isomer, may be present and lead to erroneous results.

There are so many organic compounds to be made that we can seldom afford the time to prepare any one compound in more than one way and, for that reason, many of the determinations of properties are in error. A compound nearly always retains more or less impurities derived from the materials from which it is produced, or from by-products in the reactions involved. If it is a solid and is recrystallized to a constant melting point, we assume that it is pure, but we may still have a mixture. If the same substance is prepared in an entirely different way from other materials and by different reactions, it will also carry impurities, but they will probably be different. Now if the two lots are purified separately till their properties are identical, we will be far more sure of the reliability of the data.

A good example of this is thio-carbanilide,[5] one of the standbys in our courses in organic preparations. When it became necessary to manufacture this substance on the large scale, a process avoiding the use of alcohol had to be devised. The crude product from the new process had a higher melting point than the most carefully purified product made by the classical method. When produced in alcohol solution, it contained phenylurethane which resulted from a side reaction and which could not be eliminated.

It is valuable to read atomic-weight determinations to see how one source of error after another has been discovered and eliminated.

---

[5] Information from the laboratory of Arthur D. Little, Inc.

Louis Agassiz said: "The temptation to impose one's own ideas upon Nature, to explain her mysteries by brilliant theories rather than by patient study of the facts as we find them, still leads us astray." Huxley is said to have prayed: "God give me strength to face a fact though it slay me."

When we have a theory we are prone to choose experiments which are designed to prove our theory and omit those which might turn out the other way. Rigid honesty demands that we be just as keen to devise experiments which may put our pet theory on the rack. If it is sound it will survive the severest ordeal and come out all the stronger; if it is damaged, well and good.

It is morally and scientifically dangerous to become a partisan of a theory. When a scientist becomes a partisan, he is in danger of losing his standing as a scientist. When the judge takes sides in a case, he is no longer fit to be judge. The judge must see that every credible witness has a fair show in court.

It has happened more than once, and almost any chemist of experience can supply names and dates, that a professor has outlined experiments to a student and has indicated how he expected the results to come out, and the student has brought in reports exactly as expected, which were subsequently found to have been obtained by the "paper and pencil method," sometimes even without going through the tedious operation of preparing substances and setting up apparatus. In fortunate cases some slip or some overexact analysis has aroused suspicion in time and the results have been checked up and the crookedness located before the results were printed, while in other cases a humiliating retraction had to be made of published work. The possibility of such a misfortune is a nightmare to those who direct research.

In rare cases the director of the investigation was to blame by being so set in his ideas as to refuse to accept any results at variance with them. In some such cases the student, finding that only such and such results are accepted, turned in only such and got along famously.

It is deep in human nature to want to make the

best appearance possible. There is indeed little hope for one who does not wish to appear well before his fellows, but this desire may lead to concealment or pretense. The chemist is tempted to make his preparation of materials appear to be more thorough than it actually was, to mention precautions in the experiments which were not actually taken or which were not always adhered to, or to describe a more perfect form of apparatus than was in reality employed, thus making his work appear better than it actually was. Suppressing results that vary from the mean is another way of doing the same thing.

RESEARCH ETHICS

Though not given specifically to chemists, the "golden rule" may be taken as a guide. We like to receive recognition for what we have done, so let us be generous in according credit to others. Our ideas, however new and fresh they may look to us, bear some relation to the ideas of those who have gone before. Courtesy demands that we should not horn in on the investigations of others.

A gentleman does not need a set of rules for his treatment of others; chemists should be gentlemen.

HARD WORK

The reason that get-rich-quick schemes catch so many is that so many of us are looking for easy money. If the vendors of goldmine and oil stock—I have bought both—would not come after us we would go after them, as their wares appeal to the human race. It is an almost universal belief—except in those who have tried it—that somewhere there is a machine in which we can drop pennies and dollars will fall out; that sometime in our lives we can invest a few dollars in a sure-thing proposition and draw thousands or millions in dividends.

In young chemists there is the lurking hope that a few offhand experiments will bring fame and fortune, but the sooner that idea is dissipated the better for all concerned. The only sure road to success in chemistry is the long road, and there are many rough and sandy stretches in it and all the grades are upgrades. Sometimes there seems to be no bottom to the sand and no end to the hills. The chemist must count on hard work and then more work. Investigation is slow and often tedious, but results come in the end, and success that is won is a thousand times sweeter than that which just happens.

When success comes too easily and too early, as it did to Little Jack Horner, the results are apt to be disastrous. He started out in life with two misconceptions: that everything is easy, and that he had a superior intellect. It is presumed that he grew to manhood, but on the pages of English history there is no record of any achievements of Mr. Horner.

Much quantitative work is involved in investigation, and quantitative work is essentially slow. So many are tempted to slight or abridge the quantitative part. It takes so long to calibrate weights, pipets, burets, and pycnometers. It requires so much trouble and time to make sure, while it is so easy and quick to take things for granted. A vast deal of moral courage is necessary to hold one's self to the road, to plod right straight through.

In upper South Carolina, there is a stream called Hard Labor Creek because, on one of its sudden rises, it swept away the rails which had cost months of hard labor of two brothers to split. As a boy I often crossed that creek, as a man I have many times felt that I was standing on its brink as I have seen the fruits of my hard labor lost, not indeed in its turbid waters but by the breaking of a flask or the explosion of a sealed tube. It is no rare experience to the chemist to see materials, which it has cost months of labor to prepare, lost or ruined in a moment by an accident to his apparatus, and to the injury of the loss is frequently added the insult of having to spend the rest of the day cleaning up the resulting mess. No matter what precautions are taken, disheartening accidents come to all chemists.

One accident which seemed serious at first turned out to my advantage. I found that benzamide was converted to ethyl benzoate by ethyl alcohol containing hydrogen chloride. I reasoned that thiobenzamide might give ethyl dithiobenzoate with mercaptan and hydrogen chloride. To make thiobenzamide I needed benzonitrile. I drew out the 100 grams of benzonitrile which was in the stock room. Preliminary experiment indicated that my reasoning was correct, so I started to convert the whole stock of benzonitrile to the thiobenzamide. The mixture of benzonitrile and alcoholic ammonium hydrosulfide in a flask was placed in the left-hand back corner of the hood. I remember distinctly just where it stood. A sealed tube, which was being heated in a water bath at the other side of the hood, blew up and a piece of the glass went through the wall of the flask; my precious benzonitrile ran out in the hood and down on the floor. An unsavory mess it made. I was desolate as I knew of no benzonitrile this side of Germany. This was before Eastman came to the rescue of American chemists. I ran to the library and found that Letts, a German chemist, had made benzonitrile by heating a mixture of benzoic acid and lead thiocyanate. The reaction, as he wrote it, called for the evolution of equal molecular amounts of hydrogen sulfide and carbon dioxide. I tested the gases and found only a trace of hydrogen sulfide. I substituted zinc benzoate for the free acid and raised the yield from 45 to 95%. I got a publication out of this in addition to enough benzonitrile for the preparation of the desired ethyl dithiobenzoate. This got me interested in the preparation of nitriles, and later, having read Sabatier's *Catalysis* in the meantime, when Van Epps came to work with me, I undertook the direct synthesis of a nitrile by passing the vapor of the acid and ammonia over a catalyst in a hot tube. I never imagined that this would have any commercial application, but tons of nitriles have been made directly from the acids and ammonia.

Those who love hard work and love it all the better because it is hard, those who try and fail and keep on trying, those who can suffer the loss of months of hard labor and start all over again, those who cannot be discouraged no matter what happens, are invited to undertake research.

ORIGINALITY

You will never get ahead of a man
by following him

This is the *sine qua non* of research. Unless we do something different from what has been done, it is not research, and the more original our work the better. Unfortunately this deters many who doubt their originality from undertaking investigation. It is not that they overestimate the originality required, but that they underestimate the amount they have. Those who study fingerprints tell us that no two of us human beings have identical markings on our fingers. The convolutions of our brains are far more complicated than the whorls on our dactyl epidermis. Our varied experience, training, and environment serve still further to differentiate us. If our fingers are individual and original, our minds certainly must be.

Being different from others is originality and we are all different, so we all have originality. The real difficulty is that we do not recognize our originality, capitalize on it, and use it. When we encase our fingers in the same-style gloves they all look alike and leave no identifying clues behind, as the crooks well know; they lose their individuality and the originality of their whorl patterns. In society we cloak our individuality in conventional phrases till most of us forget that we have any. The gloves and the conventions are good in their way and serve well in society, but neither are to be adhered to in research. There it is proper to turn oneself loose, to look at things in one's own way, to work as one works best on what one can do best, to trust oneself, to draw upon oneself to the utmost. It is not that we have not enough originality. It is more often that we do not trust ourselves and use what we have. When we imitate, we are lost; when we strike out for ourselves and originate, we win. I had to find this out for myself. As a young chemist I tried to imitate the smarter and more experienced chemists with whom I came in contact. The results were poor. Then I decided to look at problems with my own eyes and to do my best in my own way and I got along much better. This was one of the greatest decisions of my life and I want to encourage others to make it. It is generally agreed that the surest way to lose a race is to keep your eyes on the other runners.

IMAGINATION

Some place poets and scientists far apart, crediting the poet with a wonderful imagination and the scientist with none at all. Of the two, the poet can get along with less imagination, or at least with a less definite one. The architect builds his cathedral first in his imagination and must see the bridge spanning the river before the blueprints are made. Chemists must see things that are doubly invisible, for cathedrals and bridges are constructed of stone and girders that we can see and the structures are visible to anyone after they materialize, while the molecules with which the chemist conjures are invisible structures built of invisible materials and are just as invisible after they are realized as before. The chemist requires a superimagination. Dalton owed his atomic theory to a vivid and materialistic imagination that insisted on seeing atoms singly and in pairs, trios, and quartets, combining with each other and changing places. While Kekulé "nodded, nearly napping," he visioned the carbon atoms linked in chains till one of these turned serpent, swallowed his tail, and rolled off as a ring. This dream did more for the science of chemistry than the labor of scores of men.

The imagination can be used to great advantage in materializing the properties of substances so that we may see the relationships between them to the end that our mathematical calculations represent realities and are not simply juggling with symbols.

Nature is not limited by the imagination of man; many discoveries go far, far beyond. Alexander Graham Bell and Marconi had great imaginations, but listening to broadcasts from Moscow and Tokyo were beyond them. When I studied physics, atoms were the ultimate in smallness, and power was measured in kilowatts. Now the atoms have been split, and explosions are rated in terms of millions of tons of TNT. Things yet to be discovered are beyond the farthest reach of the boldest imagination.

2. The development of research

EMPIRICAL RESEARCH

When *Homo sapiens* arrived and went to housekeeping, he was dissatisfied. He had no idea of what he wanted, but knew that he wanted something. So he went to work. With no theories or blueprints to guide him he had to cut and try. Results came slowly, very slowly. However, at the dawn of history, about 4000 B.C. in Egypt, later in some other countries, man was in possession of a considerable amount of technical knowledge, as is shown by the remains of his dwellings, utensils, and weapons.

The empirical method is still with us, though, with the development of scientific theory, our reliance on it has dwindled. Over the centuries a vast amount of information has been accumulated by cut and try. Much of this has gone into the development of industries and much has been classified into the sciences. Many chemical processes, such as the tanning of hides, the dyeing of cloth with indigo, and the smelting of ores, had

21

been in use many centuries before chemistry was recognized as a science. Langmuir[1] praises "the art of profiting from unexpected occurrences such as were often observed in empirical research." A number of examples of important discoveries, being made by close observation or by following up of chance observations, will be given in later chapters.

GREEK PHILOSOPHY AND ALCHEMY

Man has always been curious about his environment. The Greek philosophers made a business of speculating about things. They came up with the idea that all substances are composed of the four elements: earth, air, fire, and water. The philosophers considered thoughts so far superior to material things that they did not deign to experiment with mere matter.

There were, however, some who were more practical. If lead and gold are composed of the same four elements, differing only in the proportions, why not turn lead into gold by adding some of this and taking away some of that? Copper gives zinc the color of gold, so far so good, if they could give the brass the other properties of gold, the problem would be solved. So alchemy began and lasted for nearly two thousand years. The alchemists experimented industriously and discovered many facts which have been assimilated into the science of chemistry. Frustrated in their efforts to ennoble the baser metals, some of them debased themselves by turning to questionable methods of getting gold, mixing pretense and black magic with their chemistry.

It seems ironical that the transmutation of the elements should become an accomplished fact after its possibility had been so thoroughly disproved. The alchemists had the right idea, but they did not have the know-how. Perhaps we shall some day manufacture gold from lead but then it will have value only as a useful metal.

---

[1] Irving Langmuir, *Proc. Am. Philosophical Soc.* **92**, No. 3, 167 (1948).

AMATEURS IN THE DEVELOPMENT OF RESEARCH

The term is used here in its proper sense to designate those who engage in research for the love of it. The golden age in chemistry was when men thought not of gold, but worked for the thrill of discovery and rejoiced to tell their fellow workers all they knew. Scheele was an apothecary and experimented with chemicals when the prescriptions were all filled. It is fortunate that he did not have to use up his time making sandwiches. Priestley, a dissenting minister, sought refuge in his little home laboratory when religious discussions got too hot. His close friend, Wedgwood, experimented to improve pottery. We honor Priestley for his discoveries and still buy Wedgwood pottery. Dalton was a school teacher who loved to figure out things. Liebig and Wöhler were chemistry teachers who were driven by curiosity. Particularly in Germany, research was combined with teaching. The growth of the German synthetic dye industry stimulated research during the last third of the nineteenth century. Notable investigations were carried on in the university laboratories of England, France, and Russia.

RESEARCH IN AMERICA

Amateur research flourished in this country even in colonial times. Benjamin Franklin was a prominent example. He founded the American Philosophical Society the members of which still meet to read and discuss scientific papers. Priestley came in 1794 and settled in Northumberland, Pa., where his home is now a shrine visited by chemists.

During the nineteenth century, many notable advances in science and in its applications resulted from the work of investigators and inventors. Even in the universities research was largely an individual matter. A great impetus was given to it when Gilman used Johns Hopkins' millions to create a university of a new type, one devoted to graduate study leading to the Ph.D. degree for which the completion of a piece of research should be the chief requirement. This degree was taken up quickly by other universities, and research flourished in America.

CHEMISTRY BECOMES A SCIENCE

The discovery of oxygen and the explanation of oxidation and reduction, which followed, may be regarded as the beginning of the science of chemistry. The promulgation of the ideas of atoms of constant weight for each element and of their orderly combinations to make molecules put the science on a firm basis. It took nearly two score years to get the atomic weights and empirical formulae settled. Kekulé's quadrivalence of carbon and benzene theory (1865) completed the foundation for the structural formulae of organic compounds. By the end of the century approximately a hundred thousand organic compounds of known structure had been synthesized, characterized, named, classified, and catalogued. The third edition of *Beilstein* had been published.

In that century lived and worked the most of those whose names are written large in the annals of chemistry. They investigated the fundamentals of chemistry, never dreaming of where their discoveries might lead. They laid a broad and firm foundation for amazing developments of the twentieth century. Of course, chemistry is only one of the sciences that flourished in that century, and chemists are not the only scientists who deserve credit for the advances that were made.

Dr. Pauling places emphasis on academic research:[2]

. . . modern life is really based on *fundamental science,* on *pure research,* and . . . the nature of the world today has been determined, and the nature of the world of the future will be determined, by the work, and especially the ideas, the imagination, of a small number of people—the 'impractical scientists,' mainly university professors, who strive to add to our body of knowledge in every way, rather than to solve certain practical problems that obviously need solution. I am not minimizing the importance of development research and of industrial application of new discoveries; but am

[2] Linus Pauling, *Chem. Eng. News,* **27**, 2775 (1949).

instead pointing out that the direction in which progress occurs is in fact determined by the basic discoveries that are made, and that accordingly it is the progress of pure science that determines what the nature of the world will be a generation later.

RESEARCH BECOMES BIG BUSINESS

The nineteenth century saw tremendous technological advances. The railroads supplanted the stagecoach; steamships replaced sailing vessels; the telegraph and telephone brought in a new era in communication. Early in the century gas lights illuminated city streets; electric lights and automobiles were coming in at its close. The discovery of anesthetics made modern surgery possible. Bacteria were identified as the cause of many diseases, and antiseptics were prepared to counteract them. Cotton, bleached to a glistening white by chlorine, clothed people of many lands. These and scores of other developments were, from the applications of research, fruits of the labors of a few individuals who had been led on by curiosity to investigate phenomena that attracted their attention. However great the technological advances in that century, greater than the total of those in all the centuries before, they were still to be overshadowed by what were to follow.

Early in this, the impatient century, with its insistent demand for more and more and better and better things, it became apparent that the information accumulated by research in the past century was not sufficient. The colonists found that wild turkeys made excellent dinners. To insure an adequate supply, it became necessary to domesticate the birds. About the turn of the century, enterprising manufacturers found that the supply of information that had been accumulated by the professors and their students was inadequate to supply the needs of expanding industry. The only thing to do was to capture scientists and domesticate them. The industries were growing, not only in size but also in the complexity of their operations. In addition to general scientific knowledge, they needed information on specific problems. The industries had to take up research if they were to go forward. The situation has been well stated by Dr. Oberfell:[3]

Industry had always recognized the function of development in achieving its goals, but industrial research as a specialized and organized activity is a product of the twentieth century. Only during the past fifty years has it been realized how effectively new industries can be created by the proper control and direction of research.

The story of Du Pont research illustrates what has happened. E. I. du Pont, who had studied chemistry with Lavoisier, came to this country and set up a powder mill near Wilmington, Delaware, in 1802. He started with the best methods of his day, but for him good was never good enough. He was always trying out new ideas. His successors also were chemists and carried experimenting along with their manufacturing. Over the years they learned much, but their research was incidental to other operations.

In 1901 the Du Pont Company brought in Charles L. Reese on half time for research on a problem not connected with current operations. This was a small beginning, but it grew and grew, and soon research became the activity of a department which had equal stature with production and sales departments.

About 1921 Dr. Reese wrote:[4] "The total expenditure of the Du Pont Research Organization for the years 1912 to 1918, inclusive, was $6,051,000." He went on to say that this had led to large savings. The Company had come a long way since 1901, but it was only getting started. In 1949 the Company spent $33,000,000 on research, and in 1959, $90,000,000. This is to be compared with $33,000,000, which was the total sales in 1910. Curiously enough, these huge expenditures for research have not impaired the financial standing of the Company.

In 1900, a year before the Du Pont venture, the General Electric management decided to start research as a separate activity of the Company and selected Whitney, who was teaching at M.I.T., to direct it. He was skeptical of industrial

---

[3] G. G. Oberfell, *Chem. Eng. News*, 28, 1278 (1950).
[4] E. Emmet Reid, *Introduction to Organic Research*, New York, D. Van Nostrand, 1924, p. 49.

research, and took it, at first, on a half-time basis. They set up a laboratory in a barn belonging to Steinmetz. This was the small beginning of a research organization that has grown to a gigantic size and into which the Company has poured millions. The results of their research have been of immense benefit to the public. Incidentally, the stock holders also have fared quite well.

Other corporations, some earlier, some later, realizing the need of information not contained in chemical literature, set up research departments, which, from modest beginnings, have grown to huge size.

The figures that have been given for Du Pont research are only illustrative of the rapid expansion of the research activities of other chemical companies. In our highly competitive system, no company can afford to neglect what is bringing profits to others; ever-expanding research is the price of staying in the race. The great oil companies have vied with each other in spending huge sums of money on research in order to make more powerful gasoline so that we can drive more madly.

As narrated here, the need of the industries for research began to be realized by some early in this century, but progress was painfully slow for some years. The American public got an awful jolt when the supply of dyes and pharmaceuticals was cut off by the blockade in World War I. The manufacture of heavy chemicals, such as sulfuric acid and soda, was well established and efficient, but we had been content to buy fine organic chemicals from Germany, which had almost a monopoly on them. The dye in a fifty-dollar suit of clothes may have cost only ten cents, but what would the suit be worth if the dye faded or was washed out when the wearer got caught in the rain? Why call a physician if the pharmacist could not fill the prescription? Frantic efforts were made during the War to supply these deficiencies, and many good results were obtained, along with some poor ones. It was most fortunate that the manufacture of smokeless powder was well understood, even before 1914, and that the few small plants that were in operation were able to expand rapidly enough to supply the British and French with ammunition. Otherwise the war might have been lost before we got into it in 1917. The close of the war was the signal for full speed ahead. Now the organic chemical industry of the United States far excels that of any other country.

The tale that has been told has been of chemical research because I am a chemist, but this is only one of the many lines in which research has expanded amazingly and has accomplished spectacular results within this half century.

The phenomenal growth of the automobile industry called for a similar expansion in the production of organic compounds. A million pounds a year of any product used to sound big, but in World War II, they called for a million *tons* of synthetic rubber, and they got it.

The growth of research departments has kept pace with that of the industries. The process has been autocatalytic. Research produces new and better products, and this increases sales. More money is put into research, and sales increase again, and so on. The research laboratories of some corporations are comparable in size to their plants of a few years back.

So much has been said about research in industrial establishments because it is directly connected with commercial production, but industrial research is only a part of the total research in this country. Research activities in the Army and Navy laboratories are, for the most part, on problems related to these services, and are kept secret; but in other governmental departments, research is on problems of public interest and the results are freely published. The Agriculture Department issues many bulletins on a wide variety of subjects. Four large regional laboratories work on products peculiar to the regions in which they are located.

The Mellon Institute was the first and is the most prominent of the nonprofit research institutes which have become numerous and carry on sponsored research of many kinds. Besides these there are many commercial laboratories that serve all comers. Two notable examples of these are Arthur D. Little, Inc., established in 1886, and Foster D. Snell, Inc. In the aggregate, such establishments do a large amount of research. As has been pointed out, the development of an idea requires extensive research and large expenditures. There is often a single department for "research and development," and who knows where to draw the line? By any reckoning, the present-day expenditures for research are enormous and are increasing at a rapid rate. Just now (1961) there is talk of billions of dollars for research and development on rockets and long-range missiles. There is no way of obtaining exact information as to the amount being spent on research in the United States, but it was probably something like 12 billion for 1960.

RESEARCH MAKES BIG BUSINESS

The discovery of gold started the great rush of the "forty-niners" to California. The discovery of gold in research by a few intrepid industrialist explorers some three score years later started the greater, though less-publicized gold rush. The results have been spectacular. Many small industries have become great and many great new industries have been created. There is no point in trying to disentangle the factors that have caused the phenomenal growth of American industry within the past fifty years. There is no practical value in developing a new product unless it is to be manufactured; and this requires capital for the erection of a plant and labor for its operation. What is the relative importance of the sides, top, and bottom of a tank? Mr. Gray says:[5] "In the United States, research and development has become the most important single factor in economic growth. It provides the technological basis for our ever-expanding high standard of living."

It is by no means a coincidence that the industries which have relied on research to the greatest extent are the ones that have made spectacular advances. Wages are, or should be, directly related to the value of what is produced. The only real way of raising wages is to increase the value, not the price of the product. Research improves methods of manufacturing old products and finds new ones of greater value, thus making possible higher real wages. Research benefits the worker *and* the public.

Chemical industries were started in colonial times,

---

[5] Elisha Gray, II in Report no. 20 (1957), American Management Association.

but grew slowly through the long years. Early in this century they took on research, as was told in the preceding section, and began to grow. The results have been amazing. A few items gleaned from reliable sources will illustrate this. The sales of chemicals increased from $4,339,000 in 1939 to about $26,000,000 in 1959. The production of plastics was 20,000,000 pounds in 1928, 1,486,-000,000 in 1948, and 4,518,000,000 in 1958. Synthetic rubber rose from 2500 tons in 1938 to 1,100,000 in 1958.

Electrical research has created a number of big businesses, such as incandescent lighting, telegraph, telephone, radio and television, the last two within the past fifty years. In 1959, the sales of radios amounted to $331,000,000, of television sets $896,000,000, and of electronic equipment $7,200,000,000. The revenues of the telephone companies were $8,000,000,000.

Three interdependent industries, aviation, automobile and petroleum, have grown to gigantic size within the last fifty years as the result of research of many kinds. In 1959, the production of airplanes and rockets amounted to $11,300,000,000. The factory value of automobiles and parts was $15,080,000,000. Before the automobile came along there was a petroleum industry, but its chief product was kerosene, and stringent laws were passed to keep the refiner from putting the almost worthless gasoline into it. With the advent of the automobile, the industry has spent hundreds of millions of dollars on cracking processes for turning heavy crudes into gasoline and for raising the octane rating of the product. American motorists are currently spending $10,000,000,000 a year for gasoline.

Supplying food and clothes is big business, the biggest on earth, and the one without which there would be no other business. The immediate benefit of improvements in agriculture is the provision of better and more abundant food. With better methods and implements, fewer workers are required on the farm. A secondary result is the release of workers for other tasks. In 1860, 80 out of every 100 of the population of the United States were on the farm. By 1910, this number had been reduced to 55. At the present time only 11 are still on the farm, and they produce so much that we have difficulty in disposing of the surplus. The release from the farm of these millions of workers has made possible our enormous industrial expansion. The age-long battle between man and insects for food goes on without cessation. Time and time again, hordes of insects have swept over limited areas leaving no green thing for man or beast. It is a war of extermination and the insects might win. Our hopes are based on agrichemical research, which is hastening to the rescue.

If a large proportion of the present three billion people on the earth are hungry much of the time, how can food be provided for ʃ six· billion, the estimated population of the earth in A.D. 2000? That is the $64,000,000,000 question which research must answer.

RESEARCH AND EMPLOYMENT

In its effects on employment, research works both ways. It makes jobs and abolishes them. In creating giant new industries and in expanding old ones, research has provided employment for millions of workers. On the other hand, research has cut down the number of operators required to accomplish a given task. The expansion of the telephone industry gave employment to thousands of switchboard operators; the introduction of dial telephones led to the release of a large proportion of these.

The release of millions from farm labor has provided workers required for our enormous industrial expansion. The maintenance of employment depends on the balance between improvements in industrial operations and on their expansion.

As a result of research, we work fewer hours and at less arduous tasks than our grandparents and, in addition, enjoy a standard of living never before dreamed of.

ORGANIZATION IN RESEARCH

When research becomes big business, there must be organization and cooperation.

The development of an idea usually requires the cooperation of many minds and the addition of many other ideas, but Dr. Bronk, who is an expert on ideas, says:[6] "I know of no evidence which disproves the thesis that new ideas and concepts are formed within a single mind. Great scientific discoveries will be made by individuals, who work without direction from others, as surely as will the creation of great music and sculpture and art . . ." Dr. Calvin agrees with this:[7] ". . . it is my feeling that the 'synthesis' of a really new conception can be the product of a single mind only."

This is certainly true, but the full development of an idea, or fundamental discovery, requires contributions from other minds. Dr. Ott states the case for industry:[8]

> In the field of industrial development work, the team-approach method obviously permits bringing a development to commercial fruition more quickly with relatively specific and reasonably well-defined objectives. It is not *a priori* obvious, however, that group effort can be beneficial in research, particularly if the research is of a more fundamental nature.
>
> It is a fact, nevertheless, that even in this type of industrial activity the group effort has become more pronounced in recent years. The reason for this is not hard to find. As our total scientific knowledge has increased, it has become more difficult for any one man to master a broad segment. An increasing degree of specialization of most scientific workers has become the rule of the day. However, most problems cut across more than one field of specialization; therefore, to achieve proper results, more than one specialist must be involved. Thus, group effort becomes a necessity.

This is well illustrated by the development of rayon. A Frenchman discovered that cellulose can be put into colloidal solution by treatment with alkali and carbon disulfide. When this solution, known as viscose, is extruded into dilute acid, the cellulose is regenerated in the form of a filament, later called rayon. This looks simple. The process was brought to America. It worked, but many millions of dollars had to be spent on research and development in order to perfect the process. There are a

[6] Detlev Bronk, *Chem. Eng. News*, 33, 3281 (1955).
[7] Melvin Calvin, *Chem. Eng. News*, 34, 2754 (1956).
[8] Emil Ott, *Chem. Eng. News*, 28, 1994 (1950).

number of steps, and a variation in any one of these affects the final product. The engineering problems were as numerous and as difficult as the chemical. The dyeing of rayon presented a whole new set of problems. Cooperative effort was required to put a desirable rayon on the market.

In a research department where there are several dozen, or several hundred, chemists and engineers, there must be organization and cooperation. A few will be assigned to scouting. It is necessary to dig up a number of good ideas in order to have two or three extra-good ones for exploitation. A larger number will be employed in developing ideas. As Dr. Ott points out, a single problem may have to be attacked from several directions, which requires men of different skills. A ball team with nine star pitchers and no good basemen would win few games.

As a matter of fact, each and every one of the great achievements of modern research, a few of which are mentioned in this section, was put across by coordinated team effort. It is this way because it has to be this way. Practically all of those who go into industrial research must work, for a time at least, in groups. The ability to work with and for others is an asset to any chemist.

THIS AMAZING HALF CENTURY

One, perhaps the most important, distinguishing characteristic of this amazing half century is the recognition by industry and by government of the paramount importance of research. The result has been the unprecedented intensification of research and the spectacular advances of old industries and the creation of huge new ones.

The bit by bit accumulation of technical knowledge, described earlier in this chapter, which was so slow for thousands of years, gained speed in the nineteenth century and has become explosively rapid within the past fifty years. Within this period, more progress has been made in science and in its dependent technology than in all time since *Homo sapiens* first trod this planet. The candle by which my father studied was little, if any, better than the one which the woman lit two thousand years ago to search for her lost coin. I went through college with the light of a kerosene lamp, my children did their home work under a tungsten light bulb, I write under a fluorescent light. The first man who straddled a horse rode as fast as George Washington could travel, many centuries later. In 1832, the early cars on the B. & O. railroad were drawn by horses; then came the steam locomotive which was followed by the Diesel. Recently I was talking to a flyer friend who remarked: "I was in Africa yesterday."

Fifty years ago, automobiles and airplanes were just getting started. Now there are sufficient cars in the United States that every man, woman, and child might ride at the same time.

To make driving easy, thousands and thousands of paved roads have replaced muddy dirt roads. Our motorists spend $10,000,000,000 a year for gasoline on which they pay $5,000,000,-000 in taxes. The development of airplanes has been even more spectacular; now planes compete with railroads and steamships for passengers. Our huge petroleum industry has grown up to supply high-grade gasoline for the cars and planes.

I remember when the then amazing announcement was made that Morse code could be transmitted three miles without wires. This distance was stretched to hundreds and then to thousands of miles. Then came radio which was soon followed by television.

When we look around we note that things such as electric lights, movies, talkies, artificial fibres, plastics, stainless steel and aluminum utensils, and a host of others which are now commonplace are recent developments. The Queen of Sheba was impressed with what she saw in Solomon's palace; if she could come here now she would find more comforts and conveniences in the humblest cottage than were in the king's palace. In this country, paved roads and rural electrification have spread these conveniences to the remotest regions. There is scarcely a spot so isolated that you cannot hear the news of the world, the best in music, or the hottest in rock and roll by turning a knob. These advantages are enjoyed, to a greater or lesser extent, in other countries. When my father was in Nigeria a hundred years ago, freight was carried on the heads of women; now they have paved highways for cars and landing strips for planes.

Within this terrific half century, there have been two world wars, fought on a scale never before approached. The first was started by the Germans, who then held undisputed leadership in chemical research and technology. Conventional weapons were used by both sides until the Germans introduced chemicals. After this, decisive battles were fought in chemical laboratories. An important result of this war was the stimulation of research, both scientific and applied. This took place in all lines, but here the emphasis is on chemical research. Chemical departments of universities had to be enlarged to provide chemists for industry. Now the American Chemical Society is the largest in the world with 90,000 members, compared to 11,000 in the German Gesellschaft. Half of the chemical publications of the world are in English, with a part from other countries. Research has been a key factor in our development into the mightiest nation on earth with the highest standard of living ever known.

Physics, rather than chemistry, was to the fore in the second world war, in which airplanes were so important. The Germans started the war confident of their superiority in the air. Their scientists concentrated on jet planes and rockets. These were too late getting into production; German industries had already been bombed. Since the War, the development of jet planes and rockets has led to spectacular results. Commercial jet planes carry heavy loads of passengers across the ocean at high speeds. Experimentally, speeds above 2500 miles per hour have been reached. This was the figure when I sent the manuscript to the publisher. By the time the galley proofs arrived the figure was 3140; I cannot guess what it will be by the time the book is published.

Rockets attain fantastic speeds and can hit targets thousands of miles away. As a propaganda stunt, the Russians put Sputnik into orbit around the earth. At last report there were sixteen "artificial moons" circling the earth, fifteen of them "Made in U.S.A."

By intensive cooperative research, our scientists accomplished atomic fission in time to put Japan out of the War. Less than a score of years ago, atomic fission was a dream of a few scientists; now it is a nightmare for all of us. There are enough A-bombs and H-bombs in storage to destroy the inhabitants of two continents. The Nautilus has voyaged under the North Pole ice pack. Atomic power plants are being constructed to furnish immense amounts of electric power.

This turbulent half century has seen a plethora of political upheavals and dislocations, some peaceful, some violent. More than a dozen former colonies are now independent nations with seats in the United Nations. Hundreds of millions of citizens of advanced countries have been enslaved. Rapid transportation by airplanes and instantaneous communication by radio have caused the world to shrink. You can eat breakfast in New York, fly to London, close a business deal, and be back home for dinner. What is said in Timbuctoo can be heard in Kalamazoo. What happens anywhere is known everywhere within minutes. Nations, friendly and unfriendly, are huddled together. Torrents of information and misinformation inundate the world. We have political debates on the radio and television; speakers, though separated by thousands of miles, may appear on the same screen.

It is great to have lived in this miraculous half century. What wonders will the next bring forth?

"Eye hath not seen, nor ear heard, neither hath it entered into" the imagination of man what wonders are in store for them who diligently seek.

THE URGE FROM WITHIN AND
THE REWARD FROM WITHOUT

3. Incentives

INTRODUCTION

In research, as in other human activities, the drives and rewards are many and frequently get so intertwined that it is hard to distinguish them.

Professor Remsen applied chemical terms to our motives.[1]

It is not surprising that those who enjoy mental exercise should have a desire to spend their lives in research. Those who have engaged in this kind of work know that it is very satisfying. Ask anyone who has thus spent his life what his principal motive has been, and it is certain that he will say that it has been the satisfaction he has derived from it. There are other motives, of course, for motives are always mixed. Speaking in chemical terms, motives are mixtures,

---

[1] Written by request by the late President Ira Remsen, Johns Hopkins University.

not elements. It is, however, not necessary to subject these motives to a complete analysis. It is sufficient to say that the chief constituent of those motives that lead us to undertake research is the mental satisfaction derived from it. If that were the only constituent, however, only comparatively few would be engaged in it, for fortunately it is necessary for most of us to make a living. Now, it is possible by practicing research to make a living, and this is coming more and more to be the case. The universities, the research institutes, and the more enlightened industrial establishments are calling for the services of researchers.

Research means quite different things to different people.

To the individual investigator research is really a game, an intriguing puzzle which brings keen intellectual satisfaction to the successful participant. To the layman it has something to do with the relative merits of cigarettes proclaimed in full-color, slick-paper advertisements. To the academician it is the key to the understanding of the universe. The business executive sees it as insurance of his company's future prosperity. Technologists see in research the promise of better processes and products. Governments look to it for higher standards of living and military security. Some men come to research with an almost religious desire to know all of the knowable. Others see it as a tool for the betterment of mankind. Some even see it merely as a "job." Within any or all of these definitions, industry will continue to make increasing contributions to fundamental science, but the universities must always furnish the majority of this type of data.[2]

THE DESIRE TO KNOW

Curiosity, or the desire to know, a characteristic of man and apparently of some of the higher animals, is a great driving force in investigation. It leads men to pry into the secrets of nature, and the more securely hidden they are the greater is the incentive to persist in the search.

Professor Richards says of himself:[3]

---

[2] John A. Leermakers, *Chem. Eng. News*, **29**, 5044 (1951).
[3] T. W. Richards, *Science*, **44**, 39 (1916).

In my case the incentive to the pursuit of science was primarily that intense curiosity concerning the nature of things which echoes down the ages from the time of the ancient philosophers. To the feeling of curiosity, as time went on, was added the perception that only through a knowledge of the fundamental laws of chemistry can men use the resources of the world to the best advantage. Any further gain in this knowledge must, sooner or later, directly or indirectly, give mankind more power. Even an abstract chemical generalization must ultimately be of priceless service to humanity because of the extraordinarily intimate relation between theory and practice.

Dr. Whitney describes some of the joys and benefits of increasing knowledge.[4]

To the devotee scientific research may well become a religion, but whether he sees in the infinite possibilities of matter only the necessary results of permutations among seventy-odd decaying elements or the hand of an all-wise Creator ever uncovering new principles to hopeful investigators, he cannot be blind to the blessings of new truth. This is not produced to order . . . It comes only from following with interest nature's devious and unexpected ways, studying apparently irrelevant phenomena, learning by experiment regardless of aim. And since it is important to us that pioneer effort be individualistic, wanton, clean, but vagabond, it is this type of teacher whom we must support.

The innate desire to know and to understand our surroundings manifests itself early in life. By the time children can walk, they pry into things and later they wear down their elders with incessant questions. This seems to be pure curiosity as the inquiries are seldom connected with things wanted. Sad to say that the desire for knowledge for its own sake gets lost or submerged in more mundane desires as we grow up. An unsolved problem in education is how to preserve the desire to know through the dreary years of enforced learning. Blessed are they who hunger and thirst after knowledge, for in filling themselves they increase the supply for others.

Fortunate it is for society that there are in every generation a few in whom this pure love of knowledge continues

---

[4] W. R. Whitney, *Elec. World*, 75, 152 (1920).

to grow until it becomes a consuming passion. They are the ones who devote their time and energy to research for the sheer joy of discovery, who widen our intellectual horizons, who lead us into the paths of understanding, who uncover principles the applications of which increase our material comforts and raise our standard of living.

Dr. Hammett recognizes our debt to them.[5] "A very large part of the material benefits we enjoy today can be traced back to discoveries made by scientists who were merely indulging their curiosity and had no idea at all what might be the eventual practical results of their investigations . . ." To the scientist . . . "there is no greater personal satisfaction than that found in the search for, and the occasional discovery of, a new concept or a new generalization which increases our understanding of the world around us."

Dr. Hoover believes[6] ". . . that the seeds of productive research are sown and cultivated by true scientists, men dedicated by curiosity, impelled from within by initiative and imagination. One such man with a burning faith and enthusiasm for a project can succeed where a dozen without that vital spark can fail."

Dr. Bush regards research as an act of faith.[7]

For the scientist lives by faith quite as much as the man of deep religious convictions. He operates on faith because he can operate in no other way. His dependence on the principle of causality is an act of faith in a principle unproved and unprovable. Yet he builds on it all his reasoning in regard to nature . . .

So, back of all other motivations, there is a deeper one, vague in outline, seldom expressed, often denied, yet powerful in its influence. Its ultimate expression is beyond our ability. For the present it can be expressed in the faith that man can learn to know and to understand and that it is good to exercise that power and to strive for the extension of our wisdom.

[5] Louis P. Hammett, Chem. Eng. News, **32**, 1462 (1954).
[6] John R. Hoover, Chem. Eng. News, **31**, 2850 (1953).
[7] Vannevar Bush, retiring president of the Carnegie Institution of Washington, in his final report to the board, Chem. Eng. News, **33**, 5577 (1956).

RESEARCH AS A GAME

Of all aspects of research, perhaps the view of it as a game is the most alluring to the great number who follow it. It has all of the characteristics of a game, and of a good one too. The fascination of baseball is in the infinite variety of situations and the utter impossibility of predicting from one moment to the next what will happen. Chemistry offers an even greater variety of combinations among its over one hundred player-elements, some of which can play any position on the whole diamond, and there is always enough uncertainty as to the results to keep us in suspense.

Games of chance appeal to many. There is in research the exciting element of chance, but as Professor Bartlett well says, there is much more.[8] "A sport and good fun research surely is. Only in a limited sense could it be called a game of chance. It is a game of chance like bridge, not like roulette or dice. Everybody holds some kind of hand determined by the possibilities of the phenomena he is investigating. There is all the difference in the world between the way different investigators play their hands, and this determines the difference between a piece of great research and the mere competent establishment of new facts." Several men may walk by chance through a certain territory, but only the one with a Geiger counter spots a uranium deposit. Things happen in our laboratories, but only those with eyes to see make discoveries.

Others are fond of games of skill, billiards or golf; chemical investigations give scope for the exercise of the utmost dexterity in manipulation as well as of the highest skill in construction of apparatus combined with keen discernment in planning.

Much of the zest of a game is in rivalry and the desire to excel our opponents in the contest. This element is present also in research, as we are ever in competition with other investigators, sometimes in close rivalry, in fact we are always playing a world's series, since our work must stand in comparison

[8] Written by request by Paul D. Bartlett.

with that of the whole civilized world. We must go ahead of what anyone else in the wide, wide world has done in our particular line, or our results are not worth publishing, and when we do publish, we present our results to an audience made up of thousands of chemists of all nations and tongues under heaven.

Competition is particularly keen in the industrial field; the chemists of one rubber company may be regarded as a team playing a series of games with teams from all the other rubber companies. To be sure the scores are not posted at the end of each inning, but those interested know who is winning. It is just as thrilling to outdistance another chemist by manufacturing something at 78 cents per pound which he cannot make for less than 80, as it is to go around in 78 to the other fellow's 80. The fact that the company's dividends and the chemist's prospects of promotion depend on the score does not make the game less interesting.

All in all, chemistry is a splendid game, a man's game, into which we can put the best that is in us of strength and of cunning, and not seldom of daring. If played properly, it is a clean game which trains and elevates, and develops the highest qualities.

What Dr. Whitney says of engineering, he might have said with equal force of chemistry.[9]

> No college sport could be put over if it did not contain some of the same elements which make engineering attractive. No one would play the game if it were always a copy or a repetition. If there were no feared defeat nor hoped-for victory, no new stresses applied, no new materials discovered, and no return but gate receipts, there would be no real amateurs and no sport. When this is applied to engineering proper it meets a perfect analogue. Few good engineers play for the gate receipts; they are led on by a will to accomplish. They seldom reproduce a move or repeat a major operation. They are usually trying some new stunt and are elated or depressed with emphasis because effects are relatively permanent. But the mental tools and processes are just like those of clean-cut sport.

---

[9] W. R. Whitney, *Elec. World*, **75**, 153 (1920).

Professor Metcalf believes in research for the fun of it and the love of it.[10]

The motives to research may be as varied as are the characters and interests of the men engaged in the pursuit, but the urge which seems the most productive of the highest-grade work is that of the fun of the game, the pleasure in the research itself, the love of truth and its pursuit. Ulterior motives of personal profit or even the desire to promote the progress of civilization and the well-being of society, all have an element of danger. They are likely to persuade the student, perhaps unconsciously, to control the direction of his search, turning it into so-called profitable channels. But no man can know where lie the great undiscovered truths. Truth itself is a safer guide into the unknown than is any man's guess as to the probable best line of approach to worth-while knowledge. The student who humbly goes where the subject itself seems to lead him, eager to follow whatever turn the investigation naturally takes, is the one most likely to find the richest deposits for his mining. Truth is too manifold, too unexpected, too great, and often too profoundly simple, for any man's successful anticipation. From the most unexpected sources come discoveries that open great vistas far beyond the previous imagining of any man . . . Interest in the subject itself, the desire to know the truth, the pleasure, the uplift of soul that comes with the gaining of some new vision into a hitherto unexplored field of reality, these are the safest guides, leading one to results in value far beyond fame, or financial profit, or some invention that shall increase the perhaps already too great complexity of human life . . .

EXPLORATION

One of the earliest human desires seems to have been to know what was beyond the horizon, and there were some who ventured forth to see. There has always been a fascination in exploration which has led men to endure hardships and brave dangers, known and unknown, in tropical jungles, in the frozen north, in caves of the earth, and in the depths of the sea.

---

[10] M. M. Metcalf, *Science*, 59, 27 (1924).

There are rigid limits to geographic explorations. Since Columbus blundered into the two Americas, which he could not have well missed, there are no more continents to be discovered. The North and South Poles were prime objectives. Everyone knew their exact location, but reaching them was delayed by transportation difficulties. Now there are no more poles to discover. Large-scale geographical exploration is a thing of the past. Having finished with the earth, men have turned to the exploration of space.

In chemical research, there is the same haunting mystery of the unexplored but, in sharp contrast, the more we discover, the more vistas open up, just as in astronomy, where the larger the telescope, the farther we seem to be from the limits of the universe.

Chemists have the advantage that they can make far-reaching explorations within the confines of a single laboratory, with equipment only a little more costly than the bag of gum drops with which Doc Cook made his imaginary trip to the pole.

MYSTERY STORIES

Those fond of reading mystery stories, and of testing their powers of deduction in following the half-concealed clues that are strewn along the way, should be fascinated by the stories of the discovery of the constitution of uric acid, of indigo, of mellitic acid, and of other natural products. Some of these are short shorts, while others are long and involved. The story of the determination of the structure of penicillin fills a ponderous volume.

But why stop at reading chemical whodunits? It is more satisfying to turn detective and tackle one of the many unsolved mysteries which are lying around. The by-products of many organic reactions offer interesting problems. Modern physicochemical methods are of great service in solving problems of structure.

RESEARCH FOR THE PUBLIC GOOD

The industrial wealth of the world is part material and part immaterial. The first consists of buildings, machinery, and all the other things that are reported as plant investment. These, though they appear so substantial, are actually ephemeral. Buildings are put up when needed and torn down when no longer useful; machinery wears out or becomes obsolete and is discarded. Many of the huge German chemical plants were obliterated during World War II, but within a few short postwar years better products were coming out of better buildings. The know-how by which plants are built was not touched by the bombs. The immaterial part, the priceless possession of the whole human race, is the accumulation of scientific knowledge and industrial know-how, each single item of which is the result of the thinking and experimenting of some individual, from the prehistoric hunter, fashioning the first flint arrowhead, to the atomic scientists of our day. Knowledge is the principal thing. Research, which adds to human knowledge, is a public service. This is true whether the addition is large or small. The benefit of new truth extends to the whole human race.

Regardless of its immediate objective, research serves the public. In the university, the professor may be activated by the desire to test a certain theory, while the student is particularly interested in qualifying for a degree. Medical research is, of course, directly for the public good. Various governmental departments conduct extensive research for the benefit of the public. The four Regional Laboratories were set up to investigate uses for the products of their respective regions.

Industrial research, though undertaken for private profit, results in benefits to the public. Suppose a corporation's research leads to the development of a new fiber which is patented, manufactured, and sold in a free market. Consumers buy it because they judge it to be the best for the money. The public profits. The corporation makes a profit, a large part of which goes to the government in taxes. At the end of seventeen years,

Lavoisier, Dalton, Berzelius, and Liebig, if we, too, become investigators. It is not just a high-sounding phrase but literal fact that the only way to understand and appreciate the investigations of others is to engage in similar work ourselves. This is an important reason for including research in university courses.

REFLEX INFLUENCE OF RESEARCH

Those who have been instructing students have noted the accelerated rate of their development as soon as research is taken up. A college student may be quick at grasping what is given in the lectures and retentive of what he hears or reads, but he is merely a schoolboy of larger growth till he is seasoned by research. The average student is quite bewildered when he first essays the unknown and has no laboratory manual or journal article on which to rely. He is apt to clutch at his instructor as a pupil in a swimming lesson. For a time he wants someone to okay his results and assure him that he is on the way, but soon he finds his feet on the ground and learns to walk with firmer tread, as he begins to realize that all the *terra firma* of accepted chemical knowledge was once only hazy hypothesis.

With the vanishing of the supports on which he previously leaned, the student develops self-reliance and begins to think for himself, to draw his own conclusions, and to formulate his own hypotheses; from being a follower, he becomes a leader; from memorizing results obtained by others, he produces something for others.

"Small pieces of routine research can be carried out by any intelligent student, and the results obtained are often of some direct objective value, although not by any means always. The chief value of such research is to the man who conducts it. The worker has learned to look on a problem, however small, with a clear, unprejudiced eye, to come into contact at first hand with facts, to distrust textbooks and references generally; in fine to rely upon himself." [11] Research by undergraduate students will be taken up in chapter 6.

---

[11] James Walker, *J. Soc. Chem. Ind.*, 34, 1122 (1915).

Life in the great world outside the laboratory is in verity research. New situations and unsolved problems await you every morning and follow you home at dusk. Of all parts of your training, research is that which best fits the life into which you are to plunge on graduation. It has often been noted that many who win all honors in examinations during their college course sink into oblivion soon after, while their less brilliant classmates forge steadily ahead and ultimately reach high positions. High examination grades may frequently be made by a retentive memory and judicious cramming, with little actual grasp of the subject. Independence of thought and self-reliance in the face of unforeseen difficulties, resourcefulness in surmounting obstacles, and perseverance when things look most hopeless are qualities that make for success in research and your subsequent work alike.

It does not follow that one who does well in research will make money in business. It is frequently quite the reverse, since one who concentrates his whole attention on the scientific side of a problem may fail to see the practical side. The mistake is, however, not in the research method, but in the failure to apply research to the practical as well as to the scientific part of the problems.

AMATEURS IN RESEARCH

In chapter 2 a large share of the credit for the development of chemistry into a science was given to those who worked for the love of it. The amateur is usually thought of as a half-baked, would-be professional, but in research the amateur is the one who counts. Of course, the majority of the leading investigators are in universities, research institutions, and industrial laboratories, but those who achieve results of the highest grade are amateurs at heart and investigate for the love of the results without regard to financial reward. Those whose minds are on the money have the "form of godliness but deny the power thereof."

A review of the great names in chemical history reveals a large percentage who were amateurs in the narrowest

sense, never receiving money for their research, as Priestley and
Griess, who have been already mentioned.

Scheele, the codiscoverer of oxygen, compounded
drugs for a living and mixed chemicals for the love of it. When,
after many years of struggle, he had the prospect of an income
he wrote: "Oh, how happy I am, with never a care about eating
or drinking or dwelling. . . . There is no delight like that which
springs from a discovery; it is a joy that gladdens the heart."

Lord Cavendish inherited a title and a fortune and
was utterly indifferent to both. Research was not only simply
his chief love, but was his only concern throughout the years of
his long life. He shunned human companionship and devoted
his time to experimenting, turning his large residence into a series
of laboratories.

Lavoisier was busy in politics and philanthropy and
devoted to science the fortune he made as tax collector and
business administrator.

Carey Lea, who laid the foundation for the science
of photography and discovered colloidal silver in its multifarious
forms, was an amateur and spent his long life experimenting in
a laboratory in his own home from which he published some
four hundred scientific communications.

Dr. Whitney directed the spending of millions for
research, but was intensely interested in the amateur.[12]

The part of research I am most interested in promot-
ing is what we may call the *unpaid* kind, not because it is
cheapest, but because it is most valuable. It is most neglected,
most poorly understood, most in need of appreciative support in America. The separate industries do not need en-
couragement in research nearly so much as the nation needs
it. The industries can be depended on to estimate its value
to them, for they take annual inventories. But a country,
which keeps no books, seems to have to depend on accident
for its most valuable research work.

We take a look at the past:

The great bulk of all our scientific discovery and
research in the past has been due to individual labour and

---

[12] W. R. Whitney, *Ind. Eng. Chem.*, **8**, 537 (1916).

initiative; much of it a labour of love, unrecognized at the time. Men of great genius have opened up new lines of thought or pursued private researches often with very inadequate appliances. In fact the greater part of past British research may be said to have been amateur work, not in the sense that it was lacking in the highest qualities, but only in the sense that it was pursued for the sheer pleasure and interest of it by private individuals.[13]

We strain our eyes to see the utopia of the future:[14]

There is no reason to suppose that the number of amateur investigators may not greatly increase under a more favorable form of society. In the ideal commonwealth of the future, it may not be in the least surprising to find that the communal furnaceman, after his four-hour day, is conducting elaborate investigations in paleobotany, and that the communal laundress is an acknowledged authority on colloid chemistry.

Dr. Little, who achieved notable success in industrial research, felt that it is more rewarding to work for love than for money.

I cannot forbear in this connection to refer to the opportunity which research offers to the sons of rich men. Their independent financial position enables them to attack problems, the study of which in any comprehensive way is denied to most chemists by reason of the expense involved. It is, therefore, relatively easy for the financially independent chemist to achieve distinction by intensive work in a wisely selected field. He will reap the satisfactions which come through the fellowship of science and through public recognition. There will open to him a new world of mystery and wonder and opportunity. There are many rich men's sons to whom a career in science offers far more worthy objects than the making of money which they do not need or the devotion of their lives to sport.[15]

Charles Darwin was just such an amateur. He did much for science and, incidentally, made himself famous. He derived satisfaction out of his travels. In getting for himself, he gave to others.

[13] J. A. Fleming, *Electrician*, **76**, 711 (1916).
[14] W. M. Wheeler, *Science*, **53**, 60 (1921).
[15] Written by request by A. D. Little.

Research offers an attractive way of life for a person of independent means. One so situated can try to tackle any problem that beckons and follow where the trail leads. Not having examinations to prepare for, lectures to give, or committee meetings to attend, the whole of one's time and energies can be concentrated on the chosen problem. In my opinion, there is nothing in the material realm so satisfying as working with one's own hands on a problem of one's own choosing. I look back on two happy years, 1909 to 1911, which were spent at Johns Hopkins University as Johnson Scholar. My entire time was spent on research, without restrictions or interruptions. In that period, I began work on organic sulfur compounds which has continued for fifty years.

A free-lance researcher may attach himself to some university in order to have library facilities and congenial associations.

THE PASSING OF THE AMATEUR

Dr. Conant lauds the amateur and wonders how science will fare if he does disappear:[16]

In general, the great scientific advances of this period were made by amateurs, as they had been from the seventeenth century on. Not until we reach the second and third quarters of the nineteenth century do we find that those who were most prominent in advancing science were devoting their entire time to scientific activities by which they earned their living. Today, the scientific amateur, in the sense that I am using the word, has all but disappeared.

The second point is that the revolutionary advances in theoretical science were made very largely by amateurs. And clearly almost all the great advances in industry until this century were made by the independent inventor. These men have passed. They have no intellectual descendants. Will their twentieth-century equivalents—the professional scientist, the applied-science laboratory, the engineering group—be able to carry on? Perhaps; but I submit it is too soon to draw definite conclusions. There is such a thing as momentum in human affairs as well as in physics. And I

---

[16] James B. Conant, *Chem. Eng. News* **29**, 2262-4 (1951).

submit that we of the mid-twentieth century have been moving forward to a considerable degree because of the momentum accumulated in the days of the amateur and the lone inventor. At all events, there is sufficient doubt about the ability of the new ways to be substituted for the old for us to examine the problem with some care.

PRESERVING THE AMATEUR SPIRIT

No one who ever saw Babe Ruth swat a ball over the back fence could doubt that the Babe loved to play baseball. He kept the amateur spirit in spite of being paid, and paid rather well.

Most of those who devote their time to research are paid, as otherwise they would have to find some other way of making a living. The question for the individual is: Are you paid because you do research or do you do research because you are paid? No one begrudges a comfortable living to a capable researcher who works for the love of it, but one wonders whether research that is done just for the pay is worth the cost. No one thinks to ask a garbage collector whether or not he enjoys his work; it probably does not matter. In creative thinking it is different.

It happens with considerable regularity that the problem assigned by management to a recent recruit is one in line with the company's interests rather than with the chemist's tastes. Perhaps an uninviting problem is handed out more to see what it will do to the chemist than to see what he will do to it. What then? A problem is a challenge, and no knight can ignore a challenge. It has been my experience that the most unattractive problem becomes absorbingly interesting when one really digs into it. The more one works on it, the more one sees to do. Many of those who were forced to work on mustard gas during World War I continued research on it long after the war was over. After forty years, some, including myself, are still interested in it. When you really get acquainted with a problem, you are apt to fall in love with it. Then you work on it as an amateur and the check at the end of the month is only an incident—a pleasant incident to be sure.

I believe that I have preserved the amateur spirit. Participating in research with students at Johns Hopkins University I regarded as a privilege for which I would have gladly paid had I been financially independent. I never undertook or assigned to a student a problem in which I had any financial interest. I never applied for a patent on any of the results because I did not think any of them worth patenting. It was practically the same with my consulting contacts. I was paid for my time and enjoyed discussing with chemists problems in which I had no financial interest.

This is simply a statement of my own attitude toward research and is not intended as a criticism of those who do things otherwise.

RESEARCH AS A HOBBY

In chapter 2 and in this chapter, high tribute has been paid to amateurs. Few are so situated as to be amateurs for full time, but many can be on part time.

Everyone needs a vocation and an avocation, a job and a hobby. Not so many years ago, men worked in factories twelve hours a day and on the farm from sunrise to sunset. They had to work long hours just for the necessities of life. Little time was left for recreation. Thanks to the efforts of the few who have worked to devise better and quicker ways of doing things, we now have the forty-hour week as standard. Counting out one day for rest and worship leaves 144 hours of which the forty-hour week is only 28%. This means 72% for rest and recreation. Whole industries have been built up to furnish things to occupy our spare time. We used to go driving for recreation, but traffic jams have taken the fun out of that. Of late television has come in to use up spare time. I recommend research to those who love to explore, to go hunting, to put together jigsaw puzzles, or to read whodunits. Research has the thrills of all of these and, in addition, the advantage that the results may extend human knowledge.

The number of those who might take up research as a hobby, beginning modestly with small problems, is really

large. Creditable research has been done and the results published in the *Journal of the American Chemical Society* by candidates for the B.S. degree. So it seems that those who have received
that degree might do as well. Of course, only those, in either
class, who have exceptional determination will achieve results.
Since they are not pestered by examinations and deadlines, those
who have their degrees can undertake larger tasks.

Reference should be made to chapters 4 and 5 on
finding and attacking problems, and to chapter 6 on undergraduate research.

A well-equipped chemical laboratory may cost many
thousands of dollars, but a small home laboratory, adequate for
handling selected problems, may be set up for the cost of a used
car and entail less upkeep.

Berzelius, a famous chemist of a century ago, did
much of his work on the family cook stove. It is always well for
several amateurs to meet and talk as did Priestley and Wedgwood.

At first sight, it may seem absurd to suggest re-
search as a hobby for a chemist, but actually it is a logical choice.
One who has had sufficient training to qualify as a chemist
should be able to undertake a problem of some sort. Somewhere
within the broad realm of chemistry, there should be a problem,
far enough removed from one's daily occupation, to be classed
as a hobby. A chemist draws heavily on the store of accumulated
knowledge, every item of which is the result of the research of
someone. In recognition of this, he should feel obligated to add
something.

There are probably more than 100,000 chemists in
North America, 90,000 of them members of the American Chemical Society. Many of these are active in research, but many thousands are not. The routine analyst may amuse himself by teaching
an IBM machine to do his job. As he makes his rounds, a chemical salesman might well pick up an idea or two which he would
like to try out. A chemist in industrial research thinks of many
experiments that he would like to make but cannot on company
time. One condemned to sit and read reports should have the
relief of trying out an idea of his own. Any chemist is liable to

be struck by an idea. If he is not dead he will notice it and may do something about it.

Spending one's time as a chemist, particularly in research, should stimulate one's curiosity rather than stifle it. Is chemistry for you just a job in which you grow weary, or a way of life in which you find more and more satisfaction as the years go by?

ARE YOU OVER SIXTY-FIVE?

Turn backward, turn backward, O time in thy flight
Make me a chemist again with all thy might.

If you are over sixty-five, you have participated in the most active period in the development of chemistry. You have been a professional a long time, doing the things that others wanted done. Why not turn amateur and have a grand time doing just what you want to do? As a free-lance researcher you can sally forth and challenge any problem that crosses your path. As a valiant knight you may do battle with some disease which, like a fierce dragon, preys upon hapless humans.

In all these years there must have been numerous problems, some little, some big, that interested you but you could not turn aside to solve them. Now is your chance to get at them. It is fun to work just to satisfy your curiosity. If you blunder into something of commercial importance, you can turn it over to some charity and maintain your amateur status.

If you do not have a lot of problems stored up, just look in the *Chemical and Engineering News* at the exciting advertisements of chemicals, some brand new, some old but just becoming commercially available.

To those who have been active, enforced idleness is unbearable. Men deteriorate physically and mentally when they cease to have interests. There is one, and only one, way to keep active, and that is to keep active. At retirement, one can start on the decline or one can acquire new interests, which must be absorbing to be effective. I had always enjoyed getting around and meeting interesting people, so I started visiting southern institutions in the interest of research. In the course of about ten years I made 292 visits to about a dozen laboratories. This was a neat way of making enjoyable trips without any cost to me; the institutions paid my travel expenses.

A chemist has the great advantage that he can shift to some line of research which will be different enough to give a refreshing change but in which his experience will be of service. Why not renew your youth by hiking back to the laboratory where you got your start? You will find that your legs are not as good as they used to be, but your mind should be better. Your experience should enable you to plan experiments so that you can get more information with less work. Taper joints and other modern conveniences have taken much of the drudgery out of laboratory work. Do not let anyone give you an assistant, except for washing dishes. After retirement I had the use of a small laboratory. With some voluntary assistance, I prepared some hundreds of compounds in a study of regularities in the melting points of series of sulfides and ethers. Some of the results are given in my book: *Organic Chemistry of Bivalent Sulfur,* Volume II, pp. 85-96.[17] I continued experimenting on methods of preparing organic compounds until my eyes failed so that I could not see the labels on the bottles.

With the present rapid growth of the American Chemical Society, there will soon be enough oldsters to form a division. Then, perhaps, someone will offer a medal for the best paper, done with his own hands by a chemist over 65, and then one for the over-75 class. Chevreul, whose fundamental work on fats has stood the test of time, read papers at scientific meetings after he was a hundred.

Many retired chemists are not so circumstanced that they can return to the laboratory; some have been away from it for years. For them, however, there are also many interesting and important tasks. The tens of thousands of articles that are appearing contain a mass of information which needs to be studied and correlated with what has gone before in order that its full significance may be realized. The discovery of new relationships among old facts may be even more important than adding new experimental data. Reviews and monographs bring together facts

[17] New York, Chemical Publishing Co., Inc., 1959.

from various sources and present them as an orderly whole. The writing of these is best done by experienced chemists who have the required perspective and are not pressed to turn out reports to meet a deadline. Literary projects may be carried on in spite of physical disabilities. A friend of mine who falls down when he attempts to go on the street is still editing for *Chemical Abstracts*. Thinking and writing may be done in an arm chair as they have been done by another friend, Professor John R. Sampey. In 1949, while reading a paper at a scientific meeting, he suffered a stroke from which he has not yet recovered entirely. Since then he has published many papers, including eighty reviews on the chemotherapy of cancer. He abstracts articles on this subject for *Excerpta Medica* and covers thirty-two journals for *Chemical Abstracts*. Several years ago he received the Herter Medal and is now being given another award.

KEEPING YOUNG BY RESEARCH

There are but two ages of man, two divisions of life, ascending and descending, crescendo and diminuendo, growth and decay, youth and old age. It has been suggested that old men be chloroformed, and sixty has been tentatively set as the age when men become old. But senescence is in attitudes, not in years. Many are old at thirty, while others are in vigorous and expanding youth at seventy. At eighty Moses began a strenuous forty years as lawgiver and leader; at the same age, Grandma Moses began painting and is still going strong at one hundred. One starts to grow old when one passes the peak in one's life. It has happened that a chemist, who had toiled and produced and grown thereby, till he had attained fame and position, has let up on these activities on being appointed to some high professorship.

If old age begins when the crest is passed, when the mind ceases to expand and produce, then it is within the power of every individual to postpone old age, perhaps not indefinitely, since the tissues of our bodies and our brain cells do get old in time and cease to function, but at least till he is well stricken in years.

Teaching is wonderfully stimulating to the young instructor. There is exhilaration in working out new courses and putting them across, but after a time the novelty wears off. A teacher is prone to settle down into a rut and start to grow old long before the age set for his retirement. To one so circumstanced, the means of staving off old age, of keeping alive, is the finding of some interest, some endeavor into which energy and effort can be put to the quickening of the intellectual pulse.

Research supplies this need better than almost anything else and keeps one thinking, working, and growing, thus maintaining the upward slope of the curve. The publication of the results of the research is tangible evidence to the world that life is not extinct. Would that all teachers were like Nef, Emil Fischer, and Frank Whitmore, from whose laboratories papers appeared regularly right to the end—some being published after the obituaries!

Universities grow, science grows, and the professor must grow too. Shall he only grow old? Let him keep active in research and expand as rapidly as his institution; rather let him occupy his mind with problems in chemistry than worry over retirement benefits.

There are few things that enhance the respect of students for a professor as much as the knowledge that he is in the vanguard of his science.

I am even more strongly convinced of the correctness of this statement than I was when it was first written some thirty-six years ago. I believe that my interest in research has delayed my senescence. At eighty-nine, my thoughts are still on research and I am writing this book to recommend it to others.

RESEARCH AS A WAY OF LIFE

As a vocation, as an avocation, or as a combination of the two, research ranks high. It is, of course, not the only high calling, but it is the purpose of this book to extol it as one of the highest. Creative thinking does not exhaust the mind but stimulates and strengthens it, and there is no "morning after." In the research game there are winners but there are no losers.

Pasteur won, but the millions who have drunk pasteurized milk are also winners.

Only a favored few can devote all, or a major part, of their time to research, but all chemists can be, and should be, researchers in attitude and in spirit even if they are not in practice. "As a man thinketh in his heart so is he." A man may be a bank robber for years, but never have the opportunity to stage a hold-up. The attitude of mind is the real thing; the acts of the hands are only its manifestations. While making a routine analysis or a simple organic preparation, a research-minded chemist considers each step and tries to think up improvements.

It would be of immense benefit to the human race if people in all walks of life adopted the research principles of close observation, careful trial, and objective thinking. In public affairs, it would be desirable to substitute dispassionate reasoning from established facts for the torrents of partisan oratory to which we are subjected. "Prove all things, hold fast to that which is good" was said long ago, but is still good practice.

At the present time when each weekly issue of *Chemical and Engineering News,* to mention only one publication, carries pages of alluring advertisements for research chemists and engineers, there is no need to emphasize the attractiveness of research, but there is a real danger that it will come to be regarded as a gainful occupation for five days a week, from 8 to 4:30, with a coffee break and time for lunch, rather than a way of life for every waking hour of every day of the year. The real research devotee carries his problem with him as he walks by day and dreams about it when he lies down at night. From such and from only such can we expect creative thinking of a high order. A man may change his coat at the striking of the clock, but not his nature. If he is not a research chemist at 7:59 he will not be one at 8:01. If he is a research chemist he will continue to be one after he removes his laboratory coat at 4:30.

This is written to exalt research as a way of life, rather than just another way of making a living. However, a chemist must have a living in order to be productive in research. This is not a call to establish a mendicant order of scientists who abjure all else to devote themselves to research. A scientist should be a person of the highest type, a well-adjusted member of society, broadly educated and interested in all that concerns humanity. The scientist seeks truth and finds beauty in nature; he should not be oblivious to truth and beauty in human relationships and in things of the spirit either.

Dr. Pauling lauded academic research:[18] "A career of academic research—research and teaching in a university or college—is the best of all possible careers for those people who are suited to it by nature and disposition."

THE PROFIT MOTIVE

Money makes the mare go.

An individual may engage in research just for the fun of it, but corporations undertake research for profit. The development of synthetic dyes during the last part of the nineteenth century led to the organization of industrial research on a large scale which gave Germany the chemical leadership of the world. Corporations put millions of dollars into research because experience has shown that it pays and pays well. However, profits do not come automatically and seldom quickly. To achieve satisfactory results, there must be capable management and a well-directed, comprehensive plan. To make an antiseptic is a simple matter; to get a good one is not so easy; to get a really excellent one is something else; and to dig up one that is far better than any other on the market is quite a different matter. Since the results of any one excursion into the unknown are uncertain, it is desirable to follow a number of lines. Chemical directors are not all-wise, but experience enables them to make a reasonable proportion of good guesses. Since, on the average, it requires about five years to prepare a new product in the laboratory, to test its applicability for a certain use, to work out an efficient manufacturing process, to build a plant, and to put a finished product on the market, much patient money has to be spent before profits come.

Failure to realize the uncertainties of research and

---

[18] Linus Pauling, *Chem. Eng. News*, **28,** 3970 (1950).

to take into account the conditions of success has led to sad
failures. An example will illustrate this. A small manufacturer
of chewing gum heard of the large sums of money being made
as the result of research, so he set up a laboratory and hired a
friend of mine at $15,000 a year to direct research. All was rosy,
but several months went by and no million-dollar invention had
been made, so the project was discontinued with losses all around.

RESEARCH FOR SURVIVAL

The environment changed,
the dodo did not; the dodo is not.

The dodo was a slow thinker and did not realize
the necessity of adaptation.

Surrounded by powerful wild animals, *Homo sa-*
piens saw that weapons were necessary for survival and set about
devising them. From that time until this good day, men have had
to fight continuously against hunger, pestilence, floods and
drought, and, sad to say, often against other men. The most
dangerous enemies were discovered only after the invention of
the microscope.

Few realize the grim battle in which no quarter is
given and in which there is never any truce, the continuous
battle for food between man on the one side and insects and
weeds on the other. It is said that today one fourth of the world's
population does not have enough to eat. Only by research can
means be found to provide food when the population doubles,
as it probably will within a few years. In our competitive system
where one "has to run fast just to stand still" an oil company
has to push research in order to survive when all the other oil
companies are deep in research and each is making a better gasoline than any of the others. Our government is spending billions
on rocket research in order to insure our survival as a nation.

4.∎ Finding problems

PROBLEMS EVERYWHERE

Finding a problem is a serious difficulty to many, and all the more troublesome because it is imaginary. It is a difficulty until one gets started and then the problem becomes how to dodge problems. They come from the east and from the west, from within and from without; they come in droves as the locusts came to afflict Pharaoh; they disturb your reveries in church, pop into your head during your bath; they start from every page you read and even break into your dreams. The thing is to get started on some piece of research—then every experiment performed suggests two more, and each of these, two more, and so on: they multiply like broomsticks of the sorcerer's apprentice, but the multiplication process does not start till you begin to work. One who begins to work and think will never lack for something on which to work and think. The only difficulty is in

63

getting the first "think." The process is autocatalytic, the products of the reaction accelerating it.

We often hear someone say: "An idea struck me." If you expose yourself you are liable to get hit. Some of the ways in which research ideas have come, and still come, will be noted.

IDEAS FROM READING

Ideas, ideas everywhere . . .
for those who pause to think

Everything that is known about organic compounds is known because someone wrote down the results of his experiments. Such writings make up the chemical journals. In their reading, there is great reward. We read articles in these journals, not passively for entertainment, but with active minds, to get facts, to find out how these facts were discovered, and to pick up suggestions for experiments of our own. Here the emphasis is put on the last of these three. Much has been written about improving reading speed, with little said about what is to be accomplished by the reading. In reading chemical articles, the prize goes to the slow reader, the one who pauses to relate each new fact to the already known, to test the validity and implications of the conclusions and, above all, to look for suggestions for research. One should constantly ask questions: Were the experiments well planned? Were they properly carried out? What if the temperature had been higher? Would a catalyst have done any good? Are the conclusions fully supported by the experiments? What other conclusions might be drawn? What more or less analogous compounds would react similarly? What other experiments could be made to verify, modify, or contradict the conclusions?

What may happen when one reads slowly is illustrated by how an idea struck me one summer day in 1909, while reading an article on esterification. The reaction was explained by assuming the addition of the alcohol to the acid to form an intermediate which split into water and the ester:

$$\text{MeCO·OH} + \text{EtOH} \rightleftharpoons \text{MeC} \begin{array}{c} \diagup \text{OH} \\ -\text{OH} \\ \diagdown \text{OEt} \end{array} \rightleftharpoons \begin{array}{c} \text{MeCO·OEt} \\ +\text{HOH} \end{array}$$

I was not in a hurry and paused to think. The question popped up in my mind: How does the alcohol divide, Et—OH or EtO—H? if into EtO— and —H, the oxygen of the alcohol should go into the ester and the hydroxyl of the acid into the water. This question was subsequently answered by the use of tagged oxygen, which was not available in 1909. I remembered reading, one summer day, fifteen years before, in Remsen's book, that a mercaptan is the analog of an alcohol—so off I went to the laboratory and to the preparation of 1400 grams of ethyl mercaptan. Only the janitor and I were working in the laboratory and, fortunately, he had no sense of smell. When the mercaptan was heated with benzoic acid in a sealed tube, esterification did take place and the product was the thiol ester, PhCOSEt. The mercaptan had divided into EtS and H. Answering one question raised another and another. The reversibility of the reaction had to be determined, then the location of the equilibrium, then relative esterification velocities and equilibria for different mercaptans and for the *ortho, meta,* and *para* toluic acids. Ethyl dithiobenzoate, PhCS·SEt, had to be made from thiobenzamide and mercaptan. As a sequel to this work on mercaptans, the American Petroleum Institute placed at the Johns Hopkins Chemistry Laboratory a project for the preparation of a number of mercaptans and for the study of their reactions. In recent years, some 400 sulfides have been prepared from these mercaptans in a study of regularities in their melting points. After fifty years, I am still trying to find answers to questions which came up while engaged in finding answers to previous questions about mercaptans and sulfides.

It was not reading, but listening to a lecture on insulin that started Professor du Vigneaud on a long line of brilliant researches on sulfur compounds.[1]

The work on biochemically important sulfur compounds, cited in the Nobel award, formed a part of a trail of sulfur research that began approximately thirty years ago with a study of the sulfur of insulin and encompassed recently the first synthesis of a polypeptide hormone. It might, therefore, be of interest to unravel some of the stepwise evolve-

---

[1] Vincent du Vigneaud, *Science,* **123,** 967-74 (1956).

ment of our researches from insulin to oxytocin and to bring
into focus the background of the research findings and the
thinking behind the researches.

This trail becomes apparent only in retrospect. Obviously, I did not start out to study sulfur as my life's work.
And yet, as I look back over the trail of many years, I en-
counter the fact that this thread of sulfur has been the thread
of continuity running through practically all of my research
endeavors.

By reading and pondering the published investigations of others, we frequently see something that the author has
not considered properly, or think of some experiment which
would verify or disprove his hypothesis. Some of the greatest advances in chemistry have been made by men opposing each other
in an experimental debate as in the case of Stas who upheld the
idea of the definiteness of chemical combination and Bertholet
who opposed it; or the great discussion between Hantzsch, Bam-
berger, and Bloomstrand as to the constitution of diazo compounds. In each of these cases, the leaders on the two sides
marshalled many supporters and an enormous amount of careful
experimenting was done from which emerged important conclusions that were accepted by both sides and have stood the test of
subsequent investigation.

If one compares two articles on the same subject,
discrepancies are apt to be found which may not be cleared up by
the later author. Further investigation to find where the truth
lies is in order. The literature abounds in articles describing work
taken up for just such reason. In working out ideas suggested by
the work of others, great care must be taken not to infringe on
their rights.

REWORKING OLD GROUND

A good way to obtain problems is to look through
Beilstein and note compounds or reactions that have not been
studied for twenty or thirty years. There are many of these and
in almost every case, something of value can be accomplished by
repeating and extending the old experiments. New light may
make old problems look very different. Sometimes by applying

modern interpretations to the experimental data of a past generation, new relations can be seen and important deductions made, even without new experimental work. A field that has lain fallow for a score of years is apt to yield a harvest to one who tills it, particularly if improved methods of agriculture are used, just as the tailings from old mining operations sometimes yield more gold to the cyanide process than was originally obtained from the ore.

Even better than reading *Beilstein* is a thoughtful perusal of the original articles in the chemical journals. Work done fifty years ago, or at any other period in the past, was done with apparatus available at that time and the results were interpreted in terms of theories then current. With the knowledge and equipment which we now have, results are obtainable which were beyond the reach of earlier experimenters. For example, separations can be made with modern fractionating columns and by chromatography which were undreamed of only a few years ago. High-pressure equipment has made many syntheses possible. These are only examples.

This is illustrated as follows. In 1879, Bahlson bubbled ethylene through benzene containing aluminum chloride and got a small amount of ethylbenzene. For some years, I had been interested in high-speed stirring, and this appeared to be a good reaction on which to try its efficiency. Experiments showed that, with high-speed stirring, ethylene can be made to react so rapidly with benzene, containing aluminum chloride, that this is a practical method for the ethylation of benzene. This led to an extensive study of the alkylation of benzene. At that time, no one thought of ethylbenzene as having any commercial value. Later it became important for making styrene for synthetic rubber and plastics. On the plant scale, agitation under pressure is more convenient than high-speed stirring.

EXTENDING THE SCOPE OF AN OLD REACTION

To find new applications for a much-used reaction, such as the Friedel and Crafts, discovered in 1877, would seem a difficult task, but actually it is not. This and other important reactions are described in review articles in books and in journals. These give long lists of instances of their application. A study of any one of these lists will, however, suggest many additional uses. It is more interesting to think up and try out border-line cases where there is uncertainty as to whether the reaction will go in the usual direction.

From time to time compounds, which have been little more than entries in *Beilstein,* become available in quantity. These and new compounds, which are being brought out commercially, offer many opportunities for new applications of old reactions.* Advertisements of compounds such as these appear frequently in *Chemical and Engineering News.*

EXPLOITING A NEW REACTION

This is well illustrated by what happened when the Grignard reaction was announced, early in this century. Alkyl halides were plentiful and a number of aldehydes and ketones were available. Dry ether, magnesium, and a flask with a reflux condenser were the only other things required. Scores of chemists in several countries went to work and turned out, along with other things, hundreds of secondary and tertiary alcohols. There are still many possibilities in this reaction, particularly with the higher alkyl halides, octyl to octadecyl, which were not available when the interest in the Grignard reaction was at its height.

Catalytic hydrogenation, which was discovered at about the same time as the Grignard reagent, is still going strong. Other reactions have followed these and each has given a fresh impetus to research. Lithium aluminum hydride is coming into wide use as a reducing agent. The reduction of amides provides a simple, direct method for the preparation of amines. N-Propyl-N-butylacetamide can be reduced to ethyl-propyl-butyl amine which can be alkylated with methyl iodide to the quaternary ammonium salt containing four different alkyls. This is only one of several classes of reductions by this reagent.

An alert chemist is ever on the lookout for new reactions and new reagents. Other alert chemists unwittingly may

---

* This is discussed in more detail in chapter 6.

work in the same direction. Some duplication is, however, desirable. When the same compound is made by two chemists and the determinations of the properties check, we have confidence in the results.

THE IMPETUS OF A NEW THEORY

The recognition by Kekulé of the quadrivalence of carbon supplied a rational basis for the formulation of aliphatic compounds, and his benzene theory (1865) gave a clue to aromatic compounds. These ideas gave a tremendous impetus to research. In modern phrase, he supplied organic chemists with a road map and they went places. Incidentally, it may be said that reading the chemical journals, particularly the *Berichte* of the period 1865-1890, is to be recommended to students. In that period, much of what is taught in first year organic chemistry was being worked out laboriously.

Of course, epoch-making ideas, such as those of Kekulé, do not come every day, but there is a constant stream of lesser ones to keep chemists thinking. Ideas that suggest experiments are judged to be useful; a crazy idea that sends one to the laboratory rates high.

PATENTS AS SOURCES OF IDEAS

Patents should be looked over . . .
but should NOT be overlooked.

Chemical patents disclose many novel reactions, some of which are suitable for exploitation in academic research. They are considered here as sources of information and of ideas. Patents are too often disregarded by academic chemists. It must be admitted that a few patents belong on the fiction shelf along with the writings of Baron Münchausen, but the vast majority contains information from the painstaking research of highly trained chemists. The first United States patent was for a chemical process.[2]

Not all chemical patents are of interest to the aca-

---

[2] T. D. Boone, *Ind. Eng. Chem. News Ed.,* 18, 365 (1940).

demic chemists. One on an improvement in the xanthation of cellulose would be ignored, though it might be important to a manufacturer of rayon. Those that disclose new compounds and new preparation methods are to be examined. A new compound may be of interest for its own sake or as an intermediate. Any new method extends our knowledge of preparative chemistry.

The thoughtful chemist will endeavor to relate a new reaction to the known, to understand why it goes as described, and to think up possible modifications or extensions. Any new observation, particularly if it is "unexpected," should start new trains of thought.

A word of caution must be added. Patents are cunningly written. Novelty is stressed: The results stated were unexpected and contrary to all previous experience. The new products described are remarkably superior to all others for the uses suggested. The reader may be beguiled into thinking that the ultimate has been reached, that the discovery is a "flash of genius," and that to attempt any further advance would be futile. The reader must brace himself against being swept away. Research has accomplished wonders, but they are mere trifles compared to what may be accomplished in the future. Patents as primary sources of information are taken up in chapter 16.

MATERIALS FOR RESEARCH

An old recipe for making hare soup begins: "First catch the hare." An adequate supply of starting material is a prerequisite for any investigation. One reason for the leading position of German chemists in organic research, up to World War I, was their ready access to supplies of a wide variety of organic compounds of research grade. The situation in America is illustrated by conditions at Johns Hopkins University at the time I was a graduate student, 1894-1898. Each spring Remsen would plan the research for the following academic year. The necessary organic compounds were added to those required for routine organic preparations. These were ordered from Germany for September delivery. Research for the year was limited to the compounds in stock or to those that might be synthesized from them.

As late as 1912, I prepared isopropyl bromide, when it was needed, by isomerizing the *n*-propyl with homemade aluminum bromide. Some time later, I prepared some needed *tert*-butanol from methyl iodide and acetone by the Grignard reaction.

In 1919, the Eastman Kodak Co. came to the rescue of American chemists with a list of 150 organic compounds, mostly of research grade. In 1960 they list over 3800. Another company offers 5100, mostly rarer compounds. Several other concerns have smaller lists. Each of the 33 annual volumes of *Organic Syntheses* contains tried and tested methods for preparing research quantities of some 100 compounds. There is now no lack of materials for research.

Opportunity is said to knock at least once at every man's door, and happy is he who recognizes and answers the summons. Such fortune comes to a chemist in the way of some special material which is not generally available; it may be the product from some unusual local industry or something obtained through friendly relations with an industrial plant, or the by-product from some other investigation. The possession of a quantity of some unusual material is a special opportunity which should not be overlooked. The reporter who happens to be passing by when something sensational occurs burns the wires to make a "scoop" for his paper.

THE CHALLENGE OF NATURAL PRODUCTS

The chemistry of natural products is certainly NOT the place for a beginner to look for easy problems, but it is exactly where much chemical research started. However, there is no closed season for the investigation of products that may interest us. It sometimes happens that an interesting product comes our way and there is no reason for not taking a shot at it. Even if a complete solution of the problem is not reached, something will be gained by the effort.

The determination of structure is treated in chapter 12.

IDEAS FROM OTHER CHEMISTS

The discussions of Priestley and Wedgwood have been mentioned. Discussions stimulate thinking which may lead to ideas. Students sharpen their wits by talking with fellow students. There has been a definite effort by some research groups to promote "bull sessions" in which the wildest ideas are tossed about. There is much stimulation to be derived from attending chemical meetings where papers are read and discussed. In such discussions care must be taken to differentiate between "mine and thine." Some chemists have been suspected of getting ideas for patents from chance remarks of other chemists.

KEEPING RECORDS OF IDEAS

It is most helpful to keep a record of one's ideas as they occur by having library cards convenient, at home and in the laboratory, and jotting down any suggestion of an experiment that may come from one's reading, or thinking, or work. The date should be noted and the thought stated fully enough to insure its reproducibility. These cards are to be filed in a special place and to be looked over and considered from time to time. On second sight, some of one's ideas will look trivial, and some impossible, but some will still appear worth working out. In case something of commercial value should eventuate, the dated card, showing the genesis of the invention, may be of value in connection with a patent application. For better preservation, these ideas should be copied into an "idea book." For the record each item should be dated and signed. To increase its value for patent purposes, a fellow *chemist* should write, date, and sign: "Read and understood." However, a patent court gives scant consideration to a "date of conception" unless it is followed, soon afterward, by a "reduction to practice."

But what good are a thousand ideas that are not used? It was said of a certain woman that "she was full of good works, which she did." That she actually did the good works is the reason that she has been honored for nineteen centuries.

5. Attacking a problem

METHODS OF ATTACK

As there are no Marquis of Queensbury rules in research and no holds are barred, it is proper to hit a problem anywhere with anything. The story is told of a prize fighter who was knocked out in the ring but later got really mad at the champion and beat him up. So get mad at the problem and make it a grudge fight. Fortunately research is not like big-game hunting where the hunter may have only a single shot at a tiger that is about to spring. You can have many shots at a problem and it will stay right there while you go off for more ammunition. In baseball, it is three strikes and you are out; in chemistry, you can have as many strikes as you want, but you will never get a base on balls.

Problems are diverse in nature, so the method of attack must be correspondingly varied. However, all of them can be reduced to a simple formula, getting from here to there. This resolves it into three parts: finding out where you are, locating the objective, and finally devising means of getting there. In touring terms, you learn from a signpost the name of the town where you happen to be and look it up on the map. Next you find the place you want to reach. Then the road you have to take becomes evident. Chemists, old as well as young, are apt to reverse this order and start by looking for the road without knowing just where it is to start or end.

Devising methods of attack is the occupation of the chemist as well as of the general, and methods must vary according to the peculiarities of the situation and special means that are at hand.

In the ancient Greek courts, the orator stated his case in complete and logical form and later called in witnesses to substantiate his statements, while in modern practice, the witnesses are examined first and the lawyers make what they can out of the recorded testimony.

Both methods are used in chemistry. A hypothetical structure may be built up on certain assumptions, predictions made as to what will happen if so and so is tried, and then the required experiments are made to verify the assumptions. This is frequently the method of physical chemists. The other extreme is to go ahead with the experiments and later on construct theories to fit the observed results. However, theories are seldom evolved without some experimental basis, and experiments are not apt to lead anywhere unless guided by some hypothesis.

Sometimes the explorer has a definite objective: scaling a certain mountain or reaching the North Pole. A chemist may set out to prepare a certain compound whose structural formula he writes down and nails to his masthead, or he may desire a substance having certain chemical or physical properties. In such cases, the path is pretty well marked out. Another time, a chemist may start out to investigate the properties of a little-known class of compounds without any ideas as to what is coming out, believing that there must be something of interest. He tries one experiment after another and finds out as much as he can. The bag of game may be large or small, but if he is a good hunter he brings home whatever game there is.

In my opinion, stepwise planning is preferable. The

chemist plans one experiment. When this has been carried out and the results carefully studied, he is in a better position to plan the second. It is easier to set up another experiment, particularly if an industrious helper is at hand, than to think through on the one that has been done. A long table of results looks impressive but may mean little. Half of the experiments, interspersed with much hard thinking, might mean more.

Professor du Vigneaud prefers to follow the trail wherever it leads.[1]

> It is intriguing how one starts out on a trail of exploration in the laboratory not knowing where one is eventually going; starting out, to be sure, with some immediate objective in mind, but also having a vague sense of something beyond the immediate objective, toward which one is striving. True exploratory research is really the working out of a winding trail into the unknown. The investigator who is attracted to this type of research is attracted by the same thrill, albeit at a sublimated level, that was once enjoyed by the explorers in breaking through the confines of the old world. This is the kind of research that our academic and governmental administrations must be very careful to preserve. They must encourage the desire and guarantee the freedom for such exploration into the unknown, just as it was necessary and profitable to the administrations of the old world to allow individuals to explore the unknown geographic world.
>
> Project research is, of course, necessary. There are certain needs of society that must be met as soon as possible for its immediate benefit; but it is also necessary to preserve this other type of exploratory research. The latter must be guarded from attenuation by those who do not understand that this type of research is vital for our future.

"Blessed are they who have eyes to see" and use them. It is desirable to be helped by a plan but not to be hampered by it. Nature is more intricate and has vaster possibilities than we can imagine. If in a cut-and-dried, commonplace lot of experiments something extraordinary unexpectedly falls out, a good investigator is quick to see and appreciate it. The discovery of saccharine by Remsen and Fahlberg was entirely unexpected, though by no means accidental. For some years Remsen had been

---

[1] Vincent du Vigneaud, *A Trail of Research in Sulfur Chemistry and Metabolism and Related Fields,* Cornell University Press, 1952, pp. vii, viii.

investigating aromatic sulfonic acids systematically preparing one
after another and studying their reactions and properties. One of
these acids acted queerly, yielding benzoic sulfimide, or saccharine, some hundreds of times as sweet as sugar and of considerable commercial importance.

Perkin, the elder, was attempting to obtain quinine
by the oxidation of aniline, an impossibility by the way, and got
no quinine but did get a colored substance which he investigated
further till he produced mauve, the first of the aniline dyes, and
a much more important discovery than he had planned. His
greatness was manifested by the way he followed up and turned
to account an unexpected observation. An ordinary chemist
would have called the experiment a failure and poured the mess
into the sink.

The greatest discoveries, those that open up totally
new lines of thought and study, that usher in new eras in science,
are naturally unexpected. Phenomena that are entirely new cannot be predicted. Burbank did not improve the potato; he noticed
an abnormally productive plant and he knew what to do with
it. This potato was fortunate in growing in Burbank's garden.
This is no plea or excuse for haphazard experimenting. Let us
go out well prepared for the game we expect, and if a bird of
brighter plumage or a beast of richer pelt crosses our path, let
us add it to our bag. It may take extra-keen observation or unusual marksmanship.

Readers of *Popular Mechanics* some time ago selected by vote the seven wonders of the modern world. The
highest votes were received by wireless, the telephone, the
aeroplane, radium, antiseptics, antitoxins, spectrum analysis,
and X-rays. How were these originated? All of them were
produced by the identical formula. In the first place, they
were not the result of a direct attempt to accomplish what
was really attained. The end was not visible when the foundations were laid. The real work was done by thoroughly
well-trained observers—not by laymen. They were professors
in every case. They followed up a lead opened by an observation which was too insignificant to attract the attention
of less-trained men.[2]

---

[2] W. R. Whitney, *Elec. World,* **69,** 14 (1917).

All of the men who made those discoveries were trained to observe and to see the significance of what they saw. All of them were working with their own hands and seeing with their own eyes. All of them noticed something unexpected and all of them followed up these clues with painstaking experiments. In so doing, they were led into new lines of thought and made totally unexpected discoveries. There must be keen observation to get the clue and intelligent work to follow it to a logical conclusion.

According to Dr. Hammett[3] "The most important discoveries have always been the least expected ones." Balboa's discovery of the Pacific was unexpected but, unlike those listed before, did not require close observation. He claimed the ocean but does not seem to have made any use of it.

Perkin did not dip a piece of cloth into his mixture, pull it out beautifully dyed, and run to the patent office. A clue may be likened to an acorn, but there is a lot of work between an acorn and a piece of oak furniture.

Necessity is not the mother of invention; knowledge and experiment are its parents. This is clearly seen in the case of many industrial discoveries; high-speed cutting tools were not a necessity which preceded, but an application which followed, the discovery of the properties of tungsten-chromium-iron alloys; so, too, the uses of titanium in arc lamps and of vanadium in steel were sequels to the industrial preparation of these metals, and not discoveries by sheer force of necessity.[4]

In attacking a big problem, we should not be discouraged if we are not able to see the complete solution from the beginning. If we see a way to attack one part of the problem, even a small part, that justifies making an assault on it. We scale the highest peaks by ascending one step at a time. By climbing one of the foothills we can see a little farther up the mountain, and when this additional height is reached, then on till the summit is attained. As we work on a problem, the way opens before us. It is well to study the old masters and see how they met and surmounted similar difficulties.

[3] Louis P. Hammett, *Chem. Eng. News*, **32**, 1462 (1954).
[4] W. R. Whitney, *Mining and Met.*, December 1921, p. 11.

This much has been said about methods of attacking a problem to show that there is more than one way: you must find that way which suits you best. "But the centurion . . . commanded that they which could swim should cast themselves first into the sea and get to land; and the rest, some on boards, and some on broken pieces of the ship. And so it came to pass, that they escaped all safe to land."

TO THE LIBRARY

A battle is begun in the general's tent the night before, when the maps are spread out and the reports from the scouts are brought in. The attack on a problem begins in the library. A surveyor starts at the bench mark left by a previous surveyor. The purpose of research is to add to human knowledge. To do this, you must know exactly where present knowledge ends.

The amount of reading to be done will depend on the nature and size of the problem. On account of the natural desire to get started in the laboratory, there is a tendency to cut the library time to a minimum. This may lead to wasting time on poorly planned experiments. Considerable background information is necessary to enable one to see the problem in proper perspective. There are a number of ways of getting from New York to Chicago, several air lines, several railroads, and a variety of auto roads; it is now possible to go by ship. So it is in getting from "here to there" chemically. Various possible routes to the goal must be explored and arranged in the order of plausibility before they are tried experimentally. After getting all possible suggestions from the literature, it is well to give free rein to one's imagination and think up a radically different method. By all means try this first. If it works, even poorly, you have added something to human knowledge; if it fails, and you find out why it failed, you have learned something of the method of research.

It is desirable to intersperse reading and laboratory work. When a promising method is found, it is well to try it out and study the results to find out why they were good or why they were poor. Usually this means more reading. When work described in the literature is repeated, the results do not always come up to expectations. Naturally, chemists record their best experiments and say little or nothing about their failures. Parents dress up their children when they take them out.

This is the orthodox procedure, the safe and sane way, but in research one does not have to be orthodox or sane all of the time. The famous inscription: "You do not have to be crazy to work here, but it helps" is probably an overstatement, but research is a venture into the unknown where many things are to be found which are not in accordance with our present thinking. Just for the fun of it, one may occasionally try something and look it up afterward. Two examples are given. I heated potassium hydroxide and n-butanol in a pressure tube to 300° just to see what would happen. Hydrogen was evolved and a quantitative yield of potassium butyrate was obtained. Then I found that the reaction had been discovered ninety years before, but had been applied only to nonvolatile alcohols such as cetyl. The use of a pressure tube extended its applicability to volatile alcohols. The use of an aqueous solution of the alkali was an advance. On another occasion, I heated an aqueous solution of maleic acid with zinc. The reduction to succinic acid was practically complete. On looking this up I found that an able chemist had tried this and got no reduction. It is unlikely that either of these experiments would have been tried if I had gone to the library first, as I was supposed to do.

There must be a proper balance between reading and experimenting; neither may be neglected. There is sometimes the danger that the reader may be so impressed by the quality and completeness of what has been done that he may despair of making a worthy addition to it.

More about libraries will be found in later chapters.

TO THE LABORATORY

The preparation of exquisite perfumes, of delicious flavoring materials, and of beautiful dyes of all the colors of the rainbow from black, sticky coal tar is a splendid triumph of mind over matter. But oft in the laboratory, matter humiliates and exasperates the mind by flatly refusing to react according to the equations that the mind has written. Regardless of how extensive the reading has been, regardless of how much thinking has been done, and regardless of how many theories have been built up, the final contest between mind and matter must take place in the arena of the laboratory.

Problems differ widely in size, in nature, in complexity, and in urgency. All of these differences must be taken into account in planning the attack. A complicated problem may engage the attention of a university professor and his students for years. Sometimes a "crash" attack has to be made, as when British chemists were summoned to find a way to make mustard gas in World War I, which is treated in chapter 8.

The Germans launched a surprise attack with deadly mustard gas against which the Allies then had no protection. They felt safe in doing this as they knew that they alone had the necessary starting material. By intensive concerted effort, British chemists found a quicker, cheaper method of synthesis which put the Germans on the receiving end.

The mode of attack will depend, to a great extent, on the chemist and his resources. Emphasis must be placed on the individuality of the chemist. He must find *his* approach, not just *an* approach. David had this idea and made a hit with Goliath. The lumbering old giant, encased in heavy armor, really did not have a chance against a boy who could think and used his own method of attack.

In addition to personal individuality, each chemist has had some experiences which others have not had. One of these may be just the thing needed when faced with a new problem. This happened to me in the early days of our participation in World War I. When lachrymators were mentioned as useful in warfare, my mind went back to chloroacetophenone, which I had prepared some years before as an intermediate in a projected synthesis. I had wept over this as I had never before wept over a chemical. A sample was prepared and taken to Washington May 31, 1917. Lachrymators were not as important as toxics, so it did not get tested in time to be used in that war. Chloroacetophenone,

$C_6H_5COCH_2Cl$, turned out to be one of the top three lachrymators and, unexpectedly, was found to have the decisive advantage over the other two that it does not corrode steel. It has been the chief constituent of "tear gas," whose use has spread around the world. All of this came because I remembered an experience which it would have been impossible to forget. Another name for chloroacetophenone is phenacyl chloride. Closely related to this is *p*-bromophenacyl bromide which I developed as a reagent for the identification of acids. This has attained general acceptance.

An example is given of the fitting together of several past experiences to solve a present problem. I attended a conference at which the need of a plasticizer for nitrocellulose was stressed. An hour's thinking brought up dibutyl phthalate. This might be considered as a "hole-in-one" by a blind golfer or a stroke of genius. It was neither. I happened to have the pieces; putting them together was a simple matter. It was the sum of several past experiences plus a guess. For some years, I had been interested in the formation of phthalic monoesters as a means of getting primary alcohols out of mixtures, and had made derivatives of the monoesters as a way of identifying the alcohols. I had worked with *n*-butanol in the catalytic preparation of *n*-butyl mercaptan. I held to the dictum that "like dissolves like" and that a likely solvent for an ester should be another ester. The guess was that dibutyl phthalate would be sufficiently nonvolatile to stay put. As a plasticizer dibutyl phthalate exceeded expectations. The guess as to its nonvolatility was not quite right; it does evaporate from films. In spite of this, hundreds of millions of pounds of dibutyl phthalate have been used. To reduce the volatility, higher alcohols, such as 2-ethylhexyl, have been substituted for the butyl. Several other di-basic acids have been used in place of phthalic.

WORK, WATCH, THINK

If you do not work, there will be nothing to watch. If you do not observe, there will be nothing to think about. If you do not watch, and watch closely, you will miss the little

things that have big meanings. If you do not think, there is no
use working or observing. Out of his wide experience in research,
Professor Adams says:[5] "In my opinion, most of the fundamental
discoveries today arise from a chance observation while attempting to reach some entirely different goal. For example, we began
our studies on the quinone imides after synthesizing one of them
while attempting the bromination of the benzenesulfonyl derivative of a p-phenylenediamine with bromine and pyridine. We
wanted to get ring bromination but got a quinone imide instead."
Unexpected things happen frequently in chemical laboratories,
but most of them share the sad fate of the "flower that is born
to blush unseen and waste its sweetness on the desert air." Only
a keen observer sees the unexpected and only an experienced
chemist realizes its significance. Such a happening may lead to
an important discovery or to the opening up of a new line of
research, but only if a master chemist is there when it occurs.
How many times an assistant has stood between a chemist and a
discovery will never be known. It would seem logical to keep the
best chemist in an organization in the place where he is most
likely to make discoveries, that is, in the laboratory. In many
cases, the bulk of the experimenting is done by the most recent
recruits, chemists of excellent university training, but with limited
experience. In at least one laboratory, the helpers feel that the
chemist is intruding when he takes part in an experiment. One
who really loves research is happier doing it than sitting in an
office reading reports of other people's experiments. According to
the code, the chemist in the office cannot make suggestions, except in a vague way, for fear of blunting the initiative of the
men in the laboratory. To my taste, a well-stocked laboratory is
more attractive than a plush office with a blonde stenographer.

　　　　The story goes, I hope it is not true, that there was
a famous clock maker in a certain city who built a marvelous
clock, such as had not been seen before, for the town hall. As
soon as it was finished, they put out his eyes so that he could
never build another. The fact is, I wish it were not true, that
when a chemist does particularly good research, frequently something is done to him so that he cannot continue in it. In an

[5] Letter from Roger Adams.

educational institution, they make him a dean—Crafts, Remsen, Edgar Fahs Smith, and Conant were made presidents—and in an industrial corporation, they "promote" him to be a research director. His place in the laboratory is taken by a new recruit. As he goes "up," the chemist's salary increases roughly in proportion to his distance from the laboratory. It is certainly fitting and proper that a chemist should receive recognition for exceptional work, but it is bad for all concerned for him to be "promoted" *out* of research instead of *in* research. Dr. Heise laments:[6] "Productive capability of large numbers of promising technical men is lost because they abandon research for more lucrative fields." Just suppose that as soon as Bobby Jones broke 75, they had promoted him to golf supervisor and given his clubs to a new recruit.

The discourse here is of the research chemist, and nothing that is said is intended to belittle the importance of management, which also demands high intelligence and broad knowledge. That is another story which can best be told by someone else.

A story of a chemist's seeing a few crystals that were not supposed to be there, and thus making an important discovery has been told by Dr. Marsohner.[7] Parts of it are given here.

In 1940, in a small government laboratory in Frankfurt-am-Main, an up to that time unknown chemist, Friederich Bengen, was trying to find a better method of determining butter fat in pasteurized milk. Among other things he tried adding urea to aid in the separation. As this did not help, he added some n-decyl alcohol and shook the tube, but noted no improvement. He set the tube aside. Later in the day he noted crystals in this tube. They excited his curiosity. By elimination he traced their formation to the urea and n-decyl alcohol. He set out on a systematic search for other organic liquids that would combine with urea, and found many. He did not expect hydrocarbons, which are generally so inert, to react, but tried them anyhow. Surprisingly enough certain of them did react. This was the first, but by no means the last, chapter in the history of the important urea complexes.

---

[6] George W. Heise, *Chem. Eng. News,* **32,** 4178 (1954).

[7] R. M. Marsohner, *Chem. Eng. News,* **34,** 494 (1955).

In an experiment designed for quite a different purpose, J. C. Patrick caused ethylene chloride to react with sodium tetrasulfide and obtained an elastic mass which to him looked something like crude rubber. He found that it could be compounded and vulcanized under the same conditions as natural rubber and that the vulcanizate resembled vulcanized rubber and, for some uses, could take the place of natural rubber. This became the first of the Thiokol elastomers. On account of its outstanding resistance to hydrocarbons, Thiokol A, an ethylene-polysulfide polymer, was used to line the fuel tanks of the planes with which Doolittle flew over Japan. A variety of Thiokol later (1957) became a key material in the rocket program. The point is that Patrick saw something unexpected and spent years in research to develop it. An ethylene polysulfide had been prepared some seventy years earlier, but nothing was done about it except the publication of an article. It is fortunate that Patrick did not come across this until his own experiments were well along. Thiokol will be taken up again in chapter 11 and discussed more thoroughly in Volume V of my sulfur series.[8]

The prize for developing an unexpected observation must go to Lord Rayleigh and Sir William Ramsey. They set out to make accurate determinations of the densities of several gases, a task that required much painstaking labor and promised no excitement. They noticed that 1 liter of nitrogen from the air weighed about 5 mg more than a like volume of chemically prepared nitrogen. They traced this to the presence of a heavier, inert gas which they named argon. This was the first of the noble gases that fill a column in the periodic table. We have neon lights and electric light bulbs filled with argon. The presence of an inert gas in atmospheric nitrogen had been noted before, but no one did anything about it.

In his excellent book, Professor Beveridge[9] describes in some detail ten examples of epoch-making discoveries by great medical investigators. As in the examples given here, each of

[8] *Organic Chemistry of Bivalent Sulfur*, New York, Chemical Publishing Co., Inc.

[9] W. I. B. Beveridge, *The Art of Scientific Investigation*, New York, Random House, 1950 (revised edition, 1957).

these was the result of the observation of something entirely un-expected happening which would have escaped the notice of a less-trained observer. In each case, the observation was followed by experiments which made medical history.

The phenomenal success of Sherlock Holmes as a detective was due to his observation of seemingly trivial things, which escaped the attention of his friend, Watson, and to his following up of such clues.

It is said that the darkest hour is just before dawn. In research that "darkest hour" may lengthen into days, or months, and daylight may never break on a particular problem. Even if the objective is not attained, something of value can be derived from the experiments, and the experience gained may be of value in another task.

TIME FOR RESEARCH

"So teach us to number our days that we may apply our hearts unto wisdom." This prayer is attributed to Moses whose "eye was not dimmed nor his natural force abated" at the end of his hundred and twenty strenuous years. The days of the years of our sojourn are few and are crowded with duties and diversions. We must needs number them with care lest all of them are swallowed up in routine duties or casual enjoyment and none are left for higher things. We are sure that we could carry out some wonderful investigation if we only had the time but we are "cumbered with much serving"—of ourselves as well as of others—and never find time to choose the better part.

Our money will not buy as much as formerly and many other things have changed, but there are the same number of hours in the day and the same number of days in the year as in ancient times. According to astronomical observations, the year has not changed by the minutest fraction of a second since history began. If we do not accomplish as much in a day or in a year as did Berzelius or Liebig, we cannot put the blame on Father Time. In addition to having the same time that they had, we are blessed with incomparably better facilities, well-equipped laboratories, electric motors and hot plates, resistance glass and standardized reagents.

As a matter of history, many of the famous investigators of the olden times devoted only their spare time to chemistry as an avocation. This was true of Priestley and Scheele. Peter Griess was chemist for a brewery and had to see that good ale was plentiful in merry old England—not a trifling task, we may be sure. No one knows how he found time for his monumental investigation of the diazo compounds. Doubtless he made a place for research and did not wait for a convenient season.

It is wonderful how we can find time for something which we really want to do, as when fishing time comes around and they are biting good, or our favorite baseball team is going to play, or golf calls. We can make way for research if there is the will for it.

By cutting and fitting our various tasks, an astonishing amount can be packed into a day. Efficiency experts advise us to set aside a quiet period in the early morning for thinking over the day's duties, making out a schedule, allotting so much time to each, taking care to arrange the sequence so that mind and body will be refreshed by the change from one sort of occupation to another rather than wearied by unduly prolonged effort of one kind. By compressing our routine tasks into smaller space, room may be left for research.

We get mired down in absurdities when we attempt to apply the canons of efficiency to research itself. It is easy enough to tell when half of a cord of wood has been sawed, and at any moment it takes only a glance to see how fast the sawing is going forward, but it is utterly impossible to estimate progress on a research problem. Months may go by filled with feverish activity and no progress be made toward a solution and then, in the twinkling of an eye, an idea may come and the whole be clear; a chance observation may give the clue while long series of carefully executed experiments may avail nothing. *The Star-Spangled Banner* was dashed off in a tense moment under the spell of a great emotion; few know what Francis Scott Key did the rest of his life. Kekulé spent a long life in careful experimenting and clear thinking, but his one great achievement, the benzene theory, was the product of an hour of dreaming. As the clock ticked the time away, and Kekulé sat in his reverie, who could have known that a new world of chemistry was being born and that the celebration of that hour, a quarter of a century later, would draw together chemists from all lands.

We cannot say: "Let us discover a third law of thermodynamics between 3 and 5 this afternoon"; but if we are able to arrange our schedule so as to set aside time for thinking and experimenting we put ourselves in the way of discovering something.

Working out a new idea usually involves a considerable amount of laboratory drudgery, such as the preparation and purification of the necessary research materials, the isolation or estimation of reaction products, and analyses of new compounds. To this part of an investigation, efficiency methods may be applied without damage. Thus if many analyses have to be made, as in velocity studies, quicker methods may be sought or the samples may be grouped and run in sets so as to require a minimum of the operator's time and attention. At the start of a certain investigation of reaction velocities, it required nearly a day for me to analyze one sample, but, by setting up a battery of stills, I was able to make eight determinations simultaneously. Two sets of receivers were provided and one group of eight was titrated while the next eight were distilling. Thus twenty-four samples a day were handled instead of one.

6. Research by undergraduates

This designation was chosen since "undergraduate" research might be mistaken to imply that it is different in quality from or necessarily inferior to other research. Undergraduates are limited as to the size of their undertakings, but what research they do must be of standard grade.

Can a boy help his father move a pile of stones? There is no use in the boy wasting his strength tugging at a large stone, but he can carry some of the small ones. Transporting a small stone is a help if it is taken to the right place and not dropped for his father to pick up.

The object of research is to extend human knowledge. The observation of a single fact does just that—*provided* it is properly established and *provided* it was not known previously. All through this book, the emphasis has been on quality, rather than on quantity. A dime is real money and is preferable to a bogus ten-dollar note. If you doubt this, just try the two at

91

the bank and see what happens. All that has been said about research applies here with equal force; the undergraduate simply buys a small bottle of the same medicine, instead of the "economy size."

Can an undergraduate do worth-while research? Chemists settle questions by experiment rather than by argument. Undergraduates *have* done such research and published the results in the *Journal of the American Chemical Society* and in other standard journals. On numerous visits to a number of institutions, I have seen undergraduates doing standard-grade research. According to Professor Sampey,[1] *Chemical Abstracts* noted for the eight-year period, 1952 to 1959, 1120 articles from 231 "liberal arts colleges," that is, institutions not giving the doctor's degree and not having professional faculties. The distribution between B.S. and M.S. candidates is not known, but a considerable part of the work must have been done by undergraduates. Some undergraduates have messed up problems and gotten nowhere, but so have many older workers, including myself. Professor Hurd gives an account of his experience with more than 150 B.S. seniors in over a twenty-year period.[2] Twenty-four of them were coauthors of papers published in scientific journals. Many other examples could be given.

A three-day conference, in which I participated, on chemical research by undergraduates was held at Washington and Lee University sponsored by the National Science Foundation and under the guidance of Dr. W. R. Kirner. The conclusions were summed up:[3] "It is generally agreed that research is an effective tool for the superior student, stimulates the instructor, develops the student's enthusiasm and interest in research, introduces methods of science, and raises the standard of the school in the eyes of student, staff, and public. But requisites for success are the right problem, the right student, and the right teacher."

The key man is, of course, the teacher. If you have

---

[1] J. R. Sampey, *J. Chem. Ed.*, **37**, 316 (1960).

[2] C. B. Hurd, *J. Chem. Ed.*, **21**, 81-4 (1944).

[3] *Conference on Undergraduate Research in Chemistry*—National Science Foundation, Washington, D.C.; reviewed in *Chem. Eng. News*, **32**, 3837 (1954).

the mumps, you are liable to give the mumps to others, but if you just imagine that you have the mumps, your friends are in no danger. Researchitis is catching. If the teacher really has it, the students are likely to be infected.

For the student, the prime qualifications are: a burning desire to pry into the unknown and a dogged determination to get results, regardless of difficulties. With these "Mr. Britling sees it through." Students who are not research minded may look forward to some other chemical occupation. This chapter is written especially to students, those of the better sort; those who are not satisfied by predigested food but want strong meat; those who are interested to know where the facts came from that the teacher dishes out; those who have tired of being recipients only of knowledge, but long for the thrill of creating, at least, a tiny bit of it.

One of the finest things about research for undergraduates is the mutually rewarding close association of teacher and selected students in the extra hours they spend together in their concerted attack on the unknown. In the classroom the caste system keeps them apart, but in the research laboratory it is different. In answering questions about the known, the teacher has the advantage; but in asking questions about the unknown a bunch of uninhibited youngsters is hard to beat. Questions may lead to thinking, and thinking to experimenting, and experimenting to discovery.

Just how teacher and students are to work together will depend on the personalities involved and on the nature of the problem. The teacher, whose time is so largely taken up by his many duties, certainly needs help if he is to accomplish much in research. A serious difficulty is the matter of synchronizing working periods of teacher and students. There may be operations which the student cannot undertake except under the immediate supervision of the teacher, and there may be times when the student's help is needed but is not available. There is the possibility that the student may help with his hands only and excuse himself from doing any thinking. In spite of these and of other difficulties, much valuable research has been done in this way. The teacher, with the help of a student, or of a succession of students, can handle a much larger problem than can be undertaken by an undergraduate alone.

The other extreme is where the teacher deals out a number of small problems to as many students, who work independently. Of course, the teacher stands by to supervise and help when needed.

Good results can be accomplished by either method, or by some combination of the two, *provided* both teacher and students take it seriously. In spite of the advertisements, you cannot learn to play the piano in six weeks by taking five correspondence lessons. Out of long experience Professor Yoe says:[4] "There is no short cut to training in research. The only way to learn how to do research is to *do research.* You cannot learn how to analyze a limestone or a steel by reading the procedures, however carefully, although, of course, this should be done before beginning the analysis. Research is both an art and a science; it requires practice, the more the better."

The selection of a problem that is neither too large nor too small and is neither too difficult nor too easy will be discussed in later sections.

PUBLICATION

The matter of publication is of prime importance. It is to be considered at the start in proposing a problem and should be kept before the student continuously in order that the quality of his work may be maintained and that all the desired data may be secured. A player on the varsity football team will hardly strain himself in a practice game against the scrub team, but when the contest is with a rival university, before television and movie cameras and thousands of cheering spectators, it is quite a different matter. The hope of achieving results worthy of being placed before the chemists of the world spurs on the student to do his best and leads him to check and double check his data. Seeing one's name in a chemical journal for the first time is a "thrill that comes once in a lifetime" and is a recompense for long hours of toil.

---

[4] John H. Yoe, *J. Chem. Ed.,* **18,** 410-13 (1941).

Even good players do not win every game. Some research projects do not work out as planned and, on account of unexpected difficulties, others cannot be finished in the prescribed time. This is discouraging to the young chemist, but it is a part of the game. Actually this happens more frequently to older chemists since they take longer shots. The fisherman can tell a good story about the "one that got away," but the chemical journals will not publish negative results.

The researcher's task is not finished until the new information is made available to all who may want to use it. To a chemist, this means publication in a journal regularly covered by *Chemical Abstracts*.

SELLING RESEARCH TO STUDENTS

Chapter 1 brought out the fact that research is a prime mover of progress. At the present time, the shortage of chemists and other technically trained men is limiting the rate of progress. Perhaps the situation might be improved by requiring every science teacher, in high school and college, to take a course in salesmanship.

Whether the students expect to go into industry at the B.S. level, or after further study, or whether they are aiming at plant operation or industrial research, they will do well to get first-hand information about research, its methods, its joys, and its sorrows. Carload lots of commodities are sold on the basis of samples; why not sell research in the same way? The samples may be small but they must be representative; they must not be phony or make-believe.

During their undergraduate years, most students are making up their minds as to the direction they expect to take after graduation. Research beckons, but how is the student to know whether or not he will like research. Do you like olives? How did you find out? Why not give the student a taste of research and let him see for himself. Once he gets the thrill of discovery of doing something that has never been done before, he is likely to want more research. But pray do not give him a watered-down, make-believe problem that will not call for his best. A young man gets no thrill out of beating his grandmother at tennis. Professor Hurd insists that the students should have a fair deal:[5]

> No research problem for undergraduates should consist merely of hack work. Here I agree completely with others who have already expressed this idea. It is true that an instructor sometimes has developed, or has access to, a new piece of apparatus which is so efficient that one merely has to grind out results. An undergraduate could do this very well and pile up results for the older man to use. Any senior who is unfortunate enough to be assigned to such a problem of routine operation loses one of the real opportunities provided by a good research problem, namely, planning a procedure and overcoming some difficulties. He acquires a totally incorrect idea of research in chemistry and, if he has the active imagination always present in a good research man, even a beginner, he becomes discouraged in his first experience.

From long experience with undergraduates in research, Professor Sampey says:[6] "Let a student . . . experience an exciting adventure in undergraduate research and he will need no other incentive to pursue a lifetime of scientific research." Speaking of a certain group of researchers, he says: ". . . all young participants in these adventures in undergraduate research have continued their scientific careers through graduate school into industrial research, except the two young ladies who are making homes for the scientists they met under these romantic circumstances."

Professor Hurd advises assigning a problem that the student has a chance of handling:[7]

> The problem should be one capable of giving good results to a student of average ability in the time available. This condition is almost as important as the first one. We should remember that one purpose of student research is to teach technique, another, to develop interest. Any good research problem will offer plenty of difficulties which must be surmounted. Difficulties should be encountered, but the student who climbs wearily over one difficulty after another only to

[5] C. B. Hurd, *J. Chem. Ed.*, **21**, 81-4 (1944).
[6] J. R. Sampey, *School Science and Mathematics*, **57**, 396-8 (1957).
[7] Same as reference 5.

come to the end of the course with no results is almost certain to be discouraged with both research and chemistry. It will be much better for the student to obtain some fine results upon a problem which is not too difficult than to fail gloriously upon a problem which would tax a Ph.D.

Research is individual and the student who is ambitious and industrious should be encouraged to enlarge the scope of his problem. A student who does less than his best is a failure, even though he may be the top man in his class.

Professor Hurd looks back:[8] "My own undergraduate research taught me several things which I had never learned in my many other courses in college. So far as they can be separated and described, they were:

1. How to search the literature for work which had been done on the various aspects of a certain problem.

2. How to plan an attack upon a scientific problem.

3. How to do experiments for which there were no cookbook rules.

4. How to depend on my own scientific knowledge."

Only by personal contact with research can a student glimpse its attractiveness and realize his liking for it. This may incline him to go on to graduate study and to adopt research as a way of life. A large proportion of those who have had experience with research in their undergraduate days do just that.

Research is particularly desirable for a superior student. It is reported that a passenger on a slow train asked the conductor: "Can't you run faster than this?" The conductor replied: "Yes, but I have to stay with my train." There are many students who can run much faster, but they have to stay with their classes. On a research problem, the student does not have to stay with his fellow students, or even with his teacher. Professor Barbier had been working on a problem; he passed the ball to student Grignard who made a 75-yard run for a touchdown. Grignard was an advanced student, but Hall was an undergraduate when he thought up the process for making aluminum. Working on a research problem, a student may discover himself. That "mute, inglorious Milton" would not have remained that way

---

[8] Same as reference 5.

had he been awakened to his possibilities. Perhaps another Milton would have been superfluous, but industry can use thousands of well-trained chemists.

Professor Yoe feels that research is for selected students.[9]

> By all means start seniors on research; but do not start all seniors. Some are definitely not qualified and the chances are they never will be; but the select few, the more promising ones, should be assigned suitable problems and a plan of attack should be mapped out for them. The objectives of senior research should be:
> 1. To teach the undergraduates the real meaning of the word "research"
> 2. To cultivate in them the scientific spirit
> 3. To accomplish something valuable to science, however small it may be
> 4. To make the institution known for its work in a particular field of chemistry and
> 5. To act as a stimulus to all the class and laboratory work in the department—a stimulus to the professor as well as to the students.

For an undergraduate, research is a privilege which should be granted to those who use it well. Leading a group of capable, enthusiastic students is, for the teacher, a recreation rather than a task. One student who has to be carried gets the teacher down.

ATTACKING A PROBLEM

Reference should be made to chapter 5 for a general discussion of this topic.

Normally there are three parts to research: 1. literature search; 2. making the experiments; and 3. reporting the results. The student's sample should contain all three of these.

In general, the steps are the same for an undergraduate as for the most-advanced worker. The boy walks just like his father, but takes shorter steps. Some of the steps in research have been considered in chapter 5 and others will be

---

[9] John H. Yoe, *J. Chem. Ed.*, **18**, 410-3 (1941).

treated later, but they are discussed here with particular reference to the undergraduate. A typical list is as follows:

1. Selecting a problem
2. Literature study
3. To the laboratory
4. Characterization of products
5. Writing a report
6. Publication

1. Selecting a Problem

First let it be said that the student should do the selecting. The vital spark in research is the feeling that one is on one's own. However, in this finite world, there are limitations to free will. The acceptance of the status of student implies the recognition of the need of some guidance. In a cafeteria, one is limited by the varieties of food displayed, by the size of one's purse, and by one's appetite. The choice is influenced by the attractiveness with which the wares are displayed and by the prices. The professor should put before the student a liberal assortment of problems. Each should be made attractive by a statement of the end to be accomplished and its importance. Each should have a price tag in the way of an honest estimate of the difficulties involved. Selling the problem to the student is of critical importance. What he does with it will be determined largely by how it stirs his imagination. If his interest becomes intense enough, he will dream about it and be alert enough to catch the unexpected.

In choosing a problem the matter of size is critical. In the cafeteria the slices of mince pie are so small that there is little danger of indigestion, but as chemical problems are being handed out free, why not take a large one? One ambitious B.S. candidate undertook the study of the "drying" of linseed oil. The severest limitation in research is the matter of time. This is true even in the largest organization. It is most acute for the candidate for a bachelor's degree who has only two or three afternoons a week for research. The aspirant for the master's degree has more time, but still not enough for a large task. This means that the problems must be screened to size and done up in small packages.

Larger problems must be broken up into pieces. The student should be discouraged from taking a task that he has not a reasonable chance of completing.

2. Literature Study

This was considered in chapter 5 and will be discussed at greater length in a later chapter. The student, impatient to get to the laboratory, is prone to cut short his reading. An hour in the library may save many hours in the laboratory. The present problem gains significance when it is viewed in relation to what happened before. Ideas of what can be done come from a knowledge of what has been done. In painting a hand on the portrait of a man the artist must view the whole picture.

The first thing is to make doubly sure that any compound that the student is proposed to prepare is not already known. The next is to collect information about its homologs, since the methods that have been found suitable for preparing and isolating them may be adapted to present needs.

It is useful to tabulate the physical properties, melting points, boiling points, etc., of homologs and from plots of these to estimate the properties of the compound that is to be made. It is easier to isolate and recognize a desired product when one knows what to look for.

The information gained should be summarized and used as the basis of plans for laboratory work. Preparation methods proposed should be adaptations, rather than copies, of those that have been found. An attempt should be made to think up a novel method. It is better to have crazy ideas than not to think at all. Radically new ideas usually look crazy. Any idea that leads to an experiment is a good one. A thoughtful chemist learns more from an experiment that does not go as expected than from one that does.

At this point, all the information gained and the plans made should be talked over with the teacher.

3. To the Laboratory

This has been discussed so fully in chapter 5 that little need be said here. Obtaining the expected products is desirable, but the student should get far more than this out of his experiments. He should observe and think, pondering each step, asking why it is done this way and trying to contrive a better method. If several compounds are to be made by the same method, the preparation of one of them should be repeated until good results are obtained. Then the others can be run through quickly.

Frequent trips should be made to the library to get light on questions that come up while experimenting.

4. Characterization of Products

The characterization of compounds is the sequel to their preparation and might have been considered in section 3, but on account of its importance, it is singled out for separate treatment. What is desired is the accurate determination of physical properties, such as boiling points and melting points. For some compounds, it is desirable to go farther and prepare derivatives which have characteristic melting points. Undergraduates are urged to do a much better job at this than is done by many of their elders who publish in the *Journal of the American Chemical Society* and in other high-grade journals. This is simply asking the undergraduates to do their work as it should be done. As a rule they undertake the preparation of relatively simple compounds by well-known methods. The value of this is not in showing that the compounds can be made, but in supplying accurate data needed to fill blanks in the chemical literature. Accurate data are required when it comes to studying the relation of physical properties to structure and to comparing members of one series with those of another. There is lasting satisfaction in doing a neat job, particularly if it is to be put on display. In many investigations, the interest is in showing that the reaction goes in a certain way and scant attention is paid to the properties of the products. In many articles, we find lists of compounds prepared for testing as insecticides and the only interest is in whether they kill the bugs. Other articles give the preparation of compounds for testing as medicinals or for other purposes. In all of these, analyses have to be given, but information on physical properties is apt to be sketchy.

On account of their importance, melting points,

boiling points, and densities are discussed in detail in the appendix to this chapter.

5. Writing a Report

There are few who are reticent about their fishing exploits, so why should chemists be reluctant to tell about what they caught in the laboratory? Report writing will be taken up in chapter 22, but a few remarks are in order here. They do not take motion pictures of a chemist in the laboratory to see how good he is; they read his reports. It is sometimes said of a chemist that he is good in the laboratory, but is poor at writing a report. How do you know he is good? If a chemist thinks clearly and logically, he will probably write that way. Who wants to hire a chemist who does not think clearly?

Normally, a report consists of three parts:

1. Introduction and background (a condensation of the literature study)
2. Experiments
3. Conclusions and discussion.

An undergraduate will present his research results as a term paper or thesis in accordance with the requirements for the degree.

6. Publication

It may be assumed that the undergraduate is not adept in writing journal articles, but learning is by doing and this is a good time to begin. The most practical way is to locate a journal article on a similar subject and use it as a model. Of course, the teacher will have to put the article into its final shape and assume responsibility for it as a coauthor.

THE PREPARATION OF ORGANIC COMPOUNDS

The preparation of organic compounds is recommended as the most suitable field for the beginner in research. Organic chemistry is the crowning achievement of the human mind. In no other realm have so many tens of thousands of facts been so logically arranged and fitted together into such a magnificent structure. By 1910, according to Richter, 144,150 organic compounds had been prepared; by now, the number has probably reached half a million. Each of these fits into its proper niche. To complete the system, hundreds of thousands of additional niches will have to be filled.

In recommending this as a field of research for undergraduates, no disparagement of other fields is intended. For several reasons, this is a good place for the beginner to start his trek into the unknown. Columbus sailed from a port which he knew well, in ships with whose navigation he was familiar. He saw a lot of water that he had not seen before, but it was just like what he had left behind. For the student who has had a course in organic preparations, the transition to making new compounds, analogous to those already known, is easy.

There are hosts of organic compounds waiting to be prepared from readily available materials by well-known methods in standard equipment.

In organic synthesis, there are available problems of all degrees of difficulty from the simplest, which are scarcely harder than those in a course in organic preparations, to those that have baffled some of the best chemists for decades. The synthesis of new acids, esters, amides, and the like is a natural follow-up of the usual course in organic preparations. Yet, it requires considerably more than simply following directions. Laboratory manuals are so well written that a student can turn out good results with little understanding of the reactions involved, but the preparation of a new compound, even a homolog of one given in the manual, requires thought. The proportions have to be recalculated and account has to be taken of different solubilities, volatilities, and reactivities. When work is being done for publication, far more attention has to be given to purity of starting materials and to the accuracy of the determinations made.

A prime consideration with an undergraduate is the possibility of completing a task in disconnected laboratory periods. In many cases, the preparation of an organic compound can be accomplished on the installment plan. The materials and apparatus are assembled in one period, the reaction is carried out in another, and the product isolated and stored to be purified and characterized in a subsequent period.

Skill in the preparation of organic compounds is essential in many fields of research. In the quest for new and better medicinals, many thousands of organic compounds have been prepared. Certain derivatives of barbituric acid were found to have valuable soporific properties; hundreds of others have been made having all sorts of groups in all possible positions. Sulfanilamide was found to be potent; over a thousand of its derivatives and analogs have been made and tested. Some 14,000 compounds have been synthesized and tried out as antimalarials. Antiseptics, local anesthetics, and other classes of medicinals have received much attention.

Dyes, plastics, protective coatings, synthetic rubbers, nylon, and the like are products of industrial research in all of which the preparation of hosts of organic compounds was fundamental.

As was pointed out in chapter 4, starting materials for the preparation of organic compounds are available in large number and wide variety.

In past years, the necessity for analyses for new compounds was a serious obstacle in their preparation. Now analyses are available at reasonable prices.

Completing a Series

Half a million organic compounds have been described. Suppose all of these had proper names, like aniline, methane, morpholine, thialdine, phorone, anisidine, and urea, and that they were arranged alphabetically in the text book. What a task it would be to memorize the names, formulae, modes of preparation, and properties of all of these! Actually learning organic chemistry is easier now for the student than it was a century ago when the known organic compounds were few in number but not systematized.

Teaching organic chemistry is made possible by arranging the multitude of compounds in series and finding the relation of one series to others. Thus a student becomes acquainted with ethanol, its physical properties and reactions, and then learns that it is a member of a series of alcohols, the reactions of which are much the same, while their physical properties form a progression. The physical properties of the acetates of these alcohols form a somewhat similar progression. This is illustrated in figures 1 and 2 in which the properties of the first ten are plotted against the number of carbon atoms in the alcohols. The points for the alcohols are joined by solid lines, and those for the acetates by broken lines.

It will be noted that the melting points form zigzag patterns. This is true of the melting points in nearly all series.

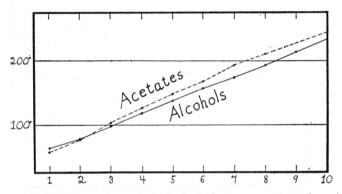

FIGURE 1. Boiling points of alcohols and acetates, plotted against the number of carbon atoms in the alcohol

The melting-point pattern characterizes a series better than anything else. It is of interest to study a series as a whole and to compare it with other series. The series may be considered the unit in organic chemistry.

It is a service to chemistry to prepare a pure compound and to put on record accurate determinations of its properties. It is a much greater service if the compound is a missing member of a series. A stamp collector would not pay a dime for just any stamp, but will bid high for a rare one needed to fill a blank in his collection.

The preparation of compounds to fill gaps in series, or to extend series is strongly recommended for undergraduates.

There are two practical considerations. One is that the new compounds can be made by slight modifications of methods that have been found satisfactory for the old ones. The other is that by plotting the properties of the new compounds along with those of the old, one can see whether the work has been done well. The regularity of the plots attests the purity of the starting materials and the accuracy of the determinations.

Of all the properties of a compound, the melting point is the most sensitive to impurities. The way it fits into the

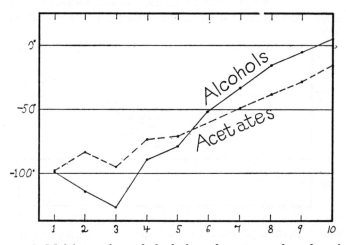

FIGURE 2. Melting points of alcohols and acetates, plotted against the number of carbon atoms in the alcohol

pattern is a far better criterion of purity than an analysis. Thus 5% of cetyl mercaptan in a sample of the octadecyl mercaptan would raise the sulfur content only 0.06%, but would knock down the melting point. A mistake in the identity of a compound may be disclosed by the melting point. Two authors have reported quite different melting points for octadecyl mercaptan. The lower melting point fits into the mercaptan pattern and the higher into the disulfide series. What the one author thought was the mercaptan was actually the disulfide. Conversely, the new melting points may show up errors in the old.

As an example of completing a series, the work of

a B.S. senior[10] may be cited. The task was to prepare three missing members of the acetanhydride series. It was found necessary to remake other members. When the researcher began, the melting point pattern was as in figure 3; when he finished it was as in figure 4.

There are many series from which the eleventh, thirteenth, fifteenth, and seventeenth members are missing.

We get amusement out of putting together the pieces of a jigsaw puzzle and seeing the picture emerge as piece is fitted to piece. It is too bad when some of the pieces are missing. There is a real thrill when, one after another of the melting points are plotted and a regular pattern takes shape. Unlike the picture of the castle, this pattern is something that has never been seen before. Sometimes the completed pattern turns out to be quite different from what was expected. There is always satisfaction in doing a neat job, whether it is a low score in golf or a

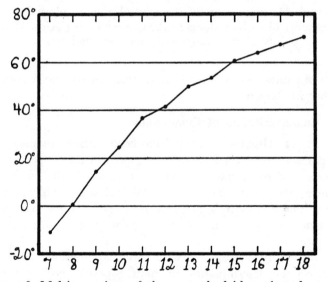

FIGURE 3. Melting points of the acetanhydrides, plotted against the number of carbon atoms in the corresponding acids. Melting points taken from the literature.

[10] J. M. Wallace and J. E. Copenhaver, *J. Amer. Chem. Soc.* **63,** 699 (1941).

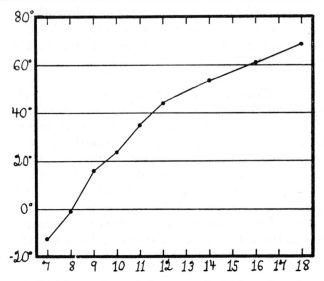

FIGURE 4. Melting points of the acetanhydrides, plotted against the number of carbon atoms in the corresponding acids. Melting points of the completed and corrected series.

piece of cabinet work. This kind of research will be considered further in chapter 9.

The Characterization of Compounds

Organic chemists have been diligent in preparing compounds, but many have been negligent in the proper characterization of the products. When one claims credit for having made a new compound, one should feel under obligation to purify it and to supply accurate information on a reasonable number of its properties. There is satisfaction in a completed task.

In the appendix to this chapter, some notes are given on the determination of melting points, boiling points, and densities. These, and refractive indices, are the properties that are commonly determined. Desirable additions would be fluidities, surface tensions, and solubilities in water and in other media.

DERIVATIVES FOR IDENTIFICATION

For several reasons, this field of research is particularly suitable for undergraduates. Minimum equipment and small amounts of materials are required and operations may be fitted into short laboratory periods. Materials are available in a wide variety. The usual course on the identification of organic compounds can be extended into new territory. Either one of two lines may be followed: 1. Old methods of identification may be applied to compounds that have not been studied, or 2. new methods may be tried out.

The identification of amines may be taken as an example. The manuals give reagents for this purpose and lists of derivatives that have been made by their use. One can go through a dealer's list to pick out additional amines and add to this list amines that have been advertised in *Chemical and Engineering News*. It is likely that a goodly number will be found of which no suitable derivatives have been prepared. Then one sets to work to secure and purify the amines that have been selected. The preparation of the derivatives follows the standard procedure. For preparing a derivative, it is usual to take about ½ gram as a sample. After one gets satisfactory results with a sample of this size, it is desirable to repeat the preparation with a much smaller sample, 10 milligrams or less. Micromethods, requiring only fractions of a milligram of material, are of great importance in working with natural products where the total quantity isolated may amount to only a few milligrams.

When one has finished with one reagent, one can go down the line with another. For the certain identification of an amine, it is desirable to prepare several derivatives even if the first turns out to be satisfactory. It is quite possible that a particular reagent may give derivatives of two amines that melt so close together that it is hard to distinguish them, but it is unlikely that this should be the case with derivatives from a different reagent. There is no one best reagent for all amines. This is illustrated in figure 5 in which the melting points of the derivatives with four reagents are plotted against the number of carbon atoms in the normal amines. It will be noted that the melting points of the derivatives of several amines with reagent III are inconveniently high and that those of amines 5, 6, and 7 with reagent I are too close together. These amines can be distinguished by using reagent IV.

With these reagents, primary amines can be identified in the presence of dialkyl amines with which they do

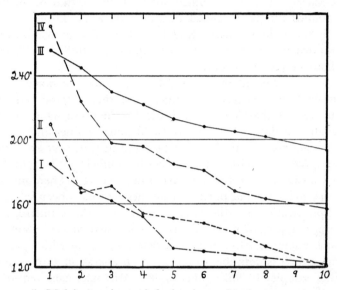

FIGURE 5. Melting points of derivatives of primary amines with four different reagents, plotted against the number of carbon atoms in the amines

not react. The reagents of figure 5 are: I, $PhNHCOCO_2Et$; II, $p\text{-}MeC_6H_4NHCOCO_2Et$; III, $p\text{-}PhC_6H_4NHCOCO_2Et$; and IV, $p\text{-}IC_6H_4NHCOCO_2Et$. The four reagents were prepared by me and handed over to Richardson for making the derivatives.[11]

From time to time, new reagents are proposed for the identification of amines. It is desirable to take one of these and go down the line with it so as to compare the new reagent

[11] A. G. Richardson, J. S. Pierce, and E. Emmet Reid. *J. Am. Chem. Soc.* **74**, 4011-12 (1952); C. A. **47**, 1008.

with those that are in use and to accumulate data for reference.

It is convenient for several students to cooperate on an undertaking of this sort, since the purified starting materials and the calibrated thermometers serve as well for several as for one. There is additional interest in the derivatives if they are chosen so as to fill in or extend a series, as is the case with those plotted in figure 5.

A third stage in the study of the identification of amines is to think up a new reagent that might give better derivatives or be more convenient to use, and then try this out on a number of amines.

The melting points of the derivatives not only show the identity of the amines, but are also a criterion of their purity.

An example of the study by an undergraduate of a new reagent for the identification of amines is the preparation of derivatives of twenty-one amines by the use of p-phenylazobenzoyl chloride.[12] The same reagent was used by two other undergraduates to prepare derivatives of twenty-four alcohols[13] and thirty phenols.[14]

What has been said about the identification of amines can be said about the identification of other classes of compounds, such as acids and alcohols. Much has been done, but there is room a plenty for more research. Derivatives can be made from new acids and alcohols with the reagents that we now have, but the search for other and better reagents should be continued. These and a few other classes of organic compounds have been pretty well cared for, but there are many for which identification methods are deficient or entirely lacking. Of late, unsaturates have become of great commercial importance, but means for the ready identification of many of them are still lacking. Years ago, the terpenes were identified by their dibromides and nitrosites. Certain mercaptans, notably thiophenol, ethanedithiol, thioglycolic acid and thioacetic acid, combine readily with unsaturates, particularly when the double bond is in the α-position.

---

[12] E. O. Woolfolk and E. H. Roberts, *J. Org. Chem.*, **21**, 436 (1956).
[13] E. O. Woolfolk, F. E. Beach, and S. P. McPherson, *J. Org. Chem.*, **20**, 391 (1955).
[14] E. O. Woolfolk and J. M. Taylor, *J. Org. Chem.*, **22**, 827 (1957).

Some of the addition products are solids and others can be converted to solids by simple reactions. Polymerizable vinyl monomers are of great importance. Ethanedithiol combines readily with acrylonitrile and should react similarly with other vinyl monomers.

The study of identification of organic compounds is a fruitful field that offers unlimited opportunities.

The advertisements in *Chemical and Engineering News* are a happy hunting ground for those who like to make compounds. Practically every issue contains a notice of at least one compound which may serve as the starting material for the synthesis of a series or a group of interesting compounds. In addition, the manufacturer asks you to write for a brochure outlining the reactions of the offered compound with literature references and suggestions of applications. Frequently he will send a generous sample, postage paid, if you will only write your name and address on a postal card. This is like lying under a tree on a South Sea island and having luscious fruit fall into your mouth.

Some of the advertised compounds are new and untouched by researchers, while others have been known, perhaps for a long time, but have not been available for extensive exploitation. An example is thiophene, the price of which has come down from 12 cents a gram to 2 dollars a pound.

Three recently advertised compounds may serve as examples:

tert-Butylamine, which has been available only to those who went to the trouble to make it, is now a commercial chemical, and beckons to those who want some interesting tasks. It should undergo most of the reactions of its isomer, *n*-butylamine, though probably at a much lower rate. The derivatives of the tertiary amine will probably have higher melting points and lower boiling points than the corresponding derivatives of the normal. It is suggested that all known derivatives of the two amines be set down in two columns and that consideration be given to the preparation of derivatives to fill the blanks. The study may be extended to take in isobutylamine and sec-butylamine. Are the reactivities of the four butylamines related to each other as are those of the four butyl alcohols?

Propargyl alcohol, HC≡C–CH$_2$OH, which for four score years has been only an entry in *Beilstein,* is now offered in drum lots. It would be interesting to make a comparative study of it and allyl and propyl alcohols. In some of their reactions the three may be alike, but in others they will probably be found to be very different. Their derivatives will show many differences.

It is also an acetylene and can be compared with other acetylenes.

1,4-Butynediol, 2-butenediol, and tetramethylene glycol will probably show more differences than similarities.

Pyromellitic acid, which was discovered by Bayer and Keibler in their classical investigation of honey stone,[15] has come down out of the musty archives to jostle other commercial chemicals. It offers many interesting possibilities. It is a double phthalic acid which is capable of all of the reactions of phthalic acid, at either, or both ends.

APPENDIX

In a course on organic preparations, stress is put on getting the desired compound, and constants are taken only to show that the product obtained is what it is supposed to be and is reasonably pure. When the object is to put on record reliable and accurate data on the physical properties of compounds, new or old, no pains should be spared to do the job as it should be done. The following pages are devoted to a discussion of methods of obtaining accurate data on melting and boiling points and on densities. This is intended to be a supplement to, and not a substitute for, instructions found in laboratory manuals.

MELTING POINTS

For compounds that melt without decomposition, the melting point is the most characteristic property. It is also the one most sensitive to impurity. A new compound, if it is a solid, is purified by recrystallization, or by any other means, until the melting point is sharp and is not raised by further treatment.

---

[15] *Annalen,* **141,** 271 (1867).

Then it is desirable to recrystallize from a different solvent. For practical purposes, a compound is said to be "pure" when further purification does not change its properties. New methods of purification may show some compounds, now considered pure, to be mixtures.

A distinction must be made between melting points and decomposition temperatures. When a compound, which has been melted and allowed to solidify, remelts at the same temperature, this is considered to be a true melting point. If there is any decomposition, the second "melting point" will be different from the first.

When a compound "melts with decomposition," the temperature observed is that at which it decomposes, rather than a true melting point. Decomposition temperatures depend somewhat on the conditions of heating and are not strictly reproducible. The melting point of phthalic acid is unknown, though many values for it are recorded. The acid does not melt instantly at 200°, though it will melt, if kept long enough, at any temperature above 131°, the melting point of the anhydride.

For taking melting points, the capillary-tube method is commonly used for compounds melting above 30°. With practice, melting points of pure compounds can be checked within 0.5°. Determination should be made on compounds of known purity until confidence is gained.

Since, as stated before, the melting point is the most characteristic property of a compound, it should be determined whenever possible. Few chemists there be who bother about the melting points of compounds that are liquid at room temperature. However, the melting points of such compounds are just as characteristic as those of any others and are needed to complete our information. Earlier in this chapter, the preparation of compounds to complete series has been stressed. The melting-point pattern of a series is its most interesting characteristic. The pattern is not complete unless the low, as well as the high, melting points are determined.

Far more accurate melting points may be obtained by plotting freezing point curves. This is the method used by physical chemists to get melting points accurate to 0.01° or even 0.001°. With only test tubes and a calibrated thermometer, melting points can be determined to 0.1°. This method can be used at high temperatures, but is particularly suitable for compounds that are liquid at room temperature.

A 5 to 10 gram sample, in a test tube, is stirred with a thermometer, while it is being cooled in a bath that is kept about 10° below the inside temperature. It is convenient to have two operators: one to stir and read the thermometer and the other to watch the time and record the readings at one-minute intervals. The temperature readings are plotted against time. Normally, there is supercooling and the temperature drops below the freezing point and jumps sharply to it when crystals start to form. If the compound is absolutely pure, the temperature remains constant until solidification is complete and then falls. If any impurity is present, the temperature plot has a downward slope. The curve is traced backward by substituting a warm bath for the cold. When the sample is melted, care is taken to leave a few crystals. Now, there will be no supercooling when the operation is repeated. It is desirable to repeat these operations several times until the results are entirely satisfactory.

This method can be used down to Dry Ice temperatures, but several difficulties are encountered. The most annoying is the condensation of moisture in the test tube. The pentane thermometers, which have to be used at low temperatures, are not accurate on account of large and uncertain stem corrections. However, accurate results can be obtained by comparison with a standard substance. Thus if the new compound is found to melt at −20.5°, the melting point of carbon tetrachloride is determined under *exactly* the same conditions. If this comes out −21.4° instead of −22.8°, the observed melting point is corrected to −21.9°. A standard substance is selected that melts in the same range. It must be one that is known to be pure.

When the downward slope of the freezing-point curve shows the presence of an impurity, the following method of purification should be tried. The thermometer is removed and the compound melted all but a few seed crystals. It is then cooled slowly until about 90% of it is solid. A roll of filter paper is pushed down into the sample to take up the liquid portion. The sample is melted, the thermometer inserted, and the freezing-point curve taken as before. If purification has been effected, the line in the plot will be higher and show less slope than before. This process may be repeated as may seem desirable.

The material in the rolls of filter paper may be recovered by suspending them in test tubes and pouring ether, or some other suitable solvent, down them.

BOILING POINTS

Distillation temperatures commonly masquerade as boiling points. A chemist prepares a new compound and, if it is a liquid, distils it, taking a cut over several degrees. This may be redistilled and a center cut taken when the temperature appears to be constant. This temperature goes into the literature as the boiling point. Some chemists are frank enough to say that the temperature is "uncorrected." This may be assumed to be generally true unless "cor." is after the figure. There may remain questions about the barometric pressure and the accuracy of the thermometer. The boiling point is the temperature at which liquid and vapor coexist in intimate contact. In an ordinary distillation, the thermometer is a long way from the liquid. The Cottrell apparatus, in which this condition is met, should be used for determining boiling points.

In vacuum distillations, there are still other sources of error. Reported "boiling points" at reduced pressures are usually unreliable. At atmospheric pressure, a change of 1 millimeter in the pressure makes a difference of only 0.05° in the boiling point, but at low pressures, where the slope of the vapor-pressure curve is slight, a small error in reading the manometer makes a large error in the boiling point. Of course, low pressures can be read accurately by the use of a special gage. The pressure shown by a manometer at a distance from the flask may be significantly different from that where the boiling is taking place. Boiling points at low pressures, as at atmospheric, should be determined with the Cottrell apparatus. For the proper characterization of a liquid, its boiling point should be determined at three or four pressures, so that its vapor-pressure curve may be drawn. Actually the determinations at several pressures can be made on the same sample of liquid and in little more time than that of just one pressure.

For making a determination, the manometer should be as close as possible to the Cottrell apparatus. The boiling is started at the lowest of the selected pressures and, when a steady state is reached, readings are made of the temperature and pressure. Adjustments are made for the next higher pressure and readings taken, and so on, to atmospheric pressure. An automatic pressure regulator is convenient, but can be dispensed with as follows. The desired pressure may be obtained by manipulating an adjustable leak, inserted next to the pump. To minimize fluctuations, connection is made with a large stout bottle. It is all right to take readings, say, at 22 and at 97 millimeters instead of at 20 and 100 millimeters and at the prevailing barometric pressure. The boiling points at 20, 100 and 760 millimeters which are to be reported are read from the curve or calculated from the equation.

To acquire skill and to establish confidence, it is desirable to make determinations on standard liquids, preferably boiling in the same range as the one in hand.

DENSITIES

These should be determined to 0.0001. With a 10-cubic centimeter pycnometer I was able to get checks to about 0.00003. This requires a well-designed pycnometer and care in the setting and in the temperature control. To gain confidence, one should make check determinations on standard liquids. Densities should be determined at 0/4 and at 25/4. This makes it possible to calculate densities at other temperatures for comparison with other data.

For the 0° bath, care must be taken that the crushed ice extends well below the bottom of the pycnometer. In case a well-regulated 25° bath is not available, a large battery jar of water will serve. If this has stood in the room for some hours, its temperature will change little in the time required for the pycnometer to come to equilibrium. Of course, this must be checked. The setting is made at the temperature of the bath and calculated to 25/4, which is reported.

7

∎ The study of known compounds

INTRODUCTION

The vast accumulation of well-coordinated information, fundamental as well as applied, which we call organic chemistry, is
but the sum of what we know about old compounds, their properties and reactions. A new fact about any one, or more, of these
is an addition to the sum of human knowledge.

Richter's *Lexikon* lists 144,150 organic compounds
as known on December 31, 1909. The main volumes of the fourth
edition of *Beilstein* have the same closing date and describe approximately the same compounds. By now, the number has
doubtless passed half a million and may be nearing a million.
Among these, we find substances of the most divergent properties.
Some have delightful odors and flavors; some are of value as
medicinals; some are virulent poisons. Some are dyes of all hues
of the rainbow; some make up fabrics such as Solomon in all his
glory never wore.

119

Our knowledge of a few of these compounds is extensive; of a considerable number, it is fair; but of the majority, it is sketchy and often of doubtful accuracy.

If we consider ethyl alcohol, which has been thoroughly studied in recent times, a bulky monograph would be required to sum up all we know about it. In the fourth decennial index (1937 to 1946) of *Chemical Abstracts,* there are approximately 1700 references to articles on ethyl alcohol. Many scores of references can be found to articles on hundreds of other compounds, while thousands of additional compounds received less attention. The fifth decennial index will include still more references to ethanol and, similarly, increased numbers to others.

Of course, alcohol is exceptional in its importance and its study is facilitated by its availability, but it has scarcely any more properties than any one of thousands of other organic compounds on which a like amount of study would produce a corresponding mass of information. Every substance has a large number of properties which may be ascertained, and the more of these we know, the better position we are in to prepare the substance, to separate it from others, to identify it, and to apply it to some useful purpose. Of the hundreds of thousands of organic compounds that have been made, there may be hundreds or even thousands which have valuable properties as pharmaceuticals, perfumes, plastics, reagents, or dye intermediates, but which blush unseen and spread their fragrance on the desert air of *Beilstein* because no one has gone to the trouble to ascertain their properties further than to take a melting point, or perchance a density or refractive index.

A thorough knowledge of the properties of individual substances is important, but the interest grows as we study a number of substances so as to compare one with another throughout the list of properties in order to trace the intricate connections between properties, and finally relate properties to constitution. A table of logarithms with one leaf torn out is of little value. A table containing inconsistent and inaccurate values for the logarithms of a minority of the numbers scattered here and there over the list would be utterly worthless for purposes of calculation, but such a table would compare most favorably with the tables we are now able to construct of the properties of organic compounds.

When we obtain accurate data for a large number of properties of all the members of a great number of series of organic compounds, we shall have the data required for attacking more efficiently the great problem of the relation of properties to constitution.

The marvelous chemical developments, both scientific and practical, that have advanced civilization resulted from a study of the properties and reactions of long-known compounds. To produce further advances, more study must be put on them.

However great the benefits that have been derived from the investigation of known substances, it is certain that even greater will be obtained. There are still fish in the sea, but it is unlikely that much larger ones will be caught. It is quite different with chemical discoveries; it is not only probable but almost certain that discoveries will be made of still greater importance than those that have been.

We say that a large proportion of the products that come from our huge chemical plants are new, not known a few short years ago. This is quite true, but these new products are made from old intermediates mostly by reactions that have been long known. The development of nylon and Dacron by Carothers and his associates was only the application of well-known reactions to old compounds. Nylon is the polyamide from adipic acid (1837) and hexamethylenediamine (1893). Dacron is the polyester from terephthalic acid (1862) and glycol (1903). As indicated by the dates given, all of these compounds had been long known. An important type of synthetic rubber is a polymer of styrene (1831) and acrylonitrile, both old compounds. Polymerization has been known for a long time, but has been exploited only recently.

While these and many other valuable things have been taken up and exploited, there is no telling how many there are that still lie buried in chemical literature. Some years ago my friend, Midgley, was looking for something to relieve the knocking of some fuels in an engine. After trying many things, he searched *Beilstein* for prospects and came across lead tetraethyl, an oddity which had been prepared in 1904. This, when tested in an engine, eliminated knocking. Its discoverer could not anticipate its use as an antiknock agent, as he was not concerned with automobiles.

Some time later, Midgley was looking for a refrigerant. Again he went to *Beilstein* and found a compound with a suitable boiling point, difluorodichloromethane, boiling at $-29°C$. This had been made by Swarts in 1907 in the course of an investigation of fluorine compounds; no one had thought of it as being useful. Probably those who looked at the formula thought that it would be toxic or that its manufacture would not be practicable. Midgley tested it and was surprised to find it to be nontoxic. As Freon, it is a much-used refrigerant.

Pharmacology is, for the most part, what we know about the physiological action of old compounds, some of which have been in use since prehistoric times. No one knows how many potent medicinals still lurk among the thousands of compounds that are described in chemical literature. Sulfanilamide had been known fifty years before a new method of testing showed it to be of medicinal value.

In spite of the immense accumulation of knowledge about old compounds, the field is so vast that there are many empty spots. What is known looks small when we contemplate the vastness of the unknown. There is yet much to be learned about the best-known compounds and a still greater lack of knowledge about thousands of others. The rest of this chapter is devoted to pointing out some of the desirable additions to our knowledge of known compounds. Consideration will be centered on physical properties, since they are the most tangible and lend themselves better to statistical treatment.

The grand science of astronomy has been built on accurate observations of the relative positions of the heavenly bodies. Great observatories in all parts of the world have cooperated in making photographic maps of the whole sky. The position of a single star is of little interest, but the relative positions of a great number are important.

The hundreds of thousands of known organic compounds and other hundreds of thousands that are yet to be prepared fit into a vast system in which each is related to all the others. This requires the accumulation of accurate information about each compound.

Any given compound has a large number of physical properties, all of which are of interest as characterizing it and as items in our study of the relation of properties to structure. Chemical properties are even more important. The practical view is that the more we know about the properties of compounds, the better position we are in to select one for a special use. For example, in lubricants, viscosity is an important characteristic. It must be suited to the machinery for which it is intended, being much lower for a watch than for a heavy machine. For an automobile lubricant, the slope of the viscosity curve must be as low as possible. Otherwise it is too difficult to start the car in cold weather and the lubricant becomes too thin when the engine warms up. A lubricant must have extremely low volatility, and be chemically inert.

CONSTITUTION AND PROPERTIES

No one doubts that the properties of a compound are dependent on its constitution. If a given number of atoms of given kinds are linked together in a certain way, the molecule has certain properties. The properties of butyric acid, for example, its density, boiling point, refractive index, solubility, odor, taste, degree of ionization, heats of formation, of solution, and of neutralization and all other imaginable properties are dependent on the atoms that make up the molecule and on their grouping. If the molecule is altered in any way, all of these properties are changed. In the far-off consummation of organic chemistry, we may expect to be able to calculate exact values for all the properties of a compound when we know its constitution and, conversely, to write the structural formula of a substance from exact measurements on a number of its properties. We are constantly endeavoring to do both of these things and frequently meet with considerable success, but our present data are not sufficiently complete or accurate enough to insure the correctness

of our deductions except in relatively few cases. Whoever measures accurately any property of an organic compound of established purity and known constitution supplies that much of the
needed data.

The crying need for extensive and persistent research on the properties of long-known compounds is realized
when we look up substances in *Beilstein*. It is a common thing to
find four or five divergent figures given for the melting or boiling point of a common substance, the highest and lowest being
frequently five or even ten degrees apart. An investigation was
held up for some time, because the melting point of piperidine
hydrochloride was given as 237° when it really is 244°. The hydrochloride of a base obtained in a certain reaction melted at 244°
and the base was supposed to be something else till piperidine
hydrochloride was prepared and found to melt at 244°.

Physical chemists accuse "organikers" of making inaccurate measurements; often we neglect to make even that kind.
The sad state of our knowledge of the properties of organic
compounds is a consequence of the way in which chemists have
worked. In the early days, pure starting materials were scarce
and only a few reactions were known. If a new compound was
a solid, it was recrystallized and its melting point determined.
Because the early chemists were not in a hurry, they obtained
good results. With liquids they did not do so well, since their
fractionation equipment was poor.

Making a new compound has been considered an
achievement, and credit has always been given to the first to make
it. Bobby Jones was far from being the first to play golf. He
achieved fame by playing an exceptionally good game. We should
give less credit to the chemist who is the first to make a particular
compound and more to the one who gets it pure and characterizes it properly.

Compounds have been made by chemists with vari-
ous objectives, frequently practical. Some have been in search
of medicinals, others of insecticides. Commonly, no effort was
made to obtain the compound in high purity. Analysis had to
be given and a boiling or melting point, and perhaps a density,
to characterize the compound. The "boiling point" was com-

monly only a distillation temperature, which may have been quite different from the true boiling point. The melting points were usually taken with any thermometer that was at hand. When interest was solely in the effectiveness of the compound for a specific use, scant attention was given to obtaining it in high purity or in ascertaining its properties accurately. The result is that, for many compounds, the available data are scanty and inaccurate.

The chief interest in the physical properties of compounds is for comparing the members of a series among themselves and with the members of other series. The melting points, boiling points, densities, and other properties of mercaptans can be compared with those of alcohols of the same carbon content.

In chapter 6, the importance of considering a series of organic compounds as a unit has been stressed. The plots of the boiling and melting points characterize these series and show the identity and purity of the individual members. When accurate determinations have been made of the properties of several members of a series, it is possible to predict the properties of the missing members, either by interpolation or from mathematical formulae.

For aliphatic hydrocarbons, branched as well as straight-chain, it is possible to calculate accurate values for boiling points, densities, and refractive indices. Aniline points, the temperatures at which hydrocarbons mix with aniline, can be predicted. These are closely related to the antiknock characteristics. For some series of alcohols and alkyl halides, formulae for calculating boiling points have been set up.

As has been stated before, numerical data for solubilities in water are scant. In table 1 the solubilities in water of some alcohols, mercaptans, alkyl bromides, and hydrocarbons are given. A striking regularity is seen in the data for the mercaptans, the only series in which the solubilities have been determined under the same conditions. It appears that any mercaptan is approximately 3.4 times as soluble as the next higher, and that any alcohol is about 138 times as soluble as the corresponding mercaptan.

In the series of esters, from acetate to caprate, as

TABLE 1

Solubilities of normal alcohols, mercaptans, alkyl bromides,
and hydrocarbons in 100 cubic centimeters of water

R	ROH	Ratio	RSH	Ratio	RBr	Ratio	RH	Ratio	ROH/RSH
Methyl	—	—	2.33	—	—	—	—	—	—
Ethyl	—	—	0.676	3.45	0.896	—	—	—	—
Propyl	—	—	0.196	3.45	0.231	3.88	—	—	—
Butyl	7.88	—	0.057	3.44	0.061	3.79	—	—	138
Amyl	2.26	3.48	0.0164	3.47	—	—	0.036	—	138
Hexyl	0.628	3.59	0.0043	3.81	—	—	0.014	2.57	146
Heptyl	0.18	3.48	0.0014	3.07	—	—	0.0052	2.69	129
Octyl	0.0538	3.35	—	—	—	—	0.0015	3.47	—
Average		3.48		3.44		3.84		2.91	138

may be seen from table 2, the ratio is approximately 3. When more extensive data become available, we shall be able to extrapolate to solubilities of the higher members of series.

The study of solubilities offers many opportunities for obtaining information of scientific interest and of practical value. Solubilities of organic compounds in water are of special importance, since it is so often necessary to get them out of, or into, aqueous solution. The determination of the solubility of a single organic compound helps. Providing data on a number of

TABLE 2

Solubilities in water of the normal acids
and of their ethyl esters

Acid		Ratio	Ester	Ratio	Acid/Ester
Formic	—	—	11 (18°)	—	—
Acetic	—	—	8.5 (15°)	1.2	—
Propionic	—	—	1.75 (20°)	4.8	—
Butyric	—	—	0.68 (25°)	2.6	—
Valeric	3.9 (16°)	—	0.24 (25°)	2.7	16.25
Caproic	0.4	9.75	0.063 (20°)	3.8	6.34
Heptylic	0.241 (15°)	1.65	0.029 (20°)	2.1	8.31
Caprylic	0.25 (100°)	—	0.007 (20°)	4.1	—
Pelargonic	—	—	0.003 (20°)	2.3	—
Capric	—	—	0.0015 (20°)	2.0	—
	Average ratio	4.06		2.95	

compounds is a greater service, particularly if they are related in a group or series.

The incompleteness of our knowledge of the properties of organic compounds is shown by an inspection of the tables given in handbooks. A table in Lange's handbook lists the properties of 6507 compounds, possibly 1% of those that have been described. These compounds have been selected as the ones most likely to be of interest. In the first thousand of these, there are 169 compounds for which boiling points are given, but no melting points. As has been pointed out in chapter 6, the melting point is the most characteristic property of an organic compound. It takes extra labor to get substances pure enough for the melting points to be reliable, and as the determination of the melting points of compounds that melt below 40°C is troublesome, chemists neglect them. Numerical values are given for the solubilities in water of 127 solids and of only 27 liquids.

An examination of the figures given by different chemists for the melting and boiling points of many compounds will show large discrepancies, as has been pointed out before. Thus one author gives the boiling point of hexyl mercaptan as 86.4°C at 90 millimeters and another as 84°C at 100 millimeters. For benzyl mercaptan we find 100°C at 22 millimeters and 99°C at 32 millimeters. In the appendix to chapter 6, some information is given on methods of obtaining correct values of melting points and boiling points.

A great service can be rendered to organic chemistry by supplying missing data and correcting inaccuracies in the old. An example of this is given in chapter 6. Three missing melting points were supplied and corrections made in others in the series of acid anhydrides. Emphasis must be put on obtaining melting points of substances that melt below 40°C and on determining the vapor pressures of slightly volatile liquids.

8. ∎ Remaking known compounds

THE NEED FOR IMPROVED METHODS

This is what the student in a course in organic preparations is doing. It is just what the great chemical corporations are doing on a large scale, and it is just what they are spending many millions of dollars to find better ways of doing.

The preparation of an organic compound involves a reaction. To obtain an improved yield of the desired compound, one must have a clearer understanding of the reaction and a more precise knowledge of the factors which influence its progress. The academic chemist will be more interested in why the reaction goes and in its mechanism; the industrial chemist, who wants a high yield of the product, is pretty dumb if he fails to study the reaction.

There are countless problems of many kinds, some of which are little more than a follow-up of routine organic preparations, and some that require the combined efforts of groups of experienced chemists.

At first sight, the preparation of a known organic compound looks like a trivial task, not a research project. We have dozens of excellent laboratory manuals of organic preparations, which are written so well that even students who do not understand the reaction can get good results. Then there are larger books filled with more difficult procedures. We have thirty odd volumes on *Organic Syntheses* which give tested directions for making useful quantities of some hundreds of compounds. However, the total number of compounds covered in all of these books is only a tiny fraction of the hundreds of thousands that have been described. The fact that books such as these have been written is evidence that the directions in the original literature are not always adequate.

IMPROVING AN OLD METHOD

The chemist who first makes a compound publishes the method he used for making it. He took so many grams of this and so many of that and heated them together for so long at such a temperature and then isolated the product in such and such a way. The rules of the game require him to tell how he actually made the compound, rather than to idealize his methods and describe one which he believes would give better results. Usually he was satisfied with obtaining enough for characterization, and possibly for testing. It mattered little whether the yield was 5 or 95%, and seldom did he make much effort to determine the best reaction conditions. The next one who finds himself in need of this particular compound repeats the preparation exactly as described and commonly gets the desired substance, though the yield is usually lower or the quality poorer than was to be expected from the description. This is natural, as it is impossible, working from written directions, to duplicate exactly the original work. Sometimes the second chemist pauses to make an effort to improve the method of preparation and publishes his findings. Other chemists may, from time to time, add further information, so that the process may gradually be improved. Anyone desiring to make this compound must read the original method and then consider all the modifications that have been suggested. The final process may be quite satisfactory or it may not be. A service, large or small according to circumstances, but a real service in any case, may be rendered the chemical world by taking up the study of the present methods of preparation of almost any organic compound.

When it comes to the large-scale manufacture of a compound, perfecting the method becomes important. This is illustrated by the case of ethyl acetate, of which hundreds of thousands of pounds are required annually. It is produced from ethanol and acetic acid in the presence of a mineral acid catalyst, just as it has been for many years, but hundreds of investigations have been required to find the most efficient and economical conditions for its manufacture, and these have to be modified to suit the scale of operations, and for other reasons. In the first forty volumes of *Chemical Abstracts,* sixty-one patents are listed on the manufacture of ethyl acetate.

DEVELOPING A PRACTICABLE PROCESS

When a compound suitable for a given purpose is discovered, the chemist is apt to pat himself on the back and consider that the great invention has been made and all that remains is to collect and spend his bonus. Actually this is only a start. The task of finding a practicable way of making the compound on a large scale remains. Usually this is a far more serious matter than the discovery itself. In an industrial establishment, the two stages are usually separated and performed by different groups of chemists; sometimes the second is passed on to an entirely different organization. This is well illustrated by the story of lead tetraethyl.

When I visited the General Motors Laboratory at Dayton right after Midgley and Boyd had discovered the remarkable power of lead tetraethyl to soothe a knocking motor, I found them making it by the reaction of zinc ethyl on lead chloride. The zinc ethyl, a spontaneously inflammable liquid, was obtained by the action of ethyl iodide on specially prepared zinc dust. Ethyl iodide is expensive and the yields in the two reactions are poor. Here was a compound ready to do an important job, but its cost was prohibitive. Dozens of chemists went to work to find a practicable method of synthesis. The one finally adopted was discovered by Professor Kraus of Clark University, but many months of research by a number of chemists were required to get lead tetraethyl into commercial production.

Similar, though less spectacular stories, could be told about neoprene, nylon, and Thiokol.

The most dramatic event in the history of chemical research was the feverish mass attack by British chemists, academic and industrial, on the synthesis of mustard gas in World War I, that was briefly referred to in a preceding section. The Germans had launched a devastating attack with this deadly agent against unsuspecting and unprotected allied troops. It was quickly identified. The British knew the German method of making it, but they did not have ethylene chlorohydrin, a necessary starting material. At that time no one in America knew a practicable method of making this compound, which is now manufactured on a large scale. The British saw the significance of some old experiments, which the all-wise Beilstein had misinterpreted, and soon mustard gas was flowing from allied plants.

FINDING NEW SOURCES OF SUPPLY

With the expansion of the organic chemical industry, which began at the end of World War I and has continued ever since at an accelerated rate, old sources of supply were being exhausted, and increasing them became a prime objective of research. Alcohol and acetic acid, in impure and dilute form, were known in antiquity as produced by the fermentation and subsequent souring of fruit juices. The fermentation was put on a factory scale and the oxidation to acetic acid was hastened, but the two steps in their manufacture remained essentially the same until well into this century.

Huge quantities of alcohol, not counting what goes into beverages, are still made by fermentation. But the supply has had to be augmented by the hydration of ethylene. In olden times ethylene, discovered in 1795, was made by the dehydration of ethanol. Whenever I needed ethylene bromide before 1915, I prepared ethylene from alcohol according to the directions in Remsen's *Organic Chemistry*. Now hundreds of tons of ethylene, needed for the production of polyethylene plastics, are made by cracking hydrocarbons.

With acetic acid it is different; old-style vinegar is used in pickles, but even as a condiment it is partially supplanted by the synthetic. Acetylene is now the starting material for the production of huge quantities of acetic acid and related products.

In the manufacture of smokeless powder, during World War I, acetone, a necessary solvent, was a critical factor. At times operations had to be halted until the acetone could be recovered from one batch for use in the second. The United States Industrial Alcohol Co. was set up to manufacture acetone by the pyrolysis of calcium acetate from acetic acid, made by the "quick vinegar" process. This method of preparing acetone had come down from its discovery in 1832. The situation was relieved by the development of a fermentation process which produced acetone and *n*-butanol. An additional supply was obtained by the oxidation of isopropanol, whose manufacture by the hydration of propylene had been put on a large scale. *n*-Butanol, which had been a curiosity since 1871, became an important chemical.

Methanol, discovered in 1661, continued to be made by wood distillation for about 260 years. As the demand for it began to outrun the supply, a high-pressure synthesis from carbon monoxide and hydrogen, worked out by Patart, made it available on an undreamed of scale. The quantity production of formaldehyde from its oxidation became a large factor in industrial expansion.

Benzene, in particular, the starting material for aniline and other dye intermediates, was so plentiful that it was sometimes added to gasoline. The demands for benzene and also for toluene have increased so greatly that the chemical industry has had to turn to petroleum for sufficient quantities.

Phenol, discovered in 1834, became scarce even during the last century, and its production by the alkali fusion of sodium benzene sulfonate was operated on a large scale. In recent years the demand for making phenolic resins, such as Bakelite, has stimulated the search for other syntheses, several of which are in large-scale operation.

The development, within the last few decades, of plastics has stimulated research on the preparation of polymerizable vinyl compounds, $RCH:CH_2$, so-called "monomers." Styrene, first obtained in 1831 by the distillation of storax, became a heavy chemical about a century later, mounting up to a billion pounds per year. There are five patents on its manufacture listed in the third decennial index of *Chemical Abstracts,* and twenty-seven in the fourth, but none in the earlier. The development of the ethylation of benzene by ethylene made possible this production of styrene. On acrylonitrile, which is polymerized with styrene to produce synthetic rubber, there are seventeen patents in the fourth decennial index, but none in the earlier. Much research has gone into these two compounds.

Rayon and cellulose acetate are made by the application of long-known reactions to cellulose, the first by the xanthate reaction, discovered by Zeise in 1815. Nylon is a polyamide from adipic acid and hexamethylenediamine, both long-known compounds. In all three cases the reactions are simple, but the development of the products into useful fibers has required a vast deal of research which has cost tens of millions of dollars.

Such examples could be multiplied. New and larger uses are constantly being found for old compounds, either as such or as intermediates for the synthesis of others. However, those that have been exploited are only a small fraction of those that are known. There is no telling how many of value may yet be discovered.

COMPARISON OF PREPARATION METHODS

For a single organic compound there may be several possible syntheses. This becomes of more than academic interest when a compound has to be produced on a large scale. Then careful comparisons have to be made to find out which process offers the best possibilities of profit. When a new synthesis is developed, it must be compared with those already known.

In the case of phenol, new processes have been developed but have not displaced the old entirely. About 1920 its manufacture by the reaction of chlorobenzene with sodium hydroxide in aqueous solution, at a high temperature under pressure, was introduced. Since 1953 several plants have been built for making it by the decomposition of cumene hydroperoxide. All three of these processes are operated on a large scale in the United States. Extensive investigations have been made on the direct air oxidation of benzene to phenol. To compare these four processes, comprehensive cost calculations on the production of phenol must be made for each. The research chemist will seldom be called upon to make these calculations, but he will have to supply an important part of the data on which they are based.

For each step in a process, the yields, corrected for losses in isolation, must be ascertained and used in the calculations of the materials required to make, say, 100 pounds of phenol. Any money received from the sale of a by-product reduces the cost of the main product. In the chlorobenzene process, phenyl ether is a by-product, but efforts have to be made to limit its production to the amount that can be disposed of. In the cumene hydroperoxide process, a molecule of acetone is produced for every one of phenol, but the market for acetone is large enough to take care of the yield.

The demand for adipic acid as one of the starting materials for nylon was the incentive for extensive investigations on ways of making it. The principal methods studied have been:

1. Oxidation of cyclohexane
2. Oxidation of cyclohexanol
3. Hydrolysis of adiponitrile.

According to *Beilstein,* adipic acid was obtained by the oxidation of a petroleum fraction. Cyclohexane is the cheapest starting material, but its oxidation gives less adipic acid and more by-products than that of cyclohexanol. The last-named process involves more steps; furfural → furane → tetrahydrofurane → 1,4-dichlorobutane → adiponitrile → adipic acid, but the reactions are more clean cut.

PREPARATION OF TAGGED COMPOUNDS

The use of radioactive isotopes provides an elegant method of studying the mechanism of organic reactions. When a tagged compound is administered to an animal, its distribution in the body and its elimination can be followed conveniently with a Geiger counter.

On account of the high cost of radioactive isotopes and of the danger of handling large quantities without elaborate precautions, syntheses must be found which give high yields of the desired compounds from available radioactive materials. It is desirable to try out a proposed method by making practice runs on a gram or less of inactive material, until satisfactory yields are obtained with certainty. The radioactive material is then diluted with ordinary material to make it up to such an amount.

FROM LABORATORY TO PLANT

This is a large problem of the industrial chemist. Nearly all processes are worked out on a laboratory scale and then have to be adapted to factory conditions. It is a long step from beakers and laboratory dishes to soap kettles 50 feet deep and 20 feet in diameter holding a million pounds, and from diazotizing in a beaker to huge vats. The need of such work has given rise to a new profession, or at least to a new designation for a profession, that of chemical engineers. A chemical engineer is one who is able to translate grams into tons, beakers into tanks, and flasks into autoclaves.

When a satisfactory laboratory process for the preparation of a compound has been worked out, the chemist's task is certainly well begun, but it may not be half done. The chemist, while working in the laboratory, should keep constantly in mind the conditions of plant operations and the possible adaptation of the proposed process to them. Unless this has been done, a process, which gives excellent results in the laboratory, may have to be reworked, or even abandoned in favor of some other, when large-scale manufacture is contemplated.

The profit from the manufacture of any product is obviously the difference between what it will bring on the market and what it costs to make. The cost of manufacture is the sum of a large number of items: raw materials, additional materials, power for heating, refrigeration, pumping, distillation, etc., labor costs, and plant amortization, to name only the chief items. Each of these items is estimated for 100 pounds of the product and the figures set down in a long column. Where two, or more, processes are being considered, this is done for each and the totals compared. It is customary to figure three years as the life of the plant. It is obvious that the preference will be given to a process which involves low-cost equipment. Labor costs are an important item and becoming more so. They depend largely on the scale of the operation; it takes one man to operate a small soap kettle, and I have seen one man taking care of a million-pound soap kettle, and he did nothing but turn a valve now and then. Labor costs must be calculated for so many pounds of product per day.

As is mentioned at the end of this chapter, the ideal is a continuous process with automatic controls which operates with little supervision.

The reaction time, particularly if the reaction has to be carried on in an autoclave, is important, since it determines how many batches can be handled in a day. The research chemist cannot be expected to supply accurate figures for all of these items, but he should realize their importance and have some idea of their magnitude.

THE SEMIWORKS

The first stop on the way from the laboratory to the plant is at the semiworks, where the proposed process is tried out on a small scale in equipment and under conditions similar to those in a plant, in order to find out how these may have to be modified.

If a preparation goes wrong in the laboratory, perhaps a dollar's worth of material and several hours of the chemist's time may be lost. To change the apparatus it is only necessary to swap a few taper joints. In the semiworks the loss from a bad run may be several times greater. If a change has to be made in the equipment, a pipe wrench or a change to another kettle may be required. In a large plant an error in operation may result in the loss of tones of valuable material and of a day's wages for a number of operatives. To make a major alteration in the design of a plant may involve the expenditure of tens of thousands of dollars and a shutdown for weeks or months. It is possible for an impatient promoter to skip the semiworks, but it is like playing Russian roulette except that the odds are five to one against you. Mistakes have to be made, but it is desirable to make 90% of them in the laboratory and the other 10% in the semiworks. I was informed, by one who knew, of a plant, costing a million dollars, that did not produce a pound of product within a year after its completion.

Taking a process through the semiworks and designing a plant are responsibilities of chemical engineers and plant designers, but they have to depend on the chemist for information about the process and product. The more accurate and complete this is, the better the prospect of a favorable outcome. It is common practice for the chemist, who is responsible for the process, to work closely with the chemical engineers, securing for them additional information as may be required. I have been told of a plant, costing several hundred thousand dollars, that was a total loss because the chemist made an erroneous identification of a product.

FROM GLASS TO METAL CONTAINERS

In going from the laboratory to the plant, the most perplexing problem is finding a substitute for glassware. No one realizes the wonderful properties of glass until it comes to doing without it. A prime quality of glass is its chemical inertness. It is unaffected by acids, except hydrofluoric, either dilute or concentrated, by oxidising or reducing agents or by free chlorine or bromine, regardless of temperature. No other material, suitable for the fabrication of reaction vessels, has been found that even approaches glass in this respect. However, various materials, or combinations of materials, have been found which are sufficiently resistant to one or more chemicals under certain conditions. Thus rubber-lined tanks can be used as containers of dilute aqueous solutions of acids at room temperature, and plain steel resists dry chlorine.

It is the job of the chemical engineer to design equipment for the semiworks tryout of the process that the chemist has devised, but much grief may be avoided if the chemist has looked forward and considered the possibilities and limitations of plant equipment. The chemist should know what the chemical reactants will do to the equipment and how traces of dissolved metals will influence the reaction or what they will do to the products. A simple example is the choice of an esterification catalyst. In the laboratory the preference is for hydrogen chloride, but this is highly corrosive to metals, so sulfuric acid is used in the plant. I once saw the whole course of a reaction, that was being run in a glass-lined kettle, altered by the tiny amount of iron that was dissolved through an unnoticed crack in the lining.

HEATING AND COOLING

Getting heat into and getting heat out of reaction mixtures give little trouble in the laboratory, but become serious matters in large-scale operations. A 10-liter flask has only 4.64 times the surface of a 1-liter flask. This means that if the two flasks, each half full of the same liquid, were placed in an oil bath, it would require more than twice as long to reach the same temperature in the larger flask. In the plant, heating surface is provided by having coils of pipe immersed in the liquid that is to be heated.

Most of the reactions with which chemists have to deal are exothermic. Just as a stone rolls downhill, the driving force in a reaction is the possibility of reaching a lower energy level. A push is needed to get the stone started, but it may pick up speed as it rolls. An exothermic reaction may require the application of heat to get it started. Whether or not the reaction will keep going, without external heating, depends on the relation of the amount of heat evolved to that lost by radiation. If the heat evolved is in excess, the temperature goes up, and for a 10°C rise the reaction rate is doubled and so is the rate of heat evolution. The spots on the laboratory ceiling are roughly proportional to the number of Skraup syntheses that have been run.

The exothermic character of a reaction may escape notice when it is run on a small scale. This was found out the hard way in a certain plant. In the laboratory 208 grams, a gram mole, of anthraquinone was sulfonated by heating with oleum at 140°C. The flask containing the mixture was heated in an oil bath and the continuous application of heat was required to maintain the desired temperature. When the reaction conditions were satisfactorily established, it was decided to make a run on a larger scale. A pound mole, 208 pounds, of anthraquinone, was mixed with the proper amount of oleum and heated. When 140° was reached the temperature continued to rise, although the heating was discontinued. Within a few minutes the whole charge was a charred mass.

The polymerization of a vinyl monomer is exothermic and may be highly so. If polymerization is initiated in a mass of such monomer, heat may be evolved so much faster than it can escape that the polymer which is produced may be damaged or even destroyed. Polymerization may take place with explosive violence. In emulsion polymerization, which is standard practice, the heat is taken care of by the water which surrounds the droplets of the monomer.

In the plant free flames are avoided on account of fire hazard. Below about 200°C heating may be by steam, the temperature being set by regulating the pressure. Dowtherm, a mixture of biphenyl, boiling at 255°, and phenyl ether, boiling at 259°, under sub- or superatmospheric pressure, may serve for the range 200° to 300°C.

MIXING AND STIRRING

When working in the laboratory, it is sufficient to shake a flask to mix its contents, but not so in the factory. An important part of nearly all large-scale operations is the mixing of the ingredients or reagents. Tanks and other containers must be provided with some form of agitator which will bring the various reagents into intimate contact and do so as quickly as possible. Even with substances that mix or dissolve to homogeneous solutions, the mixing is a much more serious matter than it appears to be to the beginner. When it comes to reactions that involve heterogeneous systems, such as washing an oil with a water solution or acting on a suspended solid by something in solution, or in the extreme case, acting on a solid suspended in a liquid by a gas which is pumped into the liquid, the question of agitation becomes much more important, in fact it frequently becomes the matter of supreme importance and the success or failure of the process may depend on the one question of the efficiency of the agitator. A sharp distinction is to be made between agitators which cause a liquid mixture to circulate as a whole and those that cause intimate internal mixing. In the case of an oil and water in a circular tank, a stirrer that causes rapid rotation of the whole mass may even aid in the separation of the oil and water, centrifugal action sending the heavier water to the outside of the tank and segregating the lighter oil in the center. Such an agitator might even unmix instead of mixing the oil and water. If a mass of homogeneous liquid is to be circulated over heating or cooling coils, such action will be satisfactory, but in case intimate contact is to be effected between the portions of a nonhomogeneous mixture, an entirely different sort of agitator is required. It is possible, by properly designed apparatus, to maintain a mass of liquid in the most intense internal mixing while the liquid, as a whole, appears almost quiescent and circulates to a minimum amount. Catalytic hydrogenation is a matter of proper agitation. In this reaction, an oil, a finely divided solid, and a gas have to be brought into the reaction. All three must be present at the same place at the same time for the reaction to take place. The result is that the process depends almost entirely on the intensity of the mixing. In this case, it is internal mixing and not the motion of the mass as a whole that is needed.

The question of designing agitators is, of course, a matter of machinery and engineering and not at all of chemistry, but the chemist is the one who must see the need of it and must see that it is provided when needed. The chemist is the one to decide whether the process is one that demands such mixing and also how much and what kind of mixing is required. After all, the chemist is likely to be the one to be blamed if the process does not work, and he is the one to make it work. Chemical action takes place only at infinitesimal distances, and if it is desired to make molecules react, they must be brought within such distances of each other and must be kept in such relation till the action is complete.

REACTIONS UNDER PRESSURE

When it comes to carrying out reactions under pressure, the use of steel containers, instead of glass, opens up new horizons. Under high pressures, many reactions go easily which do not take place under ordinary pressures. In some cases, as in the ammonia and methanol syntheses, satisfactory yields are obtained, under high pressures, in spite of unfavorable equilibria.

Small-scale experiments are made in steel shaker tubes in specially designed laboratories. Pressures up to 1000 atmospheres are common.

CONTINUOUS OPERATION

The goal in large-scale manufacturing is an automatically controlled continuous process, the reactants being fed in at one end of the equipment and the finished product coming out at the other. This goal is seldom reached, but all possible efforts are made to come as close to it as is practicable. It is a long way from the laboratory to such a plant process, but the location of the great oak was determined by the squirrel that buried the acorn. All along in the laboratory, the chemist should be looking far ahead and endeavoring to find reaction conditions suitable for continuous operation. This requires an understanding of the possibilities and the limitations of continuous processes and a deal of imagination. Large-scale batch processes in the plant are essentially magnifications of the familiar batchwise preparations of the laboratory, but laboratory-scale continuous processes that can be blown up to plant size are practically nonexistent. The development of a continuous process must begin in the semiworks, and be done by chemical engineers, but the process that is to be developed must come from the laboratory and must be suited for such development.

9. ∎ Making new compounds

INTRODUCTION

Why make new compounds? Half a million, and more, have been made. Why do we want any more? Each of these hundreds of thousands of compounds fits snugly into a niche in a vast system, the equal of which is not to be found in any other department of human knowledge. In spite of all the work that has been done, the empty niches far outnumber the ones that have been filled; millions of new compounds are needed to complete the system.

In the early days, chemists mixed this with that just to see what would happen. As theories were evolved, the preparation of new compounds became more orderly. Chemists vied with each other in elaborating new theories and in testing them by preparing the new compounds that were predicted. The chemist's reward was in the satisfaction of adding something to human knowledge and in placing his name on the record.

145

BUILDING CHEMISTRY

The preparation and description of a new compound is a brick, or perhaps it is better to say a stone, as the sizes differ, in the structure of organic chemistry. It is dumping rather than building simply to add a stone to a pile. In order that the process may be building, the stone must fit somewhere and must be added at some place in an orderly way so as to aid in carrying out the design of the structure. If we contemplate organic chemistry as a structure, we see that the building has been largely haphazard. Some parts are remarkably advanced, while others have been almost neglected with only a random stone here and there in place. The structure will grow more symmetrically if those who bring the stones will look first to see what is needed.

The individual chemist should not be discouraged by the number of compounds that are to be made, but should be heartened by the fact that whatever compounds he may make will fit into the system and be permanent additions to scientific knowledge. Instead of making just any compound, it is desirable to select one that is related to those that are already known. Thousands of hewn stones are required for the building of a cathedral. The mason adds one stone at a time at the proper place on the wall and, by and by, the magnificent edifice is complete.

The possibility of delivering a letter to John Doe in New York City depends on the fact that he lives in a numbered house on a numbered street, or avenue. As was pointed out in chapter 6, the feasibility of learning organic chemistry is linked with the fact that the myriads of compounds can be arranged in orderly series and groups which become units in the system. Many compounds are needed to fill out these series and groups.

In the study of organic chemistry, it is interesting to compare the members of a series among themselves and with those of other series.[1] In figure 6 the melting points of a num-

---

[1] The relations between the physical properties of a number of sulfur compounds to those of the corresponding oxygen compounds are discussed

ber of alkyl sulfides, RSR, are compared with those of the ethers, ROR, and hydrocarbons, RR, having the same number of carbon atoms.

It will be noted that the melting points of the sulfides are almost exactly halfway between those of the ethers and those of the hydrocarbons. Some of the sulfides and the ethers have not been prepared. When they are, their purity will be judged by the closeness of their melting points to the curve that

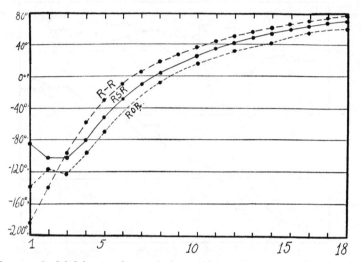

FIGURE 6. Melting points of the sulfides, RSR, compared with those of the ethers, ROR, and the hydrocarbons, RR, plotted against the number of carbon atoms in R

has been drawn. The reported melting points of two of the ethers appear to be too low.

Most of the alkyl sulfides, above decyl, of figure 6 and the higher sulfides and ethers of figure 7 were prepared by the late Mrs. Carrie Gutman Moses and myself. It is hoped that someone will prepare the missing sulfides of figure 6, then lower

in pages 43 to 53 of Volume I and pages 84 to 90 of Volume II of my series, from which many of the data in this section are taken. E. Emmet Reid, *Organic Chemistry of Bivalent Sulfur,* New York, Chemical Publishing Co., 1958, 1959.

phenyl alkyl sulfides of figure 7 and determine the missing melting point of isobutyl mercaptan for figure 7.

In figure 7 are plotted the melting points of the phenyl and 4-phenylphenyl ethers and thioethers, PhOR, PhSR, 4-PhC₆H₄OR, and 4-PhC₆H₄SR, in which R is a normal alkyl. The melting points of the lower alkyl derivatives are irregular, but there is much the same relationship between the melting

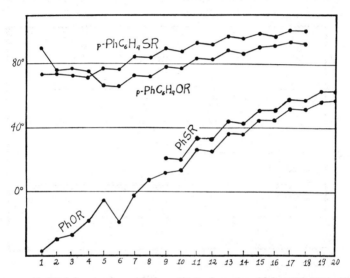

FIGURE 7. Melting points of the alkyl phenyl sulfides, PhSR, alkyl phenyl ethers, PhOR, alkyl biphenyl sulfides, p-PhC₆H₄SR, and alkyl biphenyl ethers, p-PhC₆H₄OR, plotted against the number of carbon atoms in R

points of the thioethers and those of the ethers as between the alkyl sulfides and ethers of figure 6.

In figure 8 are plotted the boiling points of the normal paraffin hydrocarbons, the alkyl chlorides, the mercaptans, and alcohols. The curves for the alkyl chlorides and the mercaptans are similar in shape. An alkyl chloride has a slightly higher molecular weight than the corresponding mercaptan, but boils lower. Heptyl mercaptan and heptyl alcohol boil at prac-

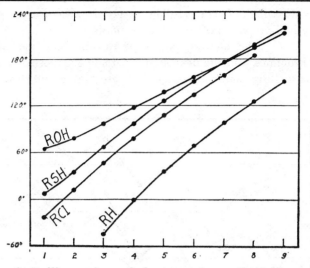

FIGURE 8. Boiling points of the normal paraffin hydrocarbons, RH, alkyl chlorides, RCl, mercaptans, RSH, and alcohols, ROH, plotted against the number of carbon atoms in R

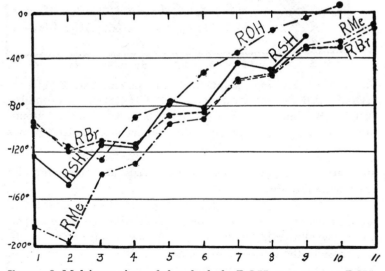

FIGURE 9. Melting points of the alcohols, ROH, mercaptans, RSH, alkyl bromides, RBr, and the next higher paraffin, RMe, plotted against the number of carbon atoms in R

tically the same temperature. The effects of association are shown by the boiling points of the lower alcohols.

The melting points of the alcohols, mercaptans, alkyl bromides, and the next higher paraffin are plotted in figure 9. The melting points of the alcohols are higher and show little

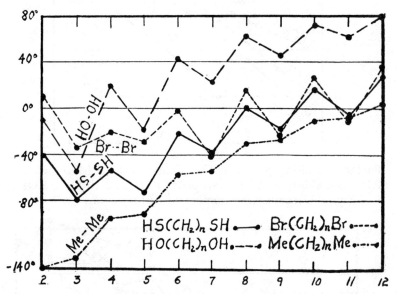

FIGURE 10. Melting points of the polymethylene glycols, $HO(CH_2)_nOH$, dimercaptans, $HS(CH_2)_nSH$, dibromides, $Br(CH_2)_nBr$, and paraffins with two more carbon atoms, $Me(CH_2)_nMe$, plotted against n, the number of methylene groups

alternation. The patterns for the mercaptans and alkyl bromides are remarkably similar.

The melting points of polymethylene glycols, dimercaptans, dibromides, and the paraffins with two more carbon atoms, are plotted in figure 10. The melting points of the glycols, like those of the alcohols, are higher, but they show alternation. The patterns for the dimercaptans and dibromides are remarkably similar.

ISOMERS

The fundamental concept, on which theoretical organic chemistry is built, is the fixedness of the bond between two carbon atoms. When this idea came to be accepted, chemists calculated the numbers of possible isomeric butanes, pentanes, and on up for the paraffin series, and set about preparing as many as possible of the isomers predicted. The American Petroleum Institute has fostered the preparation of a number of hydrocarbons, in a high state of purity, for accurate determinations of their physical properties. The remarkable differences in the engine performance of the various heptanes and octanes has led to intensive studies of these groups of isomers. During World War II, huge sums of money were spent on the synthesis of triptane, 2,2,3-trimethylbutane, the super fuel for airplane engines. Diisobutane, 2,2,4-trimethylpentane, rates 100 on the scale, while n-heptane is zero.

The study of isomers has been more extensive and more thorough for the paraffin hydrocarbons than for any other group. It is possible to predict, with considerable accuracy, the boiling point, density, and octane rating of hydrocarbons which have not yet been prepared. The octanes have been thoroughly studied, but the nonanes have been only partially covered.

The introduction of substituents increases the number of isomers greatly. Thus four butanols are derived from two butanes, and eighty-nine octanols from eighteen octanes. The boiling points of some butane derivatives are plotted in figure 11. The n-butyl derivatives have the highest boiling points, and the tert-butyl the lowest. There are interesting differences in the reactivities. n-Butanol is esterified rapidly, isobutanol slightly less rapidly, while sec-butanol goes slowly and tert-butanol hardly at all.

The melting points are plotted in figure 12. These are higher for the normal derivatives than for the secondary and iso-compounds. On account of greater symmetry, the tertiary derivatives melt much higher than the others.

Four n-octanols and eighteen methylheptanols were

included in an investigation of the relation of physical and chemical properties to structure.[2]

The astronomers of the world devote much effort to making accurate photographic maps of section after section of the heavens. Star positions are all relative. By comparing maps

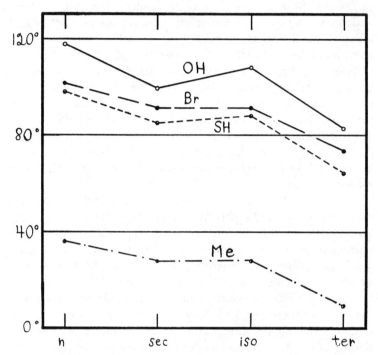

FIGURE 11. Boiling points of some isomeric butane derivatives, BuOH, BuBr, BuSH, and BuMe, plotted to show the influence of structure

made at different times, motions of celestial bodies can be detected so that distant planets and asteroids can be distinguished from the fixed stars. The proper motions of some of the "fixed" stars can be measured. As more organic compounds are prepared and gaps in series are filled, more and more comparisons can

[2] G. L. Dorough, H. B. Glass, T. L. Gresham, G. B. Malone, and E. E. Reid, *J. Am. Chem. Soc.*, **63**, 3100-10 (1941).

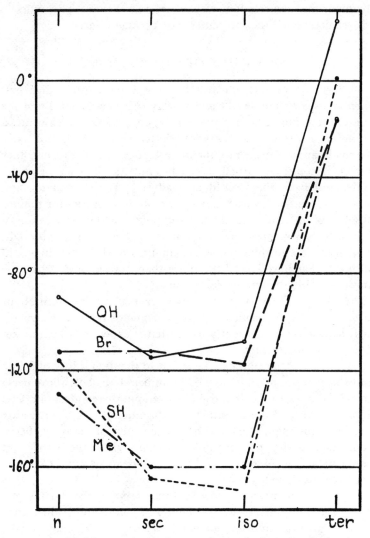

FIGURE 12. Melting points of some isomeric butane derivatives, BuOH, BuBr, BuSH, and BuMe, plotted to show the influence of structure

be made and the relations of physical and chemical properties to the structures of the molecules will become clearer.

A FAMILY OF COMPOUNDS

An early chemist hailed the preparation of a new alcohol as comparable to the discovery of a new metal. From the metal there might be obtained an oxide, a sulfide, a chloride, a bromide, a nitrate, and many other salts. From the alcohol could be made an acetate, a propionate, a benzoate, and various other esters. It could be turned into a bromide, a chloride, or an iodide; and from these could be made mercaptans, sulfides, and so on and on. Today there are even more possibilities for the utilization of an alcohol as the starting point for the preparation of a host of new compounds. Brand-new alcohols are being brought out from time to time and, what amounts to the same thing, old alcohols that have been little more than entries in *Beilstein* are now available in commercial quantities.

These new alcohols offer many opportunities for filling in gaps in chemical literature. Some of the newer alcohols will behave quite differently from what is expected, which makes them more interesting.

Attention may be called to the desirability of filling out the groups, for which the odd-numbered alcohols above decyl may be the starting materials. The even-numbered alcohols, octyl to octadecyl, and the corresponding bromides, have been readily available for some years and have been used in many syntheses. The result is that we have many series in which the higher odd numbers are missing. It would be a service to systematic chemistry to fill in these blanks.

Similarly, a new acid may serve as the starting material for the preparation of a family of compounds, which may include an acid chloride, an amide, N-alkyl amides, and esters.

Abundant supplies of the even-numbered acids, caproic to stearic, are furnished by natural products. Consequently the literature is full of their derivatives. Heptoic, pelargonic, and undecylic acids have been less available and have received less attention. The literature on tridecylic, pentadecylic, and heptadecylic acids is almost blank. Comprehensive data on derivatives of these are needed.

NEW COMPOUNDS FOR PROFIT

Is there a practical need for new compounds? As has been mentioned, more than 14,000 compounds, many of them synthesized for that purpose, have been tested as antimalarials. Some of these turned out to be good, but perhaps No. 1651 will hit the jackpot. If it does, will chemists stop there? Unlike a man with seven daughters, a chemist is never satisfied. He believes firmly that there are bigger fish in the sea than have yet been caught, and is driven on by the fear that some other chemist might catch them. Corporations that have developed superior products are building larger laboratories and hiring more chemists. Synthetic medicinals have had an important part in the great progress that has been made in the conquest of diseases. Cancer and heart ailments remain unconquered. When we look backward, we congratulate ourselves on how far we have come, but when we look forward, we see that we have just started. Thousands of compounds have been made in the search for more effective insecticides. Many good ones have been found, but in June 1957, an army of grasshoppers ate up every green thing in a California valley.

Several years ago, I was told that a certain company had tested 6,000 compounds as insecticides. Of these, 4,000 were old compounds and 2,000 had been synthesized for that purpose. They are doubtless still making and testing compounds. The testing is not always simple and certain. I know of one compound that was tested by one company and found worthless and later was patented by another company as particularly effective. Some compounds are active against certain pests and ineffective against others. Fly sprays are a special class. It is desirable to have an insecticide that will kill mosquitoes, but will not harm the bees which perform such a useful service to plants. Care must be taken that poisons applied to plants do not get into edible products. Many compounds have been tested and found to be as injurious to the plants as to the insects. The perfect insecticide, which has not yet been prepared, will eliminate all harmful pests without injury to the plants or to the bees and without contaminating the food of man or domestic animals. As has been mentioned earlier, insecticides are important weapons in the age-long battle of mankind against insects.

And what shall we say of plastics, of synthetic fibers, of food preservatives, of high-pressure lubricants, of synthetic perfumes and flavoring materials, and of scores of other products of our chemical factories? It is a curious situation; the user thinks a product is fine because it is much better than what he has had before, but the manufacturer is not satisfied with it because he thinks he can make a better one.

In making new compounds that may have practical uses, there is, of course, the possibility of material gain, but the real reward should be winning the game, winning against others, and, what is more important, winning against oneself. The golfer plays against his own record and is happy when he lowers his score. Who, after watching helplessly cancer eat away the life of a relative, would not rather find a cure for it than break the bank at Monte Carlo?

OLD REACTIONS WITH NEW MATERIALS

One or more of the well-known reactions can be applied to any one of the new starting materials which are becoming available from time to time. Many compounds, which were only entries in *Beilstein* several decades ago, are now in large-scale production. An examination of the 4th edition of *Beilstein*, closing date December 31, 1909, will disclose few esters, or other derivatives, of *n*-butanol, while there are many of isobutanol. When *n*-butanol became available commercially, chemists were quick to apply all known reactions of alcohols to it, and to prepare scores of derivatives.

NEW COMPOUNDS BY OLD REACTIONS

Certain of the more useful organic reactions, such as the Kolbe synthesis, are known by the names of their discoverers or by some other designation. Many of these have been thoroughly described in books and reviews, which give lists of the starting materials to which they have been applied and of the compounds prepared. A cursory reading of one of these articles gives the impression that the reaction is well understood and has been thoroughly exploited. On closer study, it will be found that neither of these is correct. It is not difficult to think up some new acids that can be prepared by the Kolbe synthesis. Of course, one would check recent literature before undertaking the preparation of any of these. All of the new hydroxyacids will fill blanks in series or groups, and for some, practical uses may be found.

EXPLOITING A NEW REACTION

The history of chemistry might be written in terms of the discovery of new reactions, which modify or extend theories and make possible the preparation of whole new classes of compounds that may be of scientific or industrial importance.

In the last century, a big event was the discovery of the diazo reaction which played such an important part in the development of the synthetic dye industry that gave Germany the chemical leadership of the world.

As an example of a new reaction applied to old materials, no better can be given than the Barbier-Grignard reaction, discovered in 1901 and quickly taken up by the chemists of the world. To prepare the reagent, one needs an alkyl or aryl halide. The reagent reacts with practically any aldehyde, ketone, or ester, and with a number of other classes of compounds. Thus the number of possible products is the number of available halides multiplied by the number of aldehydes, ketones, and esters, not to mention the other reactants. The number of substances that can be prepared by this reaction is extremely large. In a bibliography, 1900 to 1921, of the Grignard reaction, there were catalogued 1552 papers by about 1100 authors.[3] The index contains about 3500 entries of substances to which this reaction has been applied or which have been produced with its help. For

---

[3] C. J. West, *Reprint and Circular Series of the National Research Council*, "Organomagnesium Compounds in Synthetic Chemistry," Washington, 1922.

all this, its possibilities are far from being exhausted, and hundreds of chemists may yet busy themselves applying it to still other substances.

The cracking of hydrocarbons, on account of its immense industrial importance, has been the subject of many investigations, but practice has far outrun theory. It has, however, supplied quantities of ethylene and other unsaturates as materials for chemical industry.

In recent years the interest of many academic as well as industrial chemists has been centered on the addition reactions of unsaturates. Catalytic hydrogenation came early in the century and was followed by the addition to hydrocarbons of such things as sulfur chloride, hypochlorous acid, sulfuric acid, hydrobromic acid, and mercaptans. Polymerization, which may be regarded as self-addition, has long been known, but is here considered as a new reaction since only recently has it become an object of intensive study and large-scale commercial exploitation. Synthetic rubbers and a host of other useful plastics are polymerization products. Many chemists have been engaged in the synthesis of polymerizable vinyl derivatives and dienes.

PREPARATION OF COMPOUNDS
FOR SPECIFIC PURPOSES

A long time ago, some of our ancestors found a tree which had fallen across a stream a convenient way to get on the other side. Soon they were imitating nature and were placing trees across other streams. Later on, they constructed more elaborate bridges.

The most common method of designing a compound for a particular use is to start with a known substance which has been found to serve the purpose and work out from it. The one that is in use has proved to be good but has some drawbacks, perhaps it is somewhat too volatile, perhaps it causes discoloration, or gets rancid, or a change in the market may have raised its price too high. We set about finding something with all its desirable qualities, but without the undesirable ones, such as the perfect insecticide, which was mentioned earlier. We usually start with compounds of similar structure and progressively modify the molecule, changing one group after another. Each time we must test out our product to see whether it is better or worse than our standard substance, so as to know whether we are going in the right or wrong direction.

This is the obvious method and one that is reasonably sure of getting results. A chemist with experience and imagination should be able to get out of the beaten path and think up a new approach to the goal. What is wanted is not just an improvement on the known, but something a great deal better. If this is found, it will probably turn out to be something radically different. As was mentioned in chapter 5, chemists are prone to start out with a hazy and sometimes erroneous idea of the objective.

CHEMICAL ARCHITECTURE

Building up compounds that will have predetermined qualities may be called chemical architecture. The architect, aided by the engineer, designs structures for specific purposes. If a bridge is required, the width of the river, the character of the banks, and the sort of load to be carried are ascertained in advance and the structure designed accordingly. Engineering formulae are so exact and the strength of standard materials so well known that the shape and precise dimensions of each piece entering into the structure may be worked out. Drawings and blueprints are prepared and put into the hands of the contractor who realizes in steel or stone the visions of the designer. The specified beams, girders, rods, bolts, and nuts are fabricated and delivered to the site. When these are assembled, each piece goes into its proper place, and rarely does the completed structure fail to fulfill the expectations of the architect.

Bridges have been built by man for some thousands of years, and vast and varied is the experience that has been accumulated. Organic chemists have been designing molecular structures for only a few decades, and the specifications which have to be met are not so easily determined and cannot be stated so exactly, hence the greater difficulties and uncertainties. We have gone only a little way toward our goal, but we have made definite progress. To find a suitable material for a given purpose, we must as yet cut and try; a number of compounds must be prepared and tested before we find the one best suited. We do know enough to decide in advance against many proposals and so limit the labor.

While our knowledge of the relation of properties to structure is far from sufficient to enable us to write down a molecule that will have certain specified properties, we do have sufficient information to set some limits. This may be illustrated by a consideration of plasticizers. To confer permanent softness on a plastic, the plasticizer must remain in place, which means that its volatility must be low. Dibutyl phthalate, $C_{16}H_{22}O_4$, which has been mentioned in chapter 5, the prototype of softeners for nitrocellulose and similar plastics, boils at 343°C and evaporates slowly from films. To be permanent, a plasticizer should not boil much below 400°C. Di-2-ethylhexyl phthalate is sufficiently nonvolatile to be permanent. Cellophane, a polyhydroxyl polymer, is plasticized by glycerol and the water which it holds. These are lost in a hot, dry atmosphere, and the film becomes hard and brittle. As to the compatibility of a proposed plasticizer with the material that is to be softened, we can only guess and try. The dictum "like cures like" has been discredited, but "like dissolves like" is a "first aid" rule. The question is how like is like. Designing molecules that will have specified properties is like pitching horseshoes. We do the best we can and hope to get a ringer. If we do not, we measure the distance from the pin and try again. It is a good game anyhow.

A WIDE FIELD

The organic chemist is called upon to design chemical structures for all sorts of uses. One man wants a dye of a certain hue that will be fast to light and washing and which may be applied in a particular way; another wishes a gas that will kill boll weevil, but will not hurt the cotton plants or the laborers, and will not cost more than a fraction of the price of the crop. The medical folk are always looking for remedies which are more effective in curing the disease and are less harmful to the patient. Manufacturers of all sorts of goods are out for materials which will improve the quality or lower the cost of their products.

charge. This is due to high current load and...

10. Research in organic analysis

THE SEARCH FOR BETTER ANALYTICAL METHODS

This can hardly be called a field of research; it is more like a continent. It has been the occupation of thousands of chemists in the past and will engage the attention of a considerable proportion of those who are now on the way to research. Our hopes for the future extension of chemical knowledge are to a great extent contingent on discovering and perfecting methods of detection and estimation of organic substances.

A distinction is made between analytical research, which has to do with devising and perfecting methods, and analytical practice, which is the routine application of these methods. The two are, however, closely connected; the object of the research is to improve routine methods, and the analyst is the one in the best position to see the need for improvements. This discussion is concerned only with the research approach.

The scope of analytical chemistry has been extended to take in all means, of whatsoever kind, by which information

163

may be gained as to the composition and structure of organic compounds. As Mr. Kirklin[1] says:

> Modern organic analyses embody the principles of modern chemistry, physics, and instrumentation. It is one of the broadest of all scientific fields—ranging as it does from odor and optical tests, separations, physical tests, ultimate analysis, chemical reactions, absorption spectra, electrochemical measurements, mass spectrometry, nuclear and electron magnetic resonance—in fact all the 'eyes, ears, and yardsticks' of science that can be used for defining and describing matter.

In chapter 1 research has been heralded as the precursor of industrial progress. In the amazing developments of the past fifty years, research in organic analysis has been an important factor and has had to keep pace with research in other lines. Separations, such as were never dreamed of a few decades ago, are now possible by the use of precision fractionation columns and molecular stills. For the separation of substances which differ little in physical properties, chromatographic, countercurrent distribution, or ion-exchange methods may be applicable. Gas chromatography is particularly helpful since it can be used for separation, identification, and determination in many cases. It is becoming increasingly important now that it is possible to handle substances which are only slightly volatile by working at elevated temperatures. The fractions isolated by various chromatographic procedures are frequently used for infrared and mass spectrometric analyses. Countercurrent distribution is very important now that apparatus has been designed to give results quickly. Microchemical methods, which will be mentioned again in chapter 12, are of great service, particularly when only small amounts of material are available.

Organic analysis, which used to be a part-time occupation of many organic chemists, has become a profession. When research became big business, it had to be organized, as was mentioned in chapter 1. This meant assigning the chemists to different groups where their special skills would best serve the common interest. In every organization there has to be an analyti-

---

[1] Written at the author's request by Mr. W. A. Kirklin of the Analytical Division of Hercules Powder Co.

cal group, since analyses are required at every step of the way from scouting to manufacturing. The analytical group and the library group, which will be discussed in chapter 21, are at the center of the organization. Both of these serve all the other groups. Both are kept informed of all the interests of the company.

Dr. Hall[2] says of the members of the analytical group:

A research chemist in this field (analytical) occupies exactly the same status in the eyes of management as one in any other field of chemistry. He may be called on to identify and measure unknown products of an unknown reaction in the idea-scouting phase; again, he may be required to provide methods adequate for the laboratory assessment of a new product or process, which is far beyond the exploratory stage; and finally he must provide means of obtaining the needed information at the pilot-plant and plant stages. Here too, all the new wonders of instrumentation may come into play. Automatic, recorded control of the plant streams in many processes—only a dream a short time ago—is becoming almost commonplace. Analytical research is one of the broadest of scientific fields, embodying such a wide range of chemistry, as well as the related fields of physics and instrumentation.

QUALITATIVE ORGANIC ANALYSIS

Corresponding to qualitative and quantitative analysis, with which the most of us struggled at some time during our chemical adolescence, are the identification and estimation of organic compounds. There is, however, a great difference in the numbers of compounds involved. Analytical chemistry, as taught in the schools, has to do with less than a score of metals and about the same number of anions, while organic analysis may have to deal with any one of the half million compounds that have been described, and be prepared to cope with the thousands of new ones that are added each year.

To make life more interesting for the organic analyst, he is called upon to identify and determine the quality of

---

[2] Written at the author's request by Dr. R. T. Hall of the analytical group of the Hercules Powder Co.

hundreds of commercially important materials, which are mixtures of somewhat varying composition. Furthermore, he has to look out for adulteration with materials of much the same composition.

An enormous amount of research has gone into finding methods for the identification of organic compounds, singly or in mixtures, and introductory courses on this subject are commonly included in the training of chemists. The general plan consists of finding the class and subclass to which the unknown belongs, and finally tracking it down as an individual. The melting points of crystalline derivatives, where available, are relied upon for the final identification of particular compounds. Modern physical methods, which show the presence of double bonds or of certain groups, are of great assistance. Infrared spectrophotometry and mass spectrometry are especially helpful for identification since the spectra serve as fingerprints for the compounds to be identified. Sometimes a substance can be identified by use of infrared or mass spectrometry alone.

The use of chemicals in warfare has occasioned a great deal of research on the detection and identification of minute amounts of toxic gases in the air. Likewise, much attention has been given to the detection of noxious vapors in industrial establishments.

The development of color on treatment with a specific reagent may serve for the detection and identification of extremely small amounts of certain compounds.

The successful attack on any class of natural compounds has always waited on the discovery of methods of separation and identification suited to that particular class. Fischer's famous work on sugars was made possible by his discovery of the reactions of phenylhydrazine with the sugars to give the phenylhydrazones and the osazones, slightly soluble crystalline compounds with distinctive melting points. So it must ever be. The intricacies of terpene chemistry have been unraveled by crystalline nitrosites, dibromides, and the like.

The detection and identification of a compound, in admixture with other substances, may be effected, without isolation, provided some specific reaction can be discovered. Vitamins were shown to be present in certain foods and given designations long before they were isolated or anything was known as to their chemical constitution. However, if an individual compound can be gotten out of a mixture and purified, its identification is greatly facilitated.

In scouting research, when a chemist prepares a compound which is supposed to have a certain structure, it is sent to the analytical group for a checkup. If the elementary analysis, molecular weight, and physical and chemical properties are in accord with the assumed structural formula, all is well. If this is not the case, the chemist has guessed wrong and the chemists of the analytical group must use all the tricks of their trade to find out what the true structure may be.

Even if the yield of the desired product is high, the by-products of an organic reaction cannot well be ignored. They furnish problems for the analytical research group.

QUANTITATIVE ORGANIC ANALYSIS

An untold amount of research has gone into the finding of methods of estimating organic compounds. In the study of any reaction, all the products must be determined. To measure a reaction rate, one requires a method of determining the amount of the product formed in any desired time interval. For revenue purposes, the amount of alcohol in beverages must be known. The refinery buys truck loads of beets on the basis of the sugar content. For milk to pass inspection, it must show the prescribed percentage of butterfat. In many cases the price of a natural product depends on its content of one ingredient as shown by analysis.

Crude gasoline usually contains a variety of sulfur compounds, mercaptans, alkyl sulfides, polymethylene sulfides, and thiophenes. The amounts of these are small, as the total sulfur content is usually only a fraction of 1%. However, their detrimental effect in gasoline is serious, and a great deal of effort has been expended on schemes for determining the amounts of these four classes.

The methods of determining organic compounds

are of widely different kinds and of varying accuracy. Each compound that has to be dealt with is a separate problem, or several problems, depending on the nature of the substances with which it may be associated. In some cases high accuracy may be attained, but in others only approximations are possible. A method must be adequate for the use for which it is intended. Reliability is to be put above exactness. Thus, in determining alcohol in the breath of a man who has been involved in a road accident, a variation of 5%, more or less, makes little difference, but the test must give evidence that will stand up in court. It is much the same in cases of suspected poisoning.

The bottleneck in the development of a new process of manufacturing an organic compound is an analytical method. To follow a reaction one needs means of determining the quantity and purity of the product that is being produced. There is no use in making the second run until the results of the first have been appraised. Since delays are costly, a rapid method is desirable, even if it is only moderately accurate.

In the nitration of benzene, finding the yield is a simple matter, since there is no difficulty in separating the product, nitrobenzene, which boils at 211°, from the unreacted benzene and nonvolatile dinitrobenzene, but in other cases it is seldom so easy. The preparation of monochloroacetic acid by the chlorination of acetic acid may be taken as an example. The problem is to find the chlorination conditions that give the maximum amount of the monochloroacetic acid. What is needed is a method for estimating monochloroacetic acid in the product which contains also dichloroacetic and trichloroacetic besides some unreacted acetic acid. A chlorine determination will not help. What is required is a study of the reactions of all four acids in order to find a reaction that goes quantitatively with monochloroacetic and not at all with the others. As commercial monochloroacetic acid is apt to contain small amounts of the di- and trichloro acids, it is desirable to find specific reactions by which they can be detected and estimated. Thus for this one product three analytical methods are required.

A more or less similar story could be told of the development of the process for manufacturing almost any organic compound. In the case of monochloroacetic acid, all of the products with which one had to deal had been known and studied for many decades and their reactions had been described fully in the literature. When the manufacture of a newly discovered product is to be taken up, the situation is quite different. One cannot turn to the literature to find ready-made answers, but one must work out reactions to suit the particular case. This may involve considerable research in addition to a broad knowledge of organic reactions.

As soon as the plant begins operating, they come around and ask the chemist to streamline the analytical method so that it can be handled by a busy plant operative who may not even be a chemist. Colorimetric, potentiometric, or other automatic control methods are desirable. Automatic analyzers are available which can handle many samples, one after the other, with little supervision.

RESEARCH ON CONTROL METHODS

When, by the combined efforts of research chemists and chemical and mechanical engineers, the plant has been built and put on stream, there is great satisfaction and the expectation of living happily ever after. Turning out a product is one thing, producing a uniformly satisfactory product is quite another. The analytical research group must come up with a method of determining the quality of the product and, what is more important, of detecting the presence and estimating the amounts of impurities which may hinder the sale, or cause difficulties in the use, of the product.

In modern manufacturing, continuous processes are operated wherever possible. For such a process a continuous analytical method is desirable, that is, some way of operating on the stream as it emerges from the reactor. If the product is not up to standard, the operator needs to know this at once. He cannot wait until many gallons of an inferior product have passed by.

NATURAL PRODUCTS

In bulk and in value, products of vegetable or animal origin make up a large proportion of the articles of commerce. It has been thus since the dawn of history. Spices and perfumes were highly valued in ancient times. The caravan that took Joseph to Egypt probably carried spices. Frankincense and myrrh ranked with gold among the gifts of the Magi. Olive oil was known and prized at the time when Homer was singing those verses, the translation of which has been such a chore to college students, including myself.

As examples, two groups of natural products may be mentioned on account of their scientific and commercial importance. The "volatile" oils, such as turpentine, oil of peppermint, and mustard oil, are gotten out of plant materials as vapors, frequently by steam distillation. They are diverse in chemical nature as they are in origin. Among them are to be found hydrocarbons, primary and secondary alcohols, esters, aldehydes, and ketones, and a few sulfur and nitrogen compounds. Some are saturated and some are unsaturated. A few are nearly pure chemical entities, while most of them are mixtures. They fascinated and frustrated the early chemists and still pose problems to those of our time.

The fixed oils, with which may be put the fats, are numerous. They vary considerably in quality but are rather closely related chemically, being for the most part mixed glycerides in which stearic, palmitic, oleic, linoleic, and linolenic acids predominate. Olive, cottonseed, and linseed oils may be mentioned as representatives of this class.

On account of the commercial importance of many of the oils of these classes, an enormous amount of effort has been spent on devising methods for identifying them and determining their quality. In some of the oils, the total value is that of one constituent that can be isolated, while in others, the oil is worth far more than its known constituents. As the oils are mixtures, much reliance is put on physical properties, such as density, refractive index, and distillation range, if the oil is volatile. Distinctive constituents may be determined by conventional methods. Saponification, iodine, and certain other numbers aid. Identification is made by comparing the values found with those reported for various oils of that class. If the values found for a sample of olive oil do not fall within the accepted range for that oil, there is suspicion of adulteration or substitution, and further investigation is in order.

So it is with scores of other natural products. Each has to be studied and special methods devised for its identification and valuation. The customer wants to know whether the material in the drum is what he ordered, and if it is a tank car instead of a drum, he needs to be doubly sure. We cannot expect the peaches in the can to look exactly like the picture on the can, but they should at least be peaches.

Natural products are starting materials for manufacturing processes. Therefore, means must be provided for judging the quality as well as establishing the identity. A paint manufacturer pays eighty thousand dollars for a tank car of linseed oil and turns this into 150,000 gallons of paint which sells for a million dollars. As the painter gets about four dollars for putting on one dollar's worth of paint, the cost to the home owners is five million dollars. The paint on the house costs sixty times as much as the oil, but its value depends largely on the quality of the oil. Analytical research supplies the means of determining the quality of the oil in advance.

SPECIFICATIONS

How pure is "pure"? The word "pure" is used in so many ways that it has no definite meaning. One manufacturer advertises his product as 99.44% pure and has a chemist's certificate to prove it. This was shown to me on a visit to the plant. Nothing is said about the remaining 0.56%. It must be innocuous, as no complaints have been made about it. If, however, it were lamp black there would be no sales. Small amounts of some impurities are harmful, while larger amounts of others are not.

Pure water is taken to mean that it is uncontaminated and fit for drinking, though it may contain sodium chloride and other minerals and be unfit to put in your battery. Several decades ago, there was much discussion of the question: What is whiskey? Before a satisfactory answer was given, prohibition came on and no one asked questions. Some high-grade boot-leggers sold their product with a chemist's certificate that it contained no methanol; some went ever farther in protecting their customers, by leaving out the dangerous ethanol.

Pure may refer to origin and history. Thus pure olive oil is that which has been obtained by the pressing of olives and has been kept free from adulteration with other oils.

The designation "pure" may have reference to an intended use. A specially purified grade of alcohol, known as Cologne spirits, is sold to perfumers. It may contain nonodorous denaturants. Benzyl acetate, made by heating sodium acetate with benzyl chloride, may have the correct density and refractive index, but a perfumer will dip a copper wire in it and hold the wire in a Bunsen flame. When a green color appears he will say: Take it away. Benzene may be pure for some uses and not for others. A trace of toluene would render it unsuitable for making p-dichlorobenzene, a favorite moth repellant.

When we come across an article that is entirely satisfactory, we want to be assured that subsequent purchases will be of the same quality. In the supermarket the cans and cartons which bear brand names can be bought with confidence, since the manufacturer stakes his reputation on maintaining uniformity.

Organic chemicals are bought by specifications, rather than by brands. Where several grades of a chemical are offered, each has its set of specifications and price. Thus ethyl acetate, of which the annual United States production is over a hundred million pounds, is currently sold in three grades containing 85 to 88, 95 to 98, and 99%, respectively, of the ester. Boiling ranges and other properties are included in the specifications. The lowest grade is satisfactory as a lacquer solvent, while the highest is required for making ethyl-acetoacetate. The manufacturer must meet the requirements of prospective customers, and the user must make sure that the grade he buys is suitable for his process. This is only one of hundreds of manufactured organic compounds which are sold on specifications.

Writing specifications for a chemical demands a knowledge of the economics of its production and of the requirements of its probable applications. On the other side of the fence stands the buyer with his ideas as to what he wants. He should know, from his own experiments, what impurities are harmful and what can be tolerated. He must be realistic and ask for a grade of material that can be produced at the price he is willing to pay. For large contracts, the specifications are a matter for negotiation. Research by both maker and user must decide all questions. All purchases by the Government are on bids on materials that conform to specifications which are handed out.

Natural products also are bought and sold on specifications, though these are written in somewhat different terms. As pure linseed oil varies considerably, and as there are other oils which resemble it closely, adulteration and substitution are difficult to detect, but research is making tighter specifications possible so that the customer is more apt to get what he pays for than formerly.

Linseed oil is just one example. For natural products, in general, specifications are being written and enforced. Years ago in South Carolina, they used to say that all cottonseed oil needed was a sea voyage, preferably to an Italian port, but the sea air has since then lost its effectiveness.

THE UNITED STATES PHARMACOPEIA

This is mentioned here as an example of what has been done by research in the way of identifying and assaying natural and synthetic medicinals. A revised edition is put out every ten years by the United States Pharmacopeia Convention, which is composed of representatives of the physicians, pharmacists, and drug manufacturers. The current edition contains about 800 pages with about one drug to a page. The origin, uses, standard of purity, and method of assay are given for each medicinal.

These are recognized by law, and materials sold for medical use must conform to the specifications given. "U.S.P." on a bottle means just this.

THE ASSOCIATION OF OFFICIAL AGRICULTURAL CHEMISTS

This association publishes a fat volume of "official" methods. These are the ones that have been adopted after long trial and are sanctioned by law. In addition there are "provisional" methods which are put forward for investigation. These chemists have an important task and take it seriously. Uniform samples are distributed to a number of laboratories to be analyzed according to a proposed method. If the discrepancies in the results are too great, there is something wrong and further research is in order.

ANALYTICAL RESEARCH IN THE SERVICE OF MEDICINE

BY CHARLES F. GESCHICKTER

Professor of Pathology, Georgetown University Medical School

The amazing progress of modern medicine has been due to two things, better methods of diagnosis of diseases and more potent remedies for curing them. As is told briefly, analytical methods have been found which are of great service in the diagnosis of some diseases. What has been accomplished should inspire chemists to work to find additional methods.

Chemical analysis has a wide field of utility in clinical medicine, and in recent years it ranks with X-ray diagnosis and the determination of the patient's red- and white-cell counts as an aid to clinical diagnosis. This utility of chemical analysis is based on the fundamental physiological principle of fluid exchange within the body. All organs of the body receive their vital requirements from the blood filtrate and, in turn, excrete their waste products into it and ultimately into the urine. Chemical analysis, therefore, of the various constituents of the blood plasma reveals fairly constant values during health and corresponding alterations in disease. The same applies, to a lesser extent, to the chemical constituents of the urine. The oldest determinations of clinical use involved the blood urea or blood non-protein nitrogen as an index to the accumulation of waste products in the blood and the relative amounts of CO_2 that the blood plasma could absorb in health and disease. The amount of nitrogenous waste present is important in the diagnosis of kidney disease and the amount of CO_2 combining powers is important in the diagnosis of heart and lung disease. The determination of blood sugar (glucose) and the amount of glucose in the urine, which is normally insignificant, are equally important in the diagnosis of diabetes. These chemical analyses are routine in all hospital practice and have been so for the last thirty to forty years. Today, however, the variety of chemical analysis has been widely extended. It is now common practice to determine the percentage of protein in the blood plasma and the ratio of albumin globulin which makes up this percentage. In addition, further fractionation of these blood proteins is carried out by electrophoresis and is an important diagnostic tool in a number of the inflammatory or infectious diseases. A number of enzymes are also determined for diagnostic purposes. These include a serum amylase, which converts starch to sugar, two transaminases that are present when heart muscle is destroyed in arteriosclerotic diseases of the heart, alkaline phosphatase, which is increased in bone disease, and acid phosphatase, which is increased in the blood in cases of cancer of the prostate. Other important organic constituents are analyzed in clinical laboratory diagnosis, among which the most important are cholesterol and cholesterol esters, bilirubin (which is an excretion product in the bile derived from blood pigment), and, more rarely, fatty acids, blood lipase, steroids, porphyrines, and steroids secreted into the blood by the endocrine organs, particularly the gonads.

Determinations of the various organic constituents of blood serum are also made on the spinal fluid which is obtained by aspiration of this fluid when disease of the central nervous system is suspected. To a lesser extent, these analyses are also performed on the urine.

Equally important are the determinations performed for diagnostic purposes on the inorganic constituents of the blood and urine. The more frequently performed analyses are those on serum for calcium, phosphorus, sodium, and potassium. The quantity of these basic ions of the blood is frequently changed in diseases of the bone, the endocrine glands, and diseases of the heart and kidney. Calcium and phosphorus are usually determined by simple chemical analysis and sodium and potassium are determined by the flame photometer. Determinations of the blood chloride are usually performed when sodium and potassium values are measured. In addition, the protein-bound iodine of the serum is often determined in the diagnosis of diseases of the thyroid gland.

Not all organs of the body contribute their useful products by way of the blood stream. This is particularly true of the tissues lining the gastrointestinal tract, which contribute digestive juices to the alimentary canal. In ascertaining the functional status of such tissues, the chemical constituents secreted are often determined directly by stomach or duodenal aspiration. The free and combined hydrochloric acid in the stomach contents is measured by titration on the fasting stomach, after a test meal, or after administration of histamine, which stimulates the gastric juices. The contents of the duodenum may be drained and tested for pancreatic enzymes, such as amylase or trypsin. In addition, both the stomach and duodenal contents may be tested for the presence of blood or blood pigments.

A number of dye tests have been devised for the evaluation of liver and kidney functions, which are determined by the percentage of dye which is extracted from the blood through excretion or the rate at which it appears in the urine.

This is merely a brief review of the main battery of chemical analyses performed in chemical laboratory diagnosis and is by no means complete. Even if a complete list of the tests were given, it would be deficient or obsolete within a few years because of the rapidity with which new tests are being added for diagnostic purposes. In addition to these diagnostic tests, any type of known chemical determination for the analysis of a particular drug or poison may be utilized by specialists in this field to determine whether the patient is suffering from a particular form of poisoning or overdosage of a particular drug.

11.

■ The study of reactions

INTRODUCTION

This is chemistry. The science of chemistry is what has been learned about reactions; chemical technology is what we know about conducting reactions so that raw materials are transformed efficiently into useful products. To enlarge our scientific knowledge and to improve our manufacturing processes we must study reactions.

As we write them, chemical reactions look quite simple. We represent the oxidation of methane:

$$CH_4 + 2O_2 \rightarrow CO_2 + 2H_2O$$

This tells us that the oxidation of 16 grams of methane requires 64 grams of oxygen and that the products are 44 grams of carbon dioxide and 36 grams of water, but says nothing of how and why touching a spark can cause six hundred thousand billion billion molecules of methane to get together with twelve hundred thousand billion billion molecules of oxygen within a tiny fraction of a second. Fancy prices have been paid for machines into which one-dollar bills would go in at one end and ten-dollar bills come out at the other. Scientific curiosity should lead the prospective buyer to take the machine apart in order to learn more about the mechanism of the transformation. If a chemical manufacturer puts a dollar's worth of materials into the kettle and wants to get out ten dollars' worth of products, it is necessary for him to know a great deal about what goes on in the kettle.

The fifth volume of an encyclopedia of reactions has been published and more are to follow. Ten of a series of volumes on organic reactions have been published. A ponderous volume has been written on the reactions catalyzed by aluminum chloride. There are numerous articles in *Chemical Reviews* on reactions. There are scores of reactions, such as the Friedel-Crafts, Wilgerodt, and Grignard, which have received names. In this brief chapter all that can be done is to give a few examples of studies of reactions in the hope of stimulating interest in this line of research. An abundance of examples of all kinds of studies can be found in chemical literature which may serve as models. In fact every article in the *Journal of the American Chemical Society* and in similar journals gives information about reactions. In the preparation of new compounds, old reactions receive new applications; improvements in preparation methods result from finding more favorable conditions for conducting reactions. New reactions, and modifications of old ones, are constantly being published.

In the study of reactions, several things are to be considered: 1. scope or applicability; 2. reversibility; 3. whether of the first or of the second order; 4. reaction conditions, effects of temperature, of catalysts, ionic or free radical, and solvents.

ESTERIFICATION

Esterification is discussed as an example of reactions that has been studied in a number of different ways and because I have had a personal interest in it for many years. Its scope is exceptionally wide; hundreds of acids may react with hundreds of alcohols, the rate and limit being different for each pair of reactants. It was investigated by Berthelot[1] before Kekulé announced the structure of benzene. He heated mixtures of acids and alcohols in sealed tubes to about 200° for various times and determined the extent of esterification. He established the reversibility of the reaction and ascertained the limit for various alcohol and acid mixtures. He found that in a mixture of equivalent amounts of ethanol and acetic acid, the esterification came to a standstill at about 66.5% and that the same equilibrium was reached with a mixture of ethyl acetate and water. Then he went on to study a list of alcohols, primary, secondary, and tertiary with acetic acid. The rates and the limits for the primary alcohols were the highest and were grouped together, those for secondary alcohols lower and more scattered, and those for tertiary alcohols extremely low.

The structure of the acid was found to have an even greater effect on the esterification rate but not on the limit, in fact the limits for some of the slow acids were even slightly higher than for the faster acids.

From that day to this, esterification has continued to hold the attention of both physical and organic chemists. Many years later, I took up the study of the esterification of mercaptans[2] and found that with benzoic acid and ethyl mercaptan, esterification takes place similarly, only the limit is about 14.7% instead of 66.5%. Structures of the mercaptans and of the acids show effects similar to those with the alcohols.

The catalytic effect of mineral acids on esterification was noted early, and in all the years since has been studied as one of the most typical examples of homogeneous catalysis. Fifty years ago, I assembled a hundred articles on this subject that had been written in an effort to explain this catalysis and since then there have been many others.

Many esters are important commercially, and millions of pounds of them are produced annually. Various methods of making esters other than the simple esterification have been devised and put into service. The making of esters continues to be of both scientific and industrial interest. In Groggins' *Unit*

---

[1] *Ann. chim.* [3], **66**, 110 (1862); **68**, 274 (1863).
[2] E. Emmet Reid, *Am. Chem. J.*, **43**, 489-504; *C.A. 4*, 2270.

Processes[3] there is a chapter on "Esterification." I wrote this for the earlier editions but have been joined in the fifth by Dr. Peterson and Dr. Way. Starting in 1948, *Industrial and Engineering Chemistry* has published each September reviews on the industrial applications of various reactions. In the reviews on esterification which I wrote for seven years there are over 1000 references to articles and patents. Not all of these, however, pertain to esterification in the narrow sense in which the term is used here.

As stated before, esterification is a balanced reaction, and the amount of ester does not increase, no matter how long the heating is continued or what catalyst is used. A balanced reaction remains balanced as long as both of the reactants and both of the products are present. In the manufacture of ethyl acetate the ester is removed continuously as a ternary of the ester, alcohol, and water which boils lower than anything else that is present. To complete the esterification of decanol by acetic acid, the water may be taken off as a binary with toluene, and any excess of acid is washed out with sodium carbonate.

These are examples of how reactions can be made to go to completion in spite of their balanced character. For rate measurements, organic reactions are almost always chosen. The reason for this is that many of them take place at conveniently measurable rates. Under the influence of shock, nitroglycerine decomposes almost instantaneously, while without a catalyst, the esterification of a mixture of acetic acid and ethanol requires several years.

REACTION RATES

Reaction rates are of both theoretical and practical interest. Hundreds of investigations have been made on the rates of reactions. For comparisons, rates must be measured and expressed numerically.

The first most important requisite is to make sure

---

[3] P. H. Groggins, *Unit Processes in Organic Synthesis,* New York, McGraw-Hill Book Co.

of the reaction whose rate is to be measured. One chemist made an extensive study of the rates of alkaline hydrolysis of the methyl, ethyl, propyl, and butyl esters of the same acid in each of the four alcohols. The measurements were extensive and accurate and proved conclusively that in any one alcohol all four of the esters were hydrolized at exactly the same rate. He had overlooked the fact that all four esters underwent alcoholysis practically instantaneously when dissolved in an excess of the solvent alcohol in the presence of alkali. Thus, when dissolved in propanol, they all became the same propyl ester, which could have but one hydrolysis rate.

Another chemist published elaborate measurements on the hydrolysis of a number of substituted benzamides. To increase the solubility of the amides he added alcohol, not being aware of the fact that alcoholysis is many times faster than hydrolysis. He was measuring the combined effect of two reactions. His results were not only worthless, but worse, since they were misleading.

It is easy to make rate measurements and usually not too difficult to make them accurately, but to make reliable measurements is often quite a different matter. Scores of measurements were made of esterification velocities before someone found that a few hundredths of one percent of water in the "absolute" alcohol used made large, large differences in the rates. All of the measurements made up to that time were worthless. All the chemicals with which we work, even when purified with the utmost care, contain traces of impurities which may influence, favorably or unfavorably, reaction rates. The chemist should erect an altar to the unknown catalyst and bow before it when starting a run. This much has been said by way of warning, but it is practicable to make useful rate measurements, particularly comparative rates, such as the relative esterification rates of a group of acids. While it is impossible to eliminate all impurities, their influence can be minimized by keeping them constant throughout a series of runs. To achieve this constancy, amounts of solvents and reagents sufficient for all of the runs are to be prepared in advance.

Reaction rates are particularly sensitive to temperature changes. In general, the reaction rate doubles for a rise of 10°. This means that 1° makes a difference of 7% in the rate, and 0.1° a difference of 0.7%. Therefore, accurate temperature control is necessary. Measurements should be made at two temperatures, 10° apart, so as to be able to calculate the temperature coefficient and the heat of activation. Rate-measurement data show whether the reaction is of the first or of the second order, that is, whether it is monomolecular or bimolecular, which is important to know.

My own research began with measurements of the acid hydrolysis rates of *ortho, meta,* and *para* nitrobenzamides. Remsen had found that saccharin, an *ortho* imide, is hydrolyzed rapidly by dilute hydrochloric acid, while *p*-sulfamidobenzoic acid resists hydrolysis. This puzzled him, since Victor Meyer had shown that *ortho*-substituted benzoic esters are hydrolyzed much more slowly than the isomeric *meta* and *para* esters. Remsen handed me the problem of comparing the hydrolysis rates of the three nitrobenzamides. The study was extended to other groups of isomeric substituted benzamides. It was found that *ortho*-substituted benzamides, like the corresponding esters, are hydrolyzed much more slowly than the corresponding *meta* and *para* compounds. The analogies among acids, amides, and esters interested me and led me to study the alcoholysis of amides, then to the esterification of mercaptans and the reaction of thiobenzamides with mercaptan, which produced the dithio ester.

MEASURING REACTION RATES BY CONDUCTIVITY

Reaction rates are commonly measured either by determining the rate of formation of the products or the disappearance of one of the reactants. This requires sampling at intervals and analyses of the samples. The analyses may impose a serious burden on the operator. One of the easiest things to measure is conductivity. By inserting a pair of electrodes into a solution in which a reaction is taking place, the conductivity may be measured at suitable intervals and the results plotted. This method was used in the determination of the rate of hydrolysis of acetanhydride.[4]

In some reactions, the change in conductivity is large, as when an isothiuronium salt is formed by the reaction of butyl bromide on thiourea, neither of which is ionized. In other reactions, the change may be small, but even small changes can be followed accurately. In either case, the conductivity is taken at the start and at convenient intervals until it becomes constant. In one experiment, I stirred 5 cubic centimeters of benzoyl chloride into ethanol contained in a conductivity cell in an ice bath. The conductivity became constant in four hours. Unfortunately the conductivities are not a straight-line function of the ionic concentrations. However, if I had made similar experiments with different acid chlorides under the same conditions, the reciprocals of the times required for the conductivities to reach the 50% point would have given comparative values for the reactivities of the acid chlorides.

ADDITION REACTIONS

From the time that ethylene got the name olefiant gas, because it took up halogens to form an oil, on down to the present, addition reactions have been studied, but the interest in them has been quickened in recent years.

It has long been known that the addition of sulfuric acid to olefins takes place readily and that the acid may be hydrolyzed off, producing an alcohol as in the manufacture of isopropyl and *tert*-butyl alcohols. In chapter 8, the large-scale production of ethanol from ethylene and of isopropanol from propylene has been mentioned.

The addition of hydrogen bromide to an α-olefin takes place, normally, according to Markownikow's rule, to form a secondary alkyl bromide; but Kharasch found that, in the

---

[4] A. C. D. Ridvett and N. V. Sidgwick, *J. Chem. Soc.* **97**, 732, 1677 (1910)—C.A. **4**, 1833.

D. H. Wilson and N. V. Sidgwick, *J. Chem. Soc.* **103**, 1959 (1913)—C.A. **8**, 906.

presence of peroxides, the addition is abnormal, the product being the primary alkyl bromide. In the course of a study of the addition of ethyl mercaptan, S. O. Jones and I heated it with α-hexene and got n-hexyl ethyl sulfide.[5] We then tried the mercaptan with propylene and found the product to be isopropyl ethyl sulfide, which would be expected according to Markownikow's rule. The propylene had had no opportunity to form any peroxide. We then tried the mercaptan with a mixture of the hexene and propylene and got n-hexyl ethyl sulfide mixed with n-propyl ethyl sulfide. In this case the peroxide was supplied by the hexene.

POLYMERIZATION

We are living in the polymer age. A large segment of the chemical industry is devoted to making polymerizable compounds, and another large segment is engaged in polymerizing the monomers, as they are called.

When bromine is added to ethylene, the two bromine atoms go to the two ends of the double bond and the unsaturation disappears. The addition of an olefin to an olefin may continue indefinitely with the formation of a long-chain hydrocarbon. Actually chains of ten, a hundred, a thousand, a hundred thousand units, or even longer, may be built up. Ethylene, the simplest monomer, does not polymerize readily, but catalysts have been found which effect its polymerization. The production of polyethylene was approaching (1960) a billion pounds a year and is still increasing. The product is a somewhat branched long-chain paraffin. Tetrafluoroethylene is believed to be an unbranched chain of $-CF_2$-groups. The product, known as "Teflon," has found many uses.[6] An old example of polymerization is still one of the most important.

Styrene, discovered in 1831 by the pyrolysis of storax, is a mobile liquid which, on standing, is transformed into a glassy solid, believed to be a long-chain paraffin having phenyl

[5] S. O. Jones and E. Emmet Reid, *J. Am. Chem. Soc.* **60**, 2452-5 (1928)—C.A. **33**, 126.

[6] Special report, *Chem. Eng. News*, July 18, 1960, p. 92.

groups attached to alternate carbon atoms. A section of this
would be:

$$—CHPh·CH_2·CHPh·CH_2·CHPh·CH_2—$$

This has been long known but was not considered important
until recently. The solid has exactly the same composition as
the liquid styrene and can be separated by solvents into more or
less soluble polymers, all having exactly the same composition
as the liquid styrene but differing in molecular weights. The
conditions of polymerization determine whether the average
molecular weight will be high or low, 10,000 or above 100,000.
The polymerization of styrene, which is believed to be induced
by the presence of traces of peroxides, is inhibited by small
amounts of hydroquinone or another antioxidant.

The most-common polymerizable monomers are
vinyl compounds of the type $XCH:CH_2$, in which X is a negative
atom or group, such as Cl—, Ph—, NC—, COOEt, AcO—. The
character of the negative group influences the polymerizability
of the monomer and the character of the polymer. A substituent,
other than fluorine, in the $:CH_2$ group hinders polymerization.
However, I have observed the polymerization of ethyl cinnamate.
Maleic esters are polymerizable.

For several decades, the best efforts of a host of
chemists have been devoted to a study of polymers and polymerization. Inhibitors retard or prevent polymerization, initiators
start it, and various regulators are required to keep it going in
the right direction. It would be simple if inhibitors, initiators,
and regulators would function equally well with all monomers;
but this is far from being the case. Many polymerizations require
special treatments which differ according to whether a high or
low polymer is desired. A "homopolymer" is one from a single
monomer; thus the number of homopolymers is strictly limited.
"Copolymers" are from the copolymerization of two, or more,
monomers. From a given number of monomers there is a much
larger number of pairs; since the two monomers may be in various proportions, theoretically there may be an immense number
of copolymers. Practically, it has not been found possible to
obtain all of those predicted by theory. Two monomers in a
mixture may polymerize independently to give a mixture of

polymers, or one of them may polymerize and leave the other as a monomer, or they may copolymerize. A deal of study has been directed to the production of copolymers, and much more is needed. Polystyrene is a glassy solid; polyacrylonitrile is a fiber, known as Orlon. I have a suit composed of 50% Dacron, 25% Orlon, and 25% wool. A copolymer of styrene and acrylonitrile is a synthetic rubber, for which a billion pounds of styrene are required annually.

JOINTED POLYMERS

In polystyrene the carbon chain is continuous, but in jointed polymers, which I call polyarthrimers from the Greek word for joint as in arthritis, the carbon chain is interrupted by other atoms. If one molecule of hexamethylenediamine could be made to react with one of adipic acid with the elimination of a molecule of water, the product would be an amide having a carboxyl at one end and an amino group at the other.

$$HOOC(CH_2)_4CONH(CH_2)_6NH_2$$

The carboxyl end of this can react with a second molecule of the amine and the amino group with a second molecule of adipic acid. If this is repeated a sufficient number of times, the product is a jointed polymer in which the segments are joined together by —CONH— links. The carbon chain is not continuous as in polystyrene. If the polymerization is carried far enough, the polymer can be spun and is then nylon. While I am writing this I am wearing a nylon shirt. This was worked out scientifically by Wallace Carothers for Du Pont. He started the work on a polymer from terephthalic acid and ethylene glycol, which later became Dacron.

The reaction of ethylene chloride with sodium tetrasulfide produces a jointed polymer, a section of which would be:

$$-CH_2CH_2S_4CH_2CH_2S_4-$$

The polymer is Thiokol A, the first of the Thiokol polymers which made history in 1959 as factors in the rocket program. These polymers have been developed by J. C. Patrick.

An immense amount of research has gone into the development of jointed polymers, and there is opportunity for much more. Cellulose is a jointed polymer, the units of which are held together by oxygen atoms. This we can take apart but cannot reproduce.

CATALYSTS

The alchemists certainly missed a bet when they did not come out with catalysts. Just think of the reputation they might have achieved by sticking a rod with a bit of platinum on its tip into a mixture of air and alcohol vapor. The fairies in Grimm's famous tales never did anything as spectacular as catalysts do. Sabatier had catalysts all figured out sixty years ago. A metal such as iron, which had two stages of oxidation, could serve as an oxidation catalyst. The higher oxide would give up part of its oxygen, and the resulting lower oxide would then take up more oxygen from the air, regenerating the higher oxide, which would continue the process. This would be much like a waiter in a restaurant bringing a full dish to the diner and taking the empty dish back to the kitchen for more.

Where there was only one stage of oxidation there could be dehydration, but no oxidation. His book was beautifully written. I translated it because I wanted to remember it and feared that I would forget it if I simply read it through. So much has been learned about catalysts and so many books have been written about them that we have gotten thoroughly confused.

Seriously, for we have to take them seriously, the more we know about catalysts the less we understand them. Yet the more we find out about them the more urgently we need to learn more. Haber's discovery of a catalyst that has the magic power to cause the combination of nitrogen and hydrogen, even at a high temperature, suggests that a more active catalyst may yet be found that will effect the synthesis of ammonia at a lower temperature where the equilibrium is more favorable and such high pressures are not required. There is a similar situation in the synthesis of methanol. Finding better catalysts for these two reactions looks less unlikely than did the original finding of the present catalysts.

Hydrogenation has been one of the most spectacular achievements of catalysis. The poisoning of nickel catalysts by sulfur is a drawback. Sulfur is sudden death to nickel catalysts, while it is essential to the 'sulfactive' catalysts, which are active only at high temperatures. Palladium is indifferent to sulfur. So either make palladium as cheap as nickel, or give nickel the resistant properties of palladium.

Much progress has been made in the field of oxidation catalysis. Here the difficulty is not in getting the reaction to take place, but in disposing of the excessive amounts of heat that are evolved. It is the old problem of getting the properly roasted chestnuts out of the fire before they are burned up. There is the danger of destroying the oxidation product by the large amount of heat produced in the oxidation. The commercial oxidation of naphthalene to phthalic anhydride is highly satisfactory. It seems to me significant that in this case two molecules of carbon monoxide (m.w. 28) and two of water (m.w. 18) are formed, along with one of the desired phthalic anhydride (m.w. 148). If the reaction should take place explosively, which is certainly not the case, the momenta of the five molecules that are formed would be equal but the energies of the smaller molecules would be much greater since energies are proportional to the squares of the velocities. Thus the small molecules carry off the excess heat. Removing a difficulty which blocks our progress offers an opportunity for service. There are many opportunities in the study of catalysis.

MECHANISMS

The equations which we write represent what we put in and what we get out, but tell us nothing as to how the reactions actually take place. To the practical chemist the what is more important than the how; but the scientist wants to know the how. Pauling wrote a book on the nature of the chemical bond, but I am not sure that he knows all there is to know about it; and when it comes to finding out how these bonds shift around in a reaction so as to form new compounds, there is yet much to learn. It will be some time before we get the real story as to how chemical reactions actually take place, but we can work toward that end, and everything we find out puts us that much farther along.

In the case of the given reaction, we assemble all we know about it and the conditions under which it takes place. Then we set up a proposed mechanism from which we draw conclusions as to what effects changes in the reaction conditions would have on the course of the reaction. From a study of the experimental results we draw conclusions and think up further experiments. In this way we make progress toward the solution, even if we do not reach it.

My study of the esterification of mercaptans was taken up to throw light on the mechanism of esterification. There had been much discussion as to whether the hydroxyl of the alcohol or that of the acid is eliminated in the formation of ethyl acetate. According to one mechanism the esterification of mercaptan should give ethyl acetate and hydrogen sulfide, while according to another the products should be ethyl thiolacetate and water, which were what I obtained. This suggested, but did not prove, that it is the hydroxyl of the acid which is eliminated in esterification. Some years later this was proved by other investigators who used heavy oxygen.

TAGGED ATOMS

Since they became available, tagged atoms or molecules have done good service in the study of reaction mechanisms. As an example, it was found that the alkyl trisulfide, formed by the addition of radioactive sulfur to the disulfide, regenerated on desulfurization an inactive disulfide. This showed that the sulfur-carbon bonds had remained intact and that the radioactive sulfur had combined with the original sulfur atoms and not with the carbon.

In the synthesis of benzonitrile from lead benzoate and lead thiocyanate, mentioned in an earlier chapter, I was certain that the —CN of the thiocyanate replaced the carboxyl of the acid. Years later, someone tried this synthesis with lead benzoate in which the carboxyl contained radioactive carbon. The resulting benzonitrile proved to be radioactive, showing that I was wrong.

PRACTICAL STUDIES OF REACTIONS

It has been found by experiment that when a mixture of sugar, flour, eggs, butter, and minor ingredients, in certain proportions, is heated at the proper temperature for a definite time, a desirable product is obtained. The directions for many organic preparations read much like cookbook recipes and are regarded by some as being in the same class.

The research-minded chemist, however, looks at them in an entirely different way and asks many questions about each. What makes the reaction go? What is the mechanism? Is it of the first or second order? What are the by-products or secondary products? How is the reaction influenced by temperature and pressure? Is it acid catalyzed or base catalyzed? If a solvent is used, what is its function? Would the reaction go in its absence? Would some other solvent give better results? Is the reaction influenced favorably, or unfavorably, by the presence of impurities or of traces of unrecognized catalysts? Would the addition of a catalyst help? Such questions as these are of scientific interest, and answering them may uncover information of practical value.

IMPORTANCE OF HIGH YIELDS

If in making an organic compound the yield is less than the calculated, as is commonly the case, additional questions come up. Suppose the yield is 70%; there are several possibilities:

1. The reaction may not have been carried far enough.

2. An equilibrium may have been reached.

3. The reaction may have been complete, but 30% of the product may have undergone a secondary reaction.

4. There may have been one or more side reactions, using up 30% of the starting material.

Combinations of these are also possible.

To eliminate guesswork, it is well to start with a study of the estimation of the reaction product, either by isolation or some method of determination. If in the above case, 30% of the product is lost in the isolation, that is the step in the process that needs to be improved. In all experiments the actual yields must be corrected for isolation losses. The same applies to the estimation of unreacted starting materials.

In every run it is helpful to strike a material balance, adding up all of the products to account for the starting materials. It is desirable to determine the nature and amount of any gas that may be evolved.

1. If the recovered starting material accounts for practically all of the 30% deficiency, long reaction time, or other means, should be tried to push the reaction further toward completion. In a commercial operation, there comes a time when the value of the additional product does not justify the extra cost of getting it.

2. If a reaction is reversible, prolonging the treatment or the addition of a catalyst will not increase the yield beyond that set by the equilibrium. This point should be determined. One may, however, contrive to get high conversion. An example is the isomerization of ammonium thiocyanate to thiourea:

$$NH_4SCN \rightleftharpoons SC(NH_2)_2$$

A quantity of ammonium thiocyanate is heated under conditions found to be favorable. The cooled mixture is treated with sufficient cold water to extract the very soluble salt, and the slightly soluble thiourea filtered off. The recovered ammonium thiocyanate is recycled.

3. In a large number of cases, the primary product undergoes a further reaction, as in the sulfonation of anthraquinone. The monosulfonic acid, the primary product, is further sulfonated to a mixture of disulfonic acids. If the sulfonation is pushed until all of the anthraquinone disappears, only about

70% of the monosulfonic acid is found in the product, the rest having been converted to the unwanted disulfonic acids. The conversion is 100%, but the yield is only 70%. It has been found advantageous to stop the reaction halfway where the conversion is only 50%, but the yield of the wanted product is over 95%. The unreacted anthraquinone is recovered and reworked. The cost of recovery is balanced against the loss due to disulfonation.

4. Frequently two or more reactions go on simultaneously, in which case the yield of the desired product may be low though all of the starting material has been consumed. The nitration of toluene is a well-known example. The product is a mixture of nearly equal amounts of the *ortho* and *para* isomers with a little of the *meta,* besides some unreacted toluene and dinitrotoluenes. As the *p*-nitrotoluene is more valuable than the *ortho* isomer, many investigations have been made in the hope of finding conditions favoring its formation, but with little success. It is different with the sulfonation of anthraquinone where it has been found possible to shift the proportions of the isomers. In the sulfonation, described in the preceding section, the monosulfonic acid consists of about 95% of the beta-isomer to 5% of the alpha. A mercury catalyst speeds up the formation of the alpha-isomer to such an extent that the sulfonation can be carried out at a much lower temperature, at which practically none of the beta-isomer is formed.

When propylene and chlorine are brought together, two entirely different reactions are possible, addition to form propylene chloride, and substitution which gives allyl chloride. These two reactions are affected differently by changes in the reaction conditions, and it has been found possible to get satisfactory yields of allyl chloride. In isopentane, there are nine primary hydrogens, two secondary, and one tertiary. In chlorination under mild conditions where it is selective, the replacement of a secondary hydrogen is about three times as rapid as that of a primary, and the replacement of a tertiary about three times as fast as of a secondary. According to this, primary, secondary, and tertiary amyl chlorides should be formed in the ratios $9 \times 1:2 \times 3:1 \times 9$. If the chlorination is carried out at a high temperature where there is practically no selectivity, the products should be in the ratios 9:2:1. This is the way it is done commercially and the product is mainly the primary amyl chloride.

To the academic chemist, the aim may be getting the compound, whether the yield is high or low. In a large proportion of the thousands of preparations recorded in the journals, the yields are not mentioned, from which we may conclude that they were not high. When a man does not brag about his dog, we assume that it is not much of a dog. It does seem remarkable that a chemist who reports a 10% yield should show no sign of curiosity as to the fate of the remaining 90% of his starting material. Even a cookbook chemist should know what went with the rest. A cook who brought only 10% of a steak to the table would be asked questions.

The industrial chemist is vitally concerned with the yield of a reaction. Getting only 80% yield means throwing away 20% of the cost of raw materials, 20% of labor costs, and 20% of fixed charges. For a large plant, this would run into money. Raising the yield to 90% would cut the cost in half, which can be halved again by increasing the yield to 95%. This is assuming only one reaction. If three consecutive reactions are required to produce the final product, the losses mount higher. If the yield in each of these is 80%, the loss will be 49%. For 90 and 95% yields, the losses will be 27 and 15% respectively.

There is an additional reason for the desirability of high yields. The purification of the product is the easier and the attendant losses are the smaller, the less there is of some other product. An extreme case is the manufacture of pentaerythritol, in which the by-product is a gooey, polymeric syrup. If the yield is 50%, the desired product will be mixed with an equal amount of this syrup from which it may be impossible to separate any appreciable amount of the desired pentaerythritol.

Much of the effort of plant chemists is directed along these lines, since the commercial success of a process depends not on simply obtaining the desired material, but in making it in good quality at a cost low enough to yield a profit. It is quite possible to obtain gold from sea water, but present methods will have to be improved before it can be done economically. As yields go up, costs come down. When several concerns are competing in the manufacture of a given product, the one that can produce it for less, even if the margin is small, has the inside track and can control the market. A horse race can be decided by a nose as well as by a length.

SEPARATING THE STEPS IN A PROCESS

It is hard to name any manufacturing process that involves only one operation. The preparation of a dye usually requires a long succession of reactions, each of which demands a number of operations, such as mixing, heating, cooling, crystallizing, filtering, and drying or evaporating. The over-all yield depends on the yields in the several reactions and the perfection with which the various attendant operations are carried out.

In many cases the product from one step may not need to be purified in order to be used as the starting material for the next; it may not even be necessary to isolate it. Thus if benzene is nitrated, the crude nitrobenzene without even being dried may be reduced to aniline which is finally purified. If we start with 78 parts of benzene and nitrate and reduce and get 80 instead of 93 of aniline, we have means of knowing where the loss took place. To keep on repeating the whole process from benzene to aniline, making changes in one place or another, takes much time and does not get us anywhere. The proper way is to take the process to pieces and test each step, so that we know exactly where the losses are. When a tire leaks we do not put patches all over it, but first locate the leak; the puncture is nearly mended when we know where it is. In the before-mentioned case mechanical losses may occur, 1. in the handling of benzene; 2. by leaving nitrobenzene dissolved or suspended in spent acid; 3. by aniline remaining in the sludge. The nitration may not be complete, or dinitrobenzene may be formed and the reduction may also be faulty. The only way is to study all the steps separately till we are sure just how we stand on each of them. Then we know what part needs further study. Thus we mix a known amount of pure aniline with the volume of water that is used in the process and go through the recovery to see how much we can isolate. If the deficit is considerable, we see what can be done to cut it down. Then we try to separate a known amount of aniline from the sludge from a reduction experiment. When we have found just how to do this effectively, we are in a position to study the reduction of nitrobenzene, but this must be done with known amounts of pure dry nitrobenzene. The process is thus followed step by step from one end to the other as we would examine each link in a chain, and effort is concentrated on each weak spot.

In a process involving a large number of steps, it takes much time and trouble to isolate, purify, dry, and weigh each intermediate product, and the young chemist is tempted to take short cuts, but the long way around frequently turns out to be the shortest way through.

There is another reason why each step of the process should be studied by carrying it out with highly purified materials. Each chemical reaction in the series gives more or less of by-products, and these, if not removed, may influence the course of the subsequent reactions or may appear in the final product as impurities. When a reaction has been thoroughly studied, starting with pure materials, and the yield and quality of the product ascertained, one can repeat it using crude intermediates and find how the product is affected. Means may be found of counteracting the effects of the impurities.

Chromatography and gas chromatography, which will be mentioned again in chapter 12, have been found useful in the study of reactions, particularly in the isolation and identification of by-products.

12. Study of structure

INTRODUCTION

Organic chemistry, as we know it, is an edifice reared on structural formulae. They have become so commonplace that we seldom stop to wonder at them, to marvel at the boldness of chemists who presumed to enter into the infinitely minute and to imagine that such infinitesimals have structure, or to admire the infinite patience and consummate skill that have been displayed in working out the system and applying it to hundreds of thousands of organic compounds. Few structures built by the human mind can rival organic chemistry. Of a truth physics has gone farther and essayed to take the atoms apart, an even bolder thought.

During the siege of Paris, the news of a great city, the business letters of its merchants, and the private messages of its citizens were concentrated by photography onto tiny films to be tied to the leg of a carrier pigeon and at the destination

197

were reproduced in full. Into the structural formula of an organic compound are compressed the results of the work of perhaps scores of chemists, and if we could but read it aright, it would recall to us this mass of information. Sometimes the structural formula has seemed to be an object in itself, but it should be only a means to an end, a wonderfully compact way of setting down in minute space a large amount of information. There can hardly be a more wanton waste of mental energy than memorizing structural formulae without a full understanding of their meaning.

In times past, the determination of structural formulae was the chief occupation of the organic chemist. It must ever remain an important part of his task. Though so much labor has been put on problems of this sort and though a vast deal has been accomplished, there remain tasks in abundance, as difficult and as imposing as those that have taxed the strength of the chemical giants of the past.

The chemists of the early nineteenth century, intrigued and appalled by the number and variety of products that could be isolated from plants and fruits, went bravely to work to find out how the carbon, hydrogen, oxygen, and nitrogen atoms which they contained were put together. They had no idea of structure as we understand it, but were sure that the arrangement of the atoms within the molecule must account for the divergence of properties of compounds containing the same atoms in the same proportion. An important investigation was that of Liebig and Wöhler in 1837 of the oil of bitter almonds which resulted in the characterization of the "benzoyl radical," a group of atoms which behaved as a pseudoelement. It was only after Kekulé announced the quadrivalence of carbon and his benzene formula in 1865 that structures, as we now know them, could be written. By January 1, 1910, the structural formulae for the 144,150 compounds which Richter put in his *Lexicon* had been written, an amazing achievement. Among these there were hundreds of natural products, whose structures had been laboriously worked out, and a greater number of synthetic compounds whose structures had been deduced from the starting materials and the reactions by which they had been made. The determination of the structures of indigo and of uric acid had required the combined efforts of some of the best chemists of the time, while vanillin, salicylic acid, and many others were quickly ascertained. To appreciate our structural formulae, one must read the literature of that period. Some of these structures were incorrect, but the number is remarkably small. As has been mentioned in chapter 8, the addition product of sulfur monochloride and ethylene was put down as the disulfide instead of mustard gas. Finding this mistake did much to turn the tide in World War I. The determination of the structures of these thousands of organic compounds was an amazing achievement and made possible the work of Beilstein, who fitted each of them into its own proper niche in the great system that we know as organic chemistry.

Spectacular advances have been made in recent years in the determination of structure and synthesis of complex organic compounds. Some examples are the porphyrins, steroids, sex hormones, carotene, and cortisone. Almost as soon as an antibiotic is isolated and characterized, its structure and synthesis are announced. A hefty volume has been published on the study of the structure and synthesis of penicillin, which was the work of several teams of chemists. The synthesis of chlorophyll in American and German laboratories has been announced in July 1960.[1] The Harvard team of seventeen postdoctorate assistants, headed by Robert Woodward, had been working on this for four years.

It is not the purpose of this chapter to go into specific methods of determining structure, as there are excellent books devoted to this subject,[2] but rather to discuss the subject in general, mentioning some of the chief lines of attack. In this, as in other things, the beginner makes the best progress by studying the methods of the masters. So many chemists have published articles on the constitution of organic substances that it is easy to find an abundance of examples all the way from the time that

---

[1] *Chem. Eng. News,* July 11, 1960, p. 20.

[2] The following may be mentioned: Hans Meyer, *Analyse und Konstitutionsermittlung organischer Verbindungen,* Berlin, Julius Springer. 4th edition, 1922. H. Meyer, *Determination of Radicals in Organic Compounds* (translated by J. B. Tingle), New York, John Wiley and Sons, 1903.

chemists were struggling with type formulae and organic radicals down to recent times when all the latest and most refined methods are employed. Or we can take some of the triumphs of organic chemistry, the unravelling of the constitution of such things as indigo, alizarine, camphor, uric acid, or the sugars. A practical way is to look up a number of substances resembling the one in hand and see how they came by their accepted formulae. Of course, methods must not be followed blindly, but must be adapted to suit the present case as it is the habit of the research chemist to do.

STRUCTURE OF SYNTHETIC PRODUCTS

When we heat butanol with benzoic acid, we are sure that the product is butyl benzoate. This is true because esterification has been so thoroughly studied and because the starting compounds are so well known. The identity of the ester can be checked by its physical properties and its saponification number. In the before-mentioned case, the structure of the addition product of sulfur monochloride and ethylene was assumed to be the disulfide:

$$S_2Cl_2 + 2\ CH_2{:}CH_2 \rightarrow ClCH_2CH_2SSCH_2CH_2Cl$$

The structure was determined by arithmetic, not by chemical means. It is common experience that organic reactions do not always go exactly according to the equations which we write and that the structures of the products may not be what they are supposed to be. All along, it has required far more labor to determine the structure of reaction products than to make them. As our understanding of reactions has improved, we have less difficulty in identifying the products.

The chemical journals require that analyses be given for all new compounds in articles submitted for publication. A correct analysis shows that the substance *may* be the desired compound, but does not prove that it *is*. My hobby is plotting the melting points of the members of a series. In a certain paper on a series of esters the melting point of one ester did not fit into the pattern. This showed that it was not what it was supposed to be though its analysis was correct. It is desirable to take ultraviolet and infrared absorptions to check the assumed structure. Isomers or impurities of approximately the same composition may show up. Since the time of Brühl the refractive index of a new liquid is taken and compared with that calculated.

It happens in the best regulated laboratories that the yield in an organic preparation is considerably less than the calculated. This may mean that a by-product has been formed by a side reaction. The by-product should be isolated and its nature determined. Sometimes it turns out to be a known compound which can be identified by its melting point. If it is not a known compound, its structure should be determined.

Occasionally a reaction goes in an entirely unexpected direction. This happened to me when I heated benzamide with ethanol. I knew that ammonia displaces an alcohol from an ester. I wanted to find out whether or not the reaction is reversible so I heated benzamide with ethanol. Instead of the expected ethyl benzoate the product was N-ethylbenzamide, which was readily identified by its melting point.

Every now and then we come across compounds described in the literature which have entirely different structures from those given.

The determination of the structure of reaction products is still with us. In general, it is simpler than the investigation of a natural product. The analysis of an alloy is simpler if we are told in advance that it contains only zinc, copper, and tin. As we know the groups that are present in the starting materials, we are sure that the products must contain the same groups or modifications of them. This limits our search.

STRUCTURE OF NATURAL PRODUCTS

The first step toward the determination of the structure of an organic compound is to separate it from other organic compounds and purify it to constant properties. Differences in volatility and in solubility have been relied on for the isolation and purification of organic compounds, and have rendered excellent service. In recent years, chromatography has been added to

these and has been found to be of great value, particularly in
cases in which the limit by old methods had been reached. By
its use, compounds of the same volatility or the same solubility
can sometimes be separated. It has been found to be very useful
in obtaining and in purifying natural products.

Paper chromatography is available for the separation of small amounts of materials. Gas-phase chromatography,
which is treated in chapter 10, takes care of volatile substances.

Assuming that we have a pure compound and have
its analysis, the first thing to do is to find out whether or not it
can be split into two or more simpler compounds. Among natural
products numerous esters have been found. Two of these are
oil of wintergreen and spermaceti, both of which can be hydrolyzed by alkali. On hydrolysis, oil of wintergreen gives salicylic
acid and methanol, which are readily identified and can be recombined to regenerate the ester. Spermaceti is hydrolized to
palmitic acid and cetyl alcohol, which can be identified and
recombined. The structures of the two esters are deduced from
those of the hydrolysis products and verified by the recombina-
tion of these. The axiom: Divide and conquer applies here as
well as in warfare.

Hippuric acid is hydrolyzed to benzoic acid and
aminoacetic acid, which shows it to be a substituted benzamide.
Many complex organic compounds other than esters can be
broken into simpler parts by various means. The hydrolysis of
sucrose gives glucose and fructose. But getting these back together
so as to form sucrose is not so easy.

MICROCHEMICAL METHODS

Microchemical methods, which have been developed
in recent years, have been of enormous assistance in the study of
natural products. It happens often that a potent poison or other
interesting compound is present in minute amounts in some
plant. In such cases it has required the working up of huge
quantities of material in order to obtain a gram of the desired
compound. According to old methods, a single determination of
carbon and hydrogen would require 150 to 200 milligrams of

material, a nitrogen analysis a comparable amount, and chemical reactions even larger amounts. Fifty years ago, Dr. J. J. Abel was working on bufogen, a poison which he extracted from a toad. I ran a combustion determination of carbon and hydrogen for him and thought that I was doing well to get results with only 55 milligrams. According to modern microanalytical methods, less than 5 milligrams would have been required. Micro methods have been developed for carrying out reactions with milligram quantities. The chemistry of a new compound can be worked out with a fraction of a gram of material. In qualitative analysis courses, in many institutions, the students now use micro, or semimicro methods. A drop of a solution of thioacetamide precipitates the metals of group II. There are now whole books and journals devoted to micro methods. Such methods are used as a matter of convenience even when unlimited amounts of materials are available. Micro methods have been of immense service in the study of natural products.

DETERMINING THE SKELETON OR PARENT HYDROCARBON

If the compound cannot be split, it must be dealt with as a whole. We think of organic compounds as derived from hydrocarbons by the substitution of atoms or groups for one or more hydrogen atoms. We know the constitution of any compound when we know the hydrocarbon from which it is derived and also the kind and location of the substituents. We make much progress when we determine the parent hydrocarbon. There are various ways of doing this. One way is the old zinc-dust method, discovered by Zincke, which has done great service in certain cases. The compound is heated with zinc dust which in some way removes all the oxygen, leaving the hydrocarbon to pass on. A famous example of the use of this was the determination of the constitution of alizarine. On heating it with zinc dust, anthracene was obtained.[3] Analysis had shown the presence of four oxygen atoms in alizarine, two of which were accounted for

---

[3] Gräbe and Liebermann, *Berichte*, **1**, 49 (1868); **2**, 14 and 332 (1869); **3**, 359 and 636 (1870); *Annalen, Sup.*, **7**, 257-322 (1870); **160**, 133 (1871).

by considering it to be an anthraquinone derivative. Comparing the formula of alizarine, $C_{14}H_8O_4$, with that of anthraquinone, $C_{14}H_8O_2$, and remembering that alizarine is soluble in alkali, it was easy to conclude that the two extra oxygen atoms are present in phenol groups. It then remained to locate these two groups.

By exhaustive hydrogenation, geraniol and linalool, both of which have the formula $C_{10}H_{18}O$, are converted into 2,6-dimethyloctane. As both of these form esters and give other reactions of alcohols, they must contain hydroxyl groups which must be located. Linalool is difficult to esterify, which indicates that it is a tertiary alcohol. For it to be a tertiary alcohol, the hydroxyl would have to be at 2 or 6, but the fact that it is optically active shows that it must be in the 6-position. It then remains to locate the double bonds, which is done by careful oxidation.

Baeyer's[4] justly famous investigation on mellitic acid was all founded on the observation that benzene is produced by heating this acid with soda-lime. The elimination of carbon dioxide from benzoic acid to leave benzene was well known, so that this experiment proved to Baeyer that mellitic acid is also a carboxy derivative of benzene like benzoic acid, but having six carboxyl groups instead of one, since its composition is $C_{12}O_{12}H_6$, which he considered to be $C_6(COOH)_6$. This was the basis for the solution of the problem, though much tedious work had to be done to clear it all up.

DETERMINING THE PRESENCE OF GROUPS OR RADICALS

Since an organic compound consists of a carbon skeleton decorated with various groups, hydrogen satisfying the remaining valences, a large part of the game of constitution determination consists in identifying the groups present. Inorganic analysis rests on the assumption that copper or tungsten may be found and estimated in any of their compounds, though copper is not so easy to find in a silicate as it is in copper sulfate. In a sense, groups, or radicals, are the elements of which organic

---

[4] Adolf Baeyer, *Annalen*, Sup., **7**, 1-55 (1870).

compounds are constructed. We can now speak of hydroxyl, carboxyl, ethyl, or phenyl as elements without apology, since detectives have pried into the private life of the orthodox elements and dug up their buried past with the result that we now know that they too are complex, even more so than our organic radicals. Phenyl, ethyl, and allyl are made up of carbon and hydrogen just as chlorine and iron are constructed of positive nuclei and electrons, the properties of the radicals as well as of the elements depending on the number and arrangement of the constituent parts.

The presence of a certain group in an organic molecule causes it to have certain properties though the influence of the other constituents modifies their manifestation. Thus any compound containing a carboxyl group, —COOH, is an acid and will give the typical reactions of an acid. It may be a strong, volatile, water-soluble acid as formic, $H \cdot COOH$, or a weak, nonvolatile, practically insoluble acid as o-benzoyl-benzoic. $C_6H_5COC_6H_4COOH$. The hydroxyl group is present in ethyl alcohol and in cellulose, which are dissimilar in most respects, but both of which give nitrates and acetates, reactions characteristic of an alcoholic hydroxyl.

The groups that are commonly found in natural products are comparatively few, carboxyl, —COOH, alcoholic and phenolic hydroxyl, —OH, methoxyl, —OCH_3, aldehyde, —CHO, and acetyl, —$COCH_3$, being the most common. Synthetic products contain many others, such as the nitro, —NO_2, amino, —NH_2, mercapto, —SH, sulfonic —SO_3H, and the halogens. In the more complicated compounds, two or more groups of the same or of different kinds may occur. Thus mucic acid contains two carboxyls and four hydroxyls and vanilline, an aldehyde, a hydroxyl, and a methoxyl. A remarkable thing about organic compounds is the independent way in which the groups react. Thus vanilline shows typical aldehyde reactions as well as typical phenol reactions in one case as if it were only aldehyde and in the other as if it were solely phenol, though the aldehyde group makes the phenol group more acidic so that it can be titrated using phenolphthalein. The methoxyl group can be determined as if the others were not present.

LOCATING GROUPS ON THE SKELETON

Supposing that we have determined the hydrocarbon skeleton in a substance and the nature of the substituents; it remains to locate them. In synthetic chemistry, we sometimes start with a known hydrocarbon and introduce a known group, as in the nitration of *meta*-xylene; then the only thing that has to be found out is the position of the entering group.

The enunciation of Kekulé's famous theory of the construction of benzene[5] gave the greatest single impulse in the history of chemistry to the determination of structure, particularly of aromatic compounds of which hundreds were known but had not been properly related to each other for lack of a guiding theory. Many investigations were required to line up the numerous substitution products of benzene into the *ortho, meta,* and *para* ranks.

A study of *Beilstein* will reveal many synthetic substances whose constitutions are still in doubt. When a new compound is prepared, its maker is under obligation to determine the location of all the groups he introduces.

LOCATING DOUBLE BONDS

This is frequently a delicate task since in many compounds the double bonds may be shifted from one position to another by the very means used to locate them. Chemical literature contains many erroneous constitutional formulae for the reason that fusion with alkali and treatment with concentrated sulfuric acid have been used for this purpose. It is now known that these reagents frequently move the ethylene linkage some distance and what we find out is its new position and not where it was originally. Thus oleic acid was long considered to be $CH_3(CH_2)_{16}CH:CHCOOH$ since[6] by fusing it with caustic

---

[5] *Bull. soc. chim.* (3), **3,** 98 (1865); *Annalen,* **137,** 129 (1866). To realize the importance of this theory one must read the addresses at the celebration in 1890: *Berichte,* **23,** 1265 ff. (1890).

[6] Varrentrapp, *Annalen,* **35,** 209 (1840).

potash, palmitic and acetic acids were obtained. By shaking oleic acid with cold dilute potassium permanganate a dihydroxy stearic acid is obtained which, on further oxidation,[7] yields pelargonic and azelaic acids,

$$CH_3(CH_2)_7COOH \quad \text{and} \quad HOOC(CH_2)_7COOH$$

This shows that dihydroxy stearic acid is:

$$CH_3(CH_2)_7CH(OH)\cdot CH(OH)\cdot(CH_2)_7COOH$$

and oleic acid must be:

$$CH_3(CH_2)_7CH:CH(CH_2)_7COOH$$

Many double bonds have been located by ozonizing at low temperatures and treatment of the ozonides with water by which the compound is broken in two at the double bond, $RCH:CHR'$ becoming $RCHO + OHCR'$. With oleic acid,[8] this method gives $CH_3(CH_2)_7CHO$ and $OHC(CH_2)_7COOH$ in complete agreement with the structure listed last.

The terpenes form one of the most interesting and important groups of organic compounds. It has required decades and a large number of skillful workers to unravel their complicated relationships. As there are groups of sugars, the members of which differ only in configuration, so we have groups of terpenes, where the individuals differ only in the location of double bonds. The difficulty is made much greater by the ease with which many of these are shifted. In some of the most important terpene derivatives, geraniol, citral, citronellol, citronellal, and linalool, the position of one ethylene linkage has been difficult to determine.

BUILDING DOWN OR "ABBAU"

The German language has the word "abbauen," to build down, as "aufbauen" is to build up. When we have a building to get rid of, we call in a wrecking concern and the roof is off and the walls are pulled over in short order. Little can be learned from the debris that is hauled off as to how the house

---

[7] Edmed, *J. Chem. Soc.*, **73**, 627-34 (1898).
[8] Harries and Thieme, *Annalen*, **343**, 333-354 (1905).

looked. If we take the pains to remove one brick or one timber at a time as we tear down a structure, we can find out just how it was put up.

One of the important methods of determining the structure of complex organic compounds is by *Abbau;* we take off a carboxyl, a methoxyl, or some other group, analyze the remainder, remove another group, and so on, until we get to something we can recognize. If we know just what we have taken off we can form an idea of what the structure was. If we start with a hydrocarbon which analysis and molecular weight determination show to be $C_{10}H_{14}$ and oxidise it to $C_8H_6O_4$, which we identify as p-$C_6H_4(COOH)_2$, we see that two carbon atoms have been lost and assign the formula p-$C_6H_4(C_2H_5)_2$ to the substance. Careful oxidation is one of the most-used processes in *Abbau.*

DETERMINATION OF STRUCTURE
BY PHYSICAL METHODS

When we know the relation of physical properties to constitution as we should, we shall be able to look at a structural formula and tabulate the physical properties of the substance it represents and, conversely, write the structural formula after measuring a sufficient number of the physical properties. One versed in anatomy can look at an animal and draw an accurate picture of one of its bones. The paleontologist digs up a bone and presents us with a picture of the prehistoric animal and makes a guess as to how it walked and what it ate. While organic chemists have not arrived at that goal, we have made substantial progress in that direction and constantly use physical properties to corroborate conclusions arrived at by chemical methods or to decide between two or more formulae which agree equally well with our chemical findings.

We can start with some simple illustrations. Suppose for a moment that the butyl alcohols were unknown to us but that we came into possession of two liquids boiling at 99.5° and 117.70°, which gave analytical figures corresponding to $C_4H_{10}O$.

Molecular weight determinations might be used to confirm this formula, but would not be required, since a substance, $C_8H_{20}O_2$, could not possibly boil at so low a temperature. Comparing these boiling points with those of propyl and isopropyl alcohols, 97.2° and 82.3°, we find 117.7 − 97.2 = 20.5 and 99.5 − 82.3 = 17.2. It is more reasonable to consider the liquid boiling at 117.7° to be normal butyl alcohol and the one boiling at 99.5° as secondary butyl alcohol, the true homolog of isopropyl alcohol. Diethyl ether and methyl propyl ethers, which likewise have the composition $C_4H_{10}O$, are excluded from consideration since the boiling points given are far too high for ethers of this molecular weight.

These conclusions, based as they are on the boiling points alone, would not be sufficiently supported but should be confirmed by comparisons of densities, refractive indices, etc., and finally verified by chemical reactions.

The famous discussion on the structure of diazo compounds was finally decided on the basis of physical properties, since the chemical reactions in their formation and decomposition could be explained by either formula. The diazonium formula $C_6H_5N(N)Cl$, representing a salt containing pentavalent nitrogen, agrees well with the known facts that diazo compounds are colorless and very soluble in water, giving good conducting solutions in which the positive ion acts similarly to a tetra-alkyl-ammonium ion, while a substance having the constitution represented by the Kekulé formula, $C_6H_5N:N \cdot Cl$ would probably be colored, insoluble in water, and nonionizable.

The classical investigation of Brühl on refractive indices shows what can be done by a study of one property. His work has furnished the means for deciding the structure of many of the terpenes and of keto-enol tautomers. The refractive index of a compound multiplied by its molecular weight gives its molecular refraction. From a comparison of the molecular refractions of a number of compounds, the atomic refractions of carbon, hydrogen, and other elements were calculated. Variations in some of these were found, depending on the mode of combination. For instance, there are two different values for oxygen, one for —O— and another for O=, according to whether the oxygen is in an ether or a ketone. To decide between two possible structures of a compound, the molecular refraction is calculated for each and compared with the value found.

More recently, ultraviolet and infrared spectra have been found to give important information as to structure. Double bonds, particularly where conjugated, give characteristic absorption bands in the ultraviolet. Of all physical properties, infrared spectra give the most information as to structure. The presence of a hydroxyl group is shown by an absorption band which differs according to whether the hydroxyl is primary, secondary, or tertiary. A similar statement can be made about the amino group. The carbonyl group registers differently depending on its relation to the rest of the molecule. Other groups give characteristic absorption bands. Another important use of infrared spectra is the identification of compounds. A man can be identified by his fingerprints which is unlike that of any other man; an organic compound may be identified by its infrared spectrum, which is unlike that of any other compound. The infrared spectrum of the compound in question is compared with that of a known authentic specimen or checked against those that have been recorded. Already extensive collections of infrared spectra are available for comparisons and these are being enlarged constantly. In industrial laboratories, all new products are examined by infrared to check assumed structures and to detect by-products.

Dipole moments can be used to make decisions concerning the appropriate structure for a molecule, and such measurements do not require equipment as expensive as spectroscopic methods. Other methods which provide information are mass spectrometry and polarography. In recent years, nuclear magnetic resonance has been used rather extensively. Electron paramagnetic resonance is applicable to the study of free radicals and other substances containing at least one unpaired electron. X-ray diffraction has aided considerably in our understanding of the nature of crystals. Electron diffraction is of primary importance in the examination of gases; for solids only thin films can be used since the electrons are absorbed so readily.

As we accumulate more extensive and more accurate data on a larger number of the properties of organic compounds, physical data will play an increasingly important part in the determination of constitution. These few paragraphs are intended to call attention to a subject on which whole books have been written.[9]

VERIFICATION OF STRUCTURE BY SYNTHESIS

We are never satisfied with our conclusions as to the constitution of a compound till we build up the structure represented by our formula and prove that the synthetic compound is identical with the original. When this is done, the whole line of reasoning is vindicated and all the experiments checked. To prove that we know the structure of a watch, we must not only take it apart but also put it together again. This verification by synthesis is always desirable, but is not always possible, though persistent and ingenious thinking and working are apt to find a way. From the commercial point of view, the very object in determining the constitution of a substance is to lay a foundation for a study of its synthesis.

In two triumphs of organic chemistry, which are often mentioned, the synthesis of indigo and of alizarine, syntheses followed the determination of constitution, and plant processes were devised and perfected, so that the cultivation of madder has become only a memory and natural indigo is a rarity. In the case of rosaniline and para rosaniline, it is possible to build up the dye by reversing the process by which it was taken to pieces, but this is too expensive for the plant. The dye is manufactured by oxidation of mixtures of aniline and toluidine, in the same general way as it was before its constitution was known, but a haphazard and inefficient process has been so improved that the dye is obtained in better yield and standard quality. The knowledge of its constitution has made it possible to perfect the plant process.

[9] W. Herz, *Über die wichtigsten Beziehungen zwischen der chemischen Zusammensetzung von Verbindungen und ihrem physikalischen Verhalten,* Stuttgart, F. Enke, 1898.

Hugo Kauffmann, *Beziehungen zwischen physikalischen Eigenschaften und chemischer Konstitution,* Stuttgart, F. Enke, 1920.

Arnold Weissberger, editor, *Physical Methods of Organic Chemistry,* New York, Interscience Publishers, 1959.

13. Medical research

Research has provided us with an abundance of "better things for better living"; the task of medical research is to prolong our enjoyment of all of these wonderful things.

In what follows the subject is discussed by three who have made notable contributions to medical research.

THE LURE OF MEDICAL RESEARCH

BY JOHN C. KRANTZ, JR.

Professor of Pharmacology, University of Maryland, Medical School

Karl Wilhelm Scheele, the brilliant Swedish chemist who discovered oxygen, declared: "There is no delight like that which springs from discovery; it is a joy which gladdens the heart." The exploration of the unknown has always challenged the skill and mind of man. Today the frontier of human

213

progress is the laboratory of the chemist and allied scientists. The gains which are to be achieved embrace every facet of human endeavor, and every area of human comfort and welfare. Not the least of these is health, on which happiness and progress depend.

Medical research, therefore, offers no uncertain challenge to the embryonic chemist. Through its doors he will see unending problems which await solution. For example, half the hospital beds of our country are occupied by patients who are mentally ill. Within the decade, new drugs, such as chlorpromazine and reserpine, have been made available through the efforts of the chemist to contribute to the treatment, and in some cases cure, of these patients. But the chemistry of the living brain must be unravelled and the distortion of the normal chemical process which gives rise to mental illness must be understood. For until we know and delineate the cause of a disease, the treatment with drugs will remain empiric.

Great strides have been made in the use of drugs for the treatment of many human maladies. Diabetes has yielded to the discovery of insulin. Pernicious anemia has been thwarted by the discovery of vitamin B_{12}. Arthritis can be controlled partially by steroid therapy with the various derivatives of cortisone. And yet our advance has been halted in the attack on cancer. More research is needed; more chemists with brilliant intellects and sound basic training in the fundamentals of chemistry and biology are urgently and critically needed for this type of research before the ultimate conquest of this dreaded disease will be achieved.

Our nation is now research minded. And medical research occupies a position of high priority. Funds and opportunities are abundant in many quarters. The National Institutes of Health represent this field of endeavor on a national level. Our medical schools are all actively engaged in medical research and in the training of research workers for the numerous areas of the health program. Teaching and research make an ideal occupation for the medical research worker, for they teach best whose inspiration comes from the spirit of exploration. In addition, the many manufacturers of drugs have learned the importance of medical research and are pouring back into this field of scientific endeavor a considerable proportion of their profits.

The challenge is alluring and the rewards are equal to the challenge. The monetary reward to the medical research worker today does not suffer by comparison. His working conditions are excellent and time for freedom of thought is great, not only in the university environment but also in industry. Above all, his reward is the emotional satisfaction that springs from discovery and the knowledge that he has contributed to the great enterprise of alleviating human pain and suffering.

But the man must be equal to the challenge. He must be a dedicated man, dedicated to the search for truth. Sound training at an undergraduate level and broad training at a graduate level are essential. The ability to think through a problem, to see its ultimate utilitarian value, requires study, reading, and endless experimentation. In short, the research worker must be a scientist "who has the simplicity to wonder, the ability to question, the power to generalize, and the capacity to apply."

MEDICAL RESEARCH GUIDED BY UNDERSTANDING

BY ALFRED BURGER

Professor of Chemistry, University of Virginia

On the prescription shelves of the drugstores and in the storerooms of hospitals and physicians, one finds hundreds of medicines for almost every kind of ill. Forget about the mixtures, lotions, and pills which are advertised in newspapers, on the radio, and on television. They are ineffective in most cases. But many drugs and chemicals have been shown, by rigorous tests on numerous laboratory animals and on humans, that they furnish real relief from pain and diseased conditions. Occasionally, they can save lives and restore normal health. The discovery of such chemicals, their evaluation, and ultimately the understanding of how they effect their beneficial action constitute one of the most fascinating and challenging scientific stories.

The motivation of all research is fundamentally a longing for understanding and a vexing desire to solve a problem. But the search for new drugs has an additional motivation, more unselfish than just the satisfaction of one's own curiosity. A new and valuable drug may give renewed health and well-being to millions of our fellow men, and to sick animals. One medicinal chemist or medical scientist who discovers and develops one new medicine of even limited use can bring more health, and thus personal happiness, to a larger number of people than he could by a lifetime of practice as a physician.

At the beginning of the twentieth century, the statistical life expectancy of the average new-born in civilized countries was around forty-seven years. With the expansion of all medical facilities, and particularly the discovery of life-saving and life-prolonging drugs for several common diseases, this figure increased steeply, at the rate of four and one half years each decade. A baby born in 1960 can expect to live for seventy years, and there is no break in this curve; by the year 2020, therefore, the life expectancy should be one hundred happy and useful years. Obviously, this cannot go on forever, but an increasing knowledge of normal physiological conditions, of aging, of disease, and of new medical and chemical modes of therapy will continue to improve this golden medical age we live in.

Unfortunately, the discovery of many useful drugs has been, and still is, based purely on trial and error. "Leads" are obtained from chance observations, or from folklore about the therapeutic value of some herbal concoction. A discriminating medicinal chemist will sift such information about the beneficial effects of some ancient medicine. If there appears to be enough evidence for the validity of such claims, he will collect some of the material, and extract, concentrate, and purify the active principles. Tests in mice and other laboratory animals will often substantiate or reject the claims of medicinal properties reported for the crude natural material. For example, if an herb has been claimed to be of benefit in severe discomforts attributable to high blood pressure, it will be possible to measure in laboratory animals any blood-pressure lowering (antihypertensive) effect of the purified chemicals from the plant.

The organic chemist will now try to determine the chemical structure of the effective drug, that is, to show how the individual atoms are linked to one another in the molecule of the compound. Sometimes this task is complicated by the necessity of unravelling not only which atom is linked to another, but also in which direction, to the left or to the right, up or down, these bonds are arranged. The solution of these questions requires a detectivelike uncanny ability of tracking down little pieces of chemical evidence, and putting them together in an often bizarre jigsaw puzzle of molecular structure. To get this evidence, modern instruments which probe into electrical waves emitted by the molecule are used abundantly, but skillful, careful laboratory technique and an alert power of observation are still the most reliable means of solving such problems. The training first received in college and perfected in graduate school forms the basis for these skills.

Once the chemical structure of a medicinally active compound has been established, the chemist will ask his biological team-mates the following questions: Could the medicinal activity of the drug be improved? Is its margin of safety large enough? Has it any unwanted side effects at doses needed to produce its main desired action? It is a fallacy to assume that Nature has placed at our command the drugs best suited to treat and cure human ills. In most instances, those drugs are purely "accidents" of Nature, and their specific beneficial effect can almost always be improved by a skilled medicinal chemist. There are many rules of thumb by which this can be achieved, and only a few reasonable ways to guide us to occasional success. These intellectually more rewarding experiences shall be related here. Their shortcomings will show you how much improvement is still needed, and where advances can be brought about mostly by clear, unbiased thinking and ingenious sparks of new approaches.

Take the case of the antimetabolites. So many drugs act in such small quantities to produce profound effects in the organism that it is reasonable to assume they affect some highly vital chemicals in the body by some chemical reaction. Such vital body and cell chemicals are protein-type catalysts called enzymes. They control the speed at which chemical reactions in the body cells and fluids occur. Many of these reactions would be so infinitely slow without enzymic catalysis that one may just as well say they would not proceed in the absence of enzymes. The chemistry of the enzymes is poorly understood; some seem to operate well in a properly adjusted acidic or basic medium, while others require small amounts of vitamins as coenzymes for catalytic functioning. The chemical architecture of many vitamin molecules is known, and chemical analogs of these compounds can readily be tailor-made by a trained organic chemist. Some of these analogs can still help the protein-enzymes to speed up biochemical reactions, but others act as antivitamins. Since vitamins and similar food chemicals are needed in normal cell metabolism, such inhibitors are known as antimetabolites.

This can be demonstrated in some cases in testtube experiments. Two chemicals which are to react with each other are mixed, and a purified metabolite is added as a catalyst. The reaction will start. Then an antimetabolite is added and, as a result, the reaction will slow down or stop. In many other cases, it has not been possible to show this relation so clearly, and one relies on a certain amount of guesswork about metabolite–drug relations.

The aim of research in all sciences is to eliminate guesswork, or at least to reduce it to a minimum, and replace it by dependable data which permit predictions about the course of future experiments. In the case of the drugs, data are needed on the chemical nature of the metabolites and the extent and speed at which antimetabolites can compete with them. First of all, the nature of the chemicals on or in the living cell, with which both the metabolite and the antimetabolite must react in order to produce a physiological reaction, is completely unknown. These chemicals are often called receptors. Most medicinal chemists believe that any reliable knowledge of the chemical nature of even a few receptors will make it possible to discard the empirical search for new drugs and allow to make them "to measure," to fit the receptor.

Many biochemists who concern themselves with cell chemicals have tried to understand drug receptors, but so far almost without success. The problem is this: Suppose one has a coin and makes an impression of it to get the corresponding die. If the coin has a sharp, clear design, the die will also appear sharp and clear in reverse, provided a perfect technique is used in casting the die. But if the design on the coin is worn and diffuse, and the casting technique is not perfect, the die will not be very good. If one now makes a new coin of a different metal from this imperfect die, the new coin may resemble the original coin, to be sure, but there will be indistinct and uncertain lines and ridges also. Unless one is a real expert, the new imperfect coin may well be hard to recognize as a likeness of its prototype.

Transposed into drug–receptor relations, some effective empirical drug will represent the original coin. But since the drug almost always has side-effects, one assumes that its chemical formula in respect to its main receptor is not too unique, that is, it resembles a worn coin. Now let us try to make a die from this "hazy" drug formula. Unfortunately, receptors do not consist of plaster, but probably of proteins of very high molecular weight and complexity. Indeed, we are not at all sure of what they consist. Perhaps it is only a corner or a bay in the surface of a huge protein molecule which is a real drug receptor. Thus we are stymied in getting a good receptor-die. We can go out on a limb and disregard all the factors we do not understand, and concentrate on the few lines and ridges we have learned from the formula of the drug. But now the outlines of the receptor will have become so very indistinct that a recasting of a new molecule from this hazy surface will barely ever furnish a new drug analogous to the one we started from.

A small beginning has been made to overcome some of these difficulties. In the case of some chemically very simple drug molecules which react with soluble enzymes, a slight understanding of the reactive surface of these enzymes has become possible. The challenge for the young and imaginative medicinal biochemist is to devise novel techniques to apply these experiences to nonsoluble cell receptors. Some of the greatest rewards of therapy await him for this inspiration.

Diseases are often classified as infectious and as functional. Functional disorders occur when an organ does not function properly, or if some fundamental chemical reaction in the body has come to a halt, often when one part of the body has aged and slowed down too quickly. Among the most pressing problems in discovering drugs in this area are chemicals that could be used in diseases of the blood, bone marrow, liver, kidney, pancreas, the hormone-producing glands, the nerves, and the brain. A bare beginning has been made in the chemical treatment of arthritis, cancer, high blood pressure and mental disorders. Many infectious diseases can now be cured by antibiotics, but the germs which cause such infections have a great tendency to lose their sensitivity to antibiotics, and they become resistant. Then new chemicals are needed to overcome resistant infections, and this problem will repeat itself time and again. No really effective drugs for virus infections are known, although even here a significant beginning has been made in 1960. For the young medicinal scientist, there exists no frontier. When he solves one phase of a problem, even if he can cure a disease, there will lie the question before him: How has he really done it? There is unending excitement and fun to reward him for his efforts.

MEDICAL RESEARCH IN THE SERVICE OF MANKIND

BY RANDOLPH T. MAJOR

Professor of Chemistry, University of Virginia
Formerly, Chemical Director Merck & Co.

Some fifty years ago, a young American chemist was working in cooperation with a group of medical men in the Philippines who were trying to find a treatment for the dreaded disease, beri beri. He had prepared some extracts of rice polish, thinking that this polish might contain something needed to prevent or cure beri beri. A few years ago he wrote of one of his experiences with a patient who received some of his extracts, as follows:

"One was a boy 10 or 12 years of age in the Philippine General Hospital. When I first saw him about noon he had been unconscious for some hours. The priest had said the last rites and his parents were in the room awaiting the end. As it happened, I had an extract which I had just tested for several weeks on chickens and I thought it exceptionally potent. Blandly, I reassured the parents and directed the doctor in the injection. About 5 o'clock I came back to see my patient. As I tiptoed into the doorway he raised himself on his elbow and said that he was very hungry." [1]

The chemist who had this experience was Robert R. Williams who later determined the structure of and synthesized vitamin B_1, the elusive factor in rice polish for which he had looked for many years both in the Philippines and later in the United States.

Dr. Williams' experience in the Philippines illustrates the benefits accruing to mankind from the new medicinal products first produced by the research chemist in the medicinal field. Such chemists must dedicate their lives to the relief of pain, suffering, and death as do physicians, surgeons, pharmacists, and nurses. The research chemist, working in the medicinal field, then may enjoy the satisfactions not only of carrying on as fine chemical work as he is capable, but also of serving his fellow man in a most basic way.

In addition to the challenge to medicinal chemical research of fighting pain, sickness, and death, such research offers some of the greatest challenges to the imagination and ability of research chemists of nearly all kinds, organic chemists, biochemists, physical chemists, analytical chemists, inorganic chemists, etc. What finer research work has been done than the determination of the structure of vitamin B_{12} by a group of chemists, or the synthesis of such alkaloids as strychnine and morphine or of the steroid, cortisone.

The present medical era might be justifiably called the era of antibiotics. As defined by the discoverer of streptomycin, Dr. Selman Waksman,[2] these are chemical substances of microbial origin that inhibit the growth or the metabolic activities of bacteria and other microorganisms.

---

[1] "Current Research in the Science of Nutrition," *Nutrition Reviews*, September 1953.

[2] S. Waksman, *Microbial Antagonisms and Antibiotic Substances*, New York, The Commonwealth Fund, 1945.

The first medically important antibiotic, penicillin, was discovered by a microbiologist, but its medical significance became apparent only when a team of a medical man, a microbiologist, and a chemist investigated penicillin early in the course of World War II. Before the War was over, penicillin was being produced in great quantity in huge tanks and was saving the lives of thousands of sick and wounded soldiers. Today, it is widely used throughout the whole civilized world and has been responsible for removing most of the fear of such formerly dreaded diseases as pneumonia, syphilis, and streptococcic infections.

It is noteworthy that the early work on penicillin during World War II was carried on by a chemist in collaboration with other scientists. This is typical of nearly all medicinal chemical research. The chemist is an essential member of the team of scientists needed to find a new medicinal or improve an old one, but almost always he must work as a member of a team in order to be effective. Scientists with other training than chemical are needed in order to evaluate medicinals and to carry on medical research successfully. For example, research chemists are needed to isolate a new antibiotic, purify it, ascertain its mode of action, and determine its structure, so that later they may synthesize it or at least provide clues to better methods of isolating it or of increasing the yield. But in addition to chemists, microbiologists are needed to discover new antibiotics, to produce them by fermentation, and to increase the fermentation yields. Of course, medical men of various kinds are needed to evaluate the antibiotics in man and animals, to determine their toxicity or safety.

Thus each of the great new antibiotics, such as streptomycin, tetracycline, chloramphenicol, and erythromycin, has required teams of scientists, including chemists, to bring them to the stage of usefulness.

Many are the problems awaiting the chemist interested in medicinal chemistry. No adequate cure for most of the mental diseases is known; over half the hospital beds in this country are occupied by mentally deranged people. One out of every two people dies from diseases of the heart and blood vessels. Future medicinal chemists will undoubtedly help decrease this loss. Then there is cancer. One out of every four people suffers from some form of this disease during his lifetime. What an achievement for a chemist it would be to find a really effective cure for some type of cancer! Then the medicinal chemist must be asking himself the questions: "What are the chemical changes occurring in the body in disease, and how do drugs function?" What challenging problems these are.

It is to be hoped that many able chemists with a real interest in the alleviation of pain, suffering, and disease, and who have or can obtain the requisite training, will devote themselves to the great problems that lie ahead for medicinal research chemists.

14. ∎ Libraries

INTRODUCTION

When will some Homer arise to sing of the library, of the labors, a thousand times greater than those of Hercules, that have brought together information from every age and clime, tidings from stars whose light started on its headlong flight to the earth before Tutankhamen was born, measurements of suns in comparison with which our earth is but a speck, pictures of monsters that trod the earth in antediluvian ages, tracings of ferns of the carboniferous era, wisdom of the sages of all times, songs of poets, whisperings of lovers, secrets of antiquity? Here we find also the greatness of small things, the revelations by the microscope of empires whose contending armies do battle in a drop of blood, glimpses through the ultramicroscope of the dancing of the trillions of particles in colloidal solutions, and explorations by the scientific imagination of the interior of atoms with their solar systems of electrons. The riches in the vault of the Bank of Eng-

225

land are paltry as compared with the treasures stored in a great library. Measured in human labor, a library represents more toil in the gathering of information than the pyramids in the cutting and piling up of stone. The bank vault is protected with bolts and locks and armed guards lest someone purloin a single gold piece; the library doors open wide and over its portal is inscribed: "Whosoever will, let him come and take of the wisdom of life freely." We travel miles and stand in thoughtful reverence before the tombs where lie buried the mortal remains of Napoleon, of Shakespeare, or of the "Unknown Soldier," but here in the library the immortal thoughts of the world's great are preserved, not in sealed urns or moldy vaults, but spread open before us.

Let us pause a moment to give a tribute to the librarian, the high priest in this temple of knowledge. His is an altruistic calling, his highest ambition is to serve; his greatest reward, the opportunity for greater service. Even a physician accepts money from those whose sufferings he relieves, but the librarian is quick to serve all who come and never receives more than a thankful smile from those who profit by his helpful attention. Few even of those who use public libraries realize how much the librarian does to aid his customers and how willing he is to do it.

LIBRARIES AS TREASURE HOUSES

In earlier chapters the utter dependence of industry on scientific information and technical know-how has been stressed. This vast accumulation of knowledge, each bit of which represents the thinking and experimenting of some individual, is stored in our libraries, like water in a reservoir, to be drawn upon freely by all who can use it. Unlike water, the same information can be stored in many reservoirs and is increased, rather than decreased, by being used.

We customarily think of the value of the books in a library in terms of their purchase price. The five dollars paid for a book goes for the paper and printing, with possibly a few nickels to the author. If for each of the four million volumes in the main New York Public Library, the author's time is valued at a thousand dollars, the total cost comes to four billion dollars. This takes into account only the time required for writing down the information, which may be only a small fraction of that needed to obtain it. It may take only a few months to write a book on archaeology which may narrate the results of years of digging. As an example, I will mention my own five-volume work on the *Organic Chemistry of Bivalent Sulfur,* the third volume of which appeared in 1960. I have spent a large fraction of my time on this over a period of some thirty years, and for assistance I have paid out a large amount of my own money in addition to that received from several liberal grants. This is what it has cost to make a brief summary of 20,000 articles and patents; how shall we value the labor required of thousands of authors to produce the vast amount of information contained in the volumes of a library?

VARIETIES OF LIBRARIES

Actual libraries are of various kinds, some general and some special, each designed to serve a particular class of users. Every city boasts a public library devoted to stimulating the desire for learning in the general public. Some libraries even use radio time to advertise their free services. While such libraries must serve the general public, many of them are devoting considerable attention to building up collections of technical books and journals. Only a few examples can be mentioned.

THE NEW YORK PUBLIC LIBRARY

This great library, located on Fifth Avenue at Fortieth Street, is notable for its service to science. It has a large section with spacious working tables and long shelves filled with technical books and journals, and a section similarly equipped for pure science. Currently it receives 3000 technical and scientific journals. I have spent many profitable hours in these reading rooms, jostled by astrologers concocting fake horoscopes for the superstitious.

Next to the Patent Office in Washington, it is the best place for patent searching. It contains complete files of United States, British, German, French, Belgian, Swiss, Swedish, and Danish patents.

CHEMISTS' CLUB LIBRARY

The Chemists' Club Library is located in the Chemists' Club Building, at 52 East 41st Street, New York City. As its name and location indicate, it gives preferential treatment to members of the Club, but its services are available to all who need them. In a recent year, of over 13,000 users, only 17% were club members. I have enjoyed its hospitality.

Currently it receives 300 journals. It is the official repository of a number of technical organizations and contains much technical material not generally available. It has collected many old chemical books reaching back into alchemy. A specialty is a collection of thousands of biographical sketches and thousands of portraits of chemists and other scientists.

THE KRESGE-HOOKER SCIENCE LIBRARY

The Kresge-Hooker Science Library, located at Wayne State University, Detroit, Michigan, is the fulfillment of a dream of the late Neil E. Gordon to promote research. The nucleus of the library is the extensive private collection of old journals of Mr. Hooker, founder of the Hooker Electrochemical Company. It is predominantly chemical, though allied sciences are also included. Its aim is to make available the contents of a wide list of scientific journals to all who need information. It now receives about 1500 current periodicals and has on its shelves about 55,000 volumes of bound periodicals, and about 50,000 books.

All of these libraries maintain complete photostat and bibliofilm services and also translating and abstracting services.

UNIVERSITY LIBRARIES

When the Johns Hopkins University introduced in the United States the Ph.D. degree based on research, an adequate chemical library became a necessity. An excellent collection of journals was gotten together. Prior to World War I, only a few universities in the United States gave the doctor's degree in chemistry and had the necessary libraries. The lack of adequate library facilities limited research in less-favored institutions. For many, the acquisition of adequate journals and technical books was a painfully slow process.

In universities, the chemistry library is usually located in the laboratory for the convenience of teachers and students. Such libraries begin with the publications of the American Chemical Society and add those of the German, British, French, and other chemical societies, and other journals as funds permit. *Beilstein* and other compendiums follow. Then come books. Journals and books on the applications of chemistry take second place.

INDUSTRIAL LIBRARIES

Libraries in industrial establishments vary in size, from a shelf of books and one or two trade journals to a library with thousands of volumes and with professional librarians.

A notable example is the Lavoisier Library at the Du Pont Experimental Station in Wilmington. Its name comes from the fact that the founder of the Company studied chemistry with Lavoisier. It contains 45,000 volumes, large collections of trade literature and Government bulletins and receives 900 periodicals. It has a collection of over 500,000 patents, mostly chemical.

The particular kind of research to be done in an industrial firm determines the selection of journals and books. Emphasis is put on the applications of chemistry to the particular manufacturing processes in which the corporation is engaged.

The library must serve all who are in need of technical information. Since the development of a manufacturing process for a new product involves engineering and machinery, trade journals and machinery catalogs must be at hand.

The location of the laboratory has much to do with the contents of the library. If journals that are used only occasionally can be consulted in a nearby library, it is not necessary to purchase them. As the library is limited in funds and space, the aim must be to provide the best service to those members of the corporation who need it.

An important function of some governmental libraries is the handling of private information to which only certain people have access. At the Army Chemical Center at Edgewood, Maryland, where I have been consultant for forty years, there are stored reports from chemical warfare investigations in this and other countries which may be examined by authorized persons only. A section of the reading room is reserved for those handling "classified" documents. I have had occasion to refer to reports which I wrote during World War I. After filling out some yards of blanks, I have been cleared for the examination of secret documents.

Libraries of industrial establishments also contain collections of private information.

When a shoe manufacturer spends a million dollars in wages and other operating expenses, he must have at least a million dollars' worth of shoes, which are to be boxed up and sold. Reports are the product of a commercial research laboratory, and their value should be at least equal to their cost. The reports have to be indexed and stored so that full use may be made of the information contained in them, but only by authorized persons. In a large corporation, where the amount spent on research runs into many millions, the efficient handling of reports is a task of considerable magnitude. The only thing that can be done here is to point out the importance of handling reports so that values can be realized from them. In a later chapter emphasis is placed on the obligation of the chemist to put the full value of his research into the report.

LIBRARIES OF THE FUTURE

In consequence of the rapid expansion of research, chemical journals have grown bulkier and other publications have increased in number and size. Libraries that were half empty only a few years ago are now overflowing.

Within the last twenty-five years, the institutions featuring research have multiplied; so have industrial laboratories. This has created an insistent demand for sets of the more important chemical journals. Earlier volumes of many of the journals have become unavailable. Several early volumes of the *Journal of the American Chemical Society* have been reprinted. Some journals were printed on paper that has not stood the test of time.

For economy in cost and in storage space, journals are being photographed on bibliofilms or many pages microphotographed on a card. At some time in the future, libraries may shrink as whole sets of journals are stored in drawers only a little larger than those now used for the card catalogues. For example, I saw at the University of South Carolina a set of *Liebig's Annalen,* 554 volumes, 8 supplements and indexed, photographed, 46 pages to a card, and stored in a cabinet 33 inches wide, 17.5 deep, and 7 high. These volumes in print occupy some 43 feet of shelf space. It is estimated that microfilms take up only 5% of the space required by the printed volumes. A number of periodicals are already available on microfilms.

Experiments are underway on the recording of whole journals on magnetic tape, from which any desired section can be reproduced.

LIBRARIES UNLIMITED

All libraries are limited; in the case of great ones, such as those mentioned previously, the limits are wide, while in the lesser, they are narrow. There is nowhere in the world in any one place a collection of all the books and journals that have ever been published. However, modern library service is so well organized and so efficient that the total resources of the greatest libraries may be called upon to supplement those of the smallest. By international cooperation, it is possible to obtain a microfilm of practically any article or book that can be located. Many of the larger libraries maintain photostat and microfilm services, and the more important ones translating and abstracting services in addition.

THE MOUNTAIN COMES TO MOHAMMED

Mohammed lived long before research had perfected modern means of communication and transportation; he had to go to the mountain. Much has been said about the treasures of information that repose on the shelves of a great library, but what good is a library in New York to a researcher a thousand miles away? How can a traveler on the burning sands of the Sahara quench his thirst from Silver Springs, Florida, where a whole river of sparkling water wells from the ground? After being at Johns Hopkins for four years, 1894 to 1898, where I worked only a few steps from a library well stocked with journals, I taught for ten years at institutions where the only chemistry books and journals were those I purchased out of my own pocket. One summer I went back to Baltimore, three summers to Chicago, and one to Cambridge, Massachusetts in order to have access to libraries. However, what I read in the summer did not answer questions that came up during the rest of the year.

Now things are different; the library comes to the lone researcher, wherever he may be. He waves a magic wand and presto, a volume hops from the shelf in a distant library and opens at the desired page when it is wafted to him. Actually, the wand is a fountain pen with which he writes an order. What comes to him is not the volume itself but a photostat or a bibliofilm of the desired article.

From time to time *Chemical Abstracts* publishes a list of the journals which it abstracts. The next is due in 1961. In the front of this is a list of some prominent libraries, each with a number. Those that have microfilm or photostat service are specially indicated. After the name of each journal in the list, there are numbers designating the libraries which receive that journal. From this, one can locate one or more sources of the desired material. Thus, the isolated chemist is able to obtain needed information. Even whole books may be filmed.

FINDING BOOKS

So much emphasis is put on journals as primary sources of information that books, which are also important to chemists, are apt to be overlooked. Finding journals gives little trouble; they are all together in one section of the library, and *Berichte* follows *Annalen*. With books it is quite a different story. In a large library there may be thousands of books. To a thoughtful person it is obvious that finding a book must go before reading it. Of what use are the treasures in a library if you cannot find them? Skill in the use of the library is essential if one is to get the desired information and get it quickly. Most academic and industrial libraries are "open shelf," which means that the reader is free to wander among the stacks and take down any book in which he may be interested and carry it over to the reading table to examine it. The reader should be able to do this without the help of the librarian. In modern libraries, subjects are given numerical designations, and the books are placed on the shelves in accordance with these numbers.

Suppose the reader wants to find a book on naphthalene; he will look in the classification guide and find that this is in QD 391 and will locate that section in the stacks. He may have in mind a book on naphthalene by a certain author; he will find it there, that is, if it is in the library. Usually the interest is not in a particular book but in finding as many books as possible on the subject. All of these will be found in the one location. As the library grows, they will be moved on down the line, possibly to another stack, but that causes no trouble, as the numerical sequence remains the same. With a little study of the system and some practice in using it, the reader can locate quickly any book in the library.

In some libraries the reader must order books from

the card catalog and have them brought to the reading room. The success of this plan depends on the thoroughness with which the cataloging has been done, and on an intelligent use of the catalog with a thorough understanding of its construction, what it contains and what it does not. Even in "open-shelf" libraries, the use of the catalog can save time. If the name of the author or the title of the book is known, reference to the catalog will tell whether or not it is in the library, and its exact location if it is there. The searcher who is interested not so much in a particular book as he is in a topic will find in this location other books pertaining to it. He will make a list of these and proceed to obtain them. It is advisable to look under a number of headings which may suggest themselves as related and under which books may be found bearing on the main topic. The cataloging in various libraries differs much in the thoroughness of cross indexing. There is a minimum of two cards to a book, an author and a title, or subject, card. There may be a large number of subject cards bringing out the various topics and subtopics treated. In some cases even journal articles are indexed. The more headings under which a book is cataloged the more apt it is to be found, but if there is only one card for it, this is more likely to be located if one looks under all possible headings. The process is much the same as looking for an article in an abstract journal, and what is said about this in a later chapter applies here as well.

The main card catalog usually contains author, title, and subject cards arranged as in a dictionary. There is usually also a shelf list in which the cards are in the same sequence as the books in the library. As the books are grouped according to subject matter, the cards are similarly placed in the shelf list, and if one book on distillation is located, others on the same topic will be found on adjacent cards. Fingering the cards on the shelf list is like looking along the rows of books. This list is not always available to the reader. Some libraries have a separate author catalog.

CALL NUMBERS

In all cases the location of the book is indicated by certain markings in the corner of the card. These look enigmatical at first, but become clear by a little study. They are known as the "call numbers" since they are used in asking for a book and are all that is needed to find it. To use these important call numbers, one must understand the classification of books in modern libraries. It is also helpful to have this knowledge if one has access to the books on the shelves, since by knowing the system, one can locate the class of books one wishes by following along the call numbers, which are commonly more conspicuous than the titles. It is a common mistake to associate books with a particular section of a shelf. It must be remembered that the numbers show relative locations, i.e., relative to other books, not to library furniture. New books take their proper places in the line and do not go to the end like late arrivals at the ticket seller's window.

The two systems of classification used in American libraries are sketched here.

SYSTEMS OF LIBRARY CLASSIFICATION

Two commonly used systems of classification, or rather of designating the classification, are the Dewey, or decimal system, in which the classes are given numbers, and the Library of Congress, or the Cutter system, in which combinations of letters and figures are used. With both we may have more or less minute subdivisions according to the size and purposes of the library and the ideas of the librarian. A subject in which a particular library specializes and on which it contains a large number of books may be minutely subdivided, while books in some other line may be bunched under some broad division. The arrangement of books within the classes or subclasses is much the same. One must locate the class and then find the individual book, which is much like finding the desired street and then a given number on that street.

The more elaborate Library of Congress system is used by the more important special libraries, but the decimal system will be considered first, since its description is simpler and serves well as an introduction to the other.

The Decimal System

The Dewey decimal classification makes use of numbers to divide recorded knowledge into ten great classes 0 to 9. Each class is further subdivided into ten secondary classes and these into ten subclasses. Decimals are added to indicate the specific subdivision of each subject and this decimal division may be carried to any necessary extent. For example, 5 is natural science, 510 mathematics, 530 physics, 540 chemistry, and so on. Within each subject you have a range of ten numbers (e.g., 540 to 549) where you proceed from the general to the specific.

All the books in a class are arranged according to the first letters of the author's surname. If this begins with a consonant, only the one letter is used, but if the initial is a vowel, a second letter is added. The numbers following the initial usually show the order in which the books bearing the same initial were acquired in the library. Thus a book on agricultural chemistry might be 630.16 S 1 if it were written by Smith; if another book on this subject by Saunders is acquired, it will be 630.16 S 2, and so on.

Library of Congress or Cutter System

In this system the general classes of knowledge are designated by letters, Q denoting science—is it because scientists are always asking questions?—the several sciences being differentiated by the addition of a second letter. Thus QA is mathematics, QB astronomy, QC physics, and QD chemistry. T represents technology and TP chemical technology. Agricultural Chemistry is found in class S, agriculture; pharmaceutical chemistry in class R, medicine; and mineral industries, including metallurgy, etc., in TN. Each of these may be divided into 999 classes by the addition of figures. The lower numbers are always reserved for periodicals, collections, series, histories of the subject, subject encyclopedias and dictionaries, and other general items. Higher numbers indicate the various aspects of the subject, even the most minute. Having determined the proper number for a given item insofar as subject matter is concerned, a further letter and number are added so that this book may stand in its proper order, usually alphabetically by author or entry, with other books on the same subject. The number in this case is coded to the initial letters of the entry and is a *decimal* number. This enables the librarian to assign an almost infinite number of volumes to the same subject number, each fitted to its proper location, without disturbing the already existing books. The completed combination of letters and numbers is known as the call number and is the key to the shelving and future location for use of every book. Multivolume sets and runs of journals are assigned the same call number, differentiated one from another by the volume number within each set.

15. Use of chemical literature

THE USE OF BOOKS

In the use of each of his five senses, man is excelled by many of the beasts of the field; his powers of observation and ability to profit by experience are shared to a considerable extent by the higher animals; but man is able to transmit information so that one begins where the last left off. Every monkey has to start his investigations just where his father did, and there is little, if any, advance of technology in monkeydom. The total that a monkey can know is what one monkey can discover, but a man may know all that others have found out and written down, plus what he adds.

The science of chemistry is the orderly arrangements of the facts accumulated by the toil of thousands of chemists. If one were to live more years than Methuselah and work more hours a day than Edison, one could discover for oneself

239

only a small fraction of what has been found out by the hosts of those who have labored in chemistry for generations.

In the fourth decennial author index of *Chemical Abstracts* (1937 to 1946), there are names of about 260,000 who have contributed to the progress of chemistry during those ten years, so that on the average, each one is to be credited with 0.0004% of the advances made. From this it is obvious that if a chemist knows only as much as he learned through his own experimenting, he is acquainted with only a minute fraction of 1% of current chemistry, not to mention the vast accumulation of knowledge left by past generations of chemists.

The man who does not avail himself of books puts himself on a plane with the monkey who has to learn by his own experiments how to crack a coconut. If we are to add to human knowledge, we must know exactly how far that knowledge has gone, at least at the point where we are to do the adding; we must find the end of a rope before we can splice a piece onto it.

Hardly anything more humiliating can happen to a chemist than to publish his research and then to have someone step forward and point out that the work had been done previously and had been published in some journal that the chemist should have consulted. In industry, it would be a waste to spend thousands of dollars on experiments to find out facts which had been discovered, stored, and cataloged long before in the library and which might have been learned by an intelligent search.

There is nothing more pitiable than the spectacle of an enthusiast, fancying himself a pioneer, laboriously digging in ground already explored, exhausted, and abandoned by others. My friend Clarence King told me once how he set his heart on the ascent of a certain high peak in the Sierras. With infinite exertion, and no little peril, he scaled the precipitous mountainside, and reached at last the summit, only to find there an empty tomato can and a copy of a newspaper, relics left there by a picnic party, which had ascended by an easy trail on the other side of the mountain. A little preliminary research would have saved him from this scientific fiasco.

Your isolated and concentrated scientist must know what has gone before, or he will waste his life in doing what has already been done, or in repeating past failures. He must know something about what his contemporaries are trying to do, or he will waste his life in duplicating effort. The history of science is so vast and contemporary effort is so active that if he undertakes to acquire this knowledge by himself alone, his life is largely wasted in doing that; his initiative and creative power are gone before he is ready to use them.[1]

There are other important benefits to be derived from an acquaintance with the literature, as has been pointed out by Crane, Patterson, and Marr:[2]

The literature is not solely a storehouse of facts. It is a source of inspiration if it is gone at in the friendly and appreciative spirit which real acquaintance brings into existence. It supples new ideas, new viewpoints, and a broader vision. The literature of science as a whole merits the friendly attitude. Most of it is the product of earnest research men. Great men have usually found time to write. Familiarity with the literature of one's subject, particularly the older literature, is the only possible way of acquiring the proper historical perspective.

NEED OF LIBRARY TRAINING

Liebig is credited with the introduction of the laboratory method of teaching chemistry which has spread all over the world and given a tremendous impetus to our science. Good laboratory instruction became prevalent early in this century, but need of training in the use of chemical literature received tardy recognition. In my book: *Introduction to Organic Research,* published in 1924, this need was emphasized. At that time training in the use of chemical literature was rare; now it is commonly included in chemical curricula.

Even now the average chemist is much more capable in the laboratory than in the library. The student needs to be trained in both, for it is no more to be expected that a student will acquire good library technique without instruction than that he will become a skilful analyst without guidance. We are

---

[1] R. W. Raymond, *J. Ind. Eng. Chem.,* **7,** 331 (1915).
[2] E. J. Crane, A. M. Patterson, and E. B. Marr, *A Guide to the Literature of Chemistry,* 2nd Ed., New York, John Wiley and Sons, 1957.

born neither with laboratory dexterity nor with library facility: both have to be acquired. It is true that an individual may attain to either untaught and unaided by others, but schools exist for the purpose of shortening the toilsome road of self-instruction.

To be a chemist one must be capable of doing accurate and reliable work in the laboratory and must also be adept in searching the literature. No one wishes to employ a pseudo-chemist who bungles along in the laboratory and takes several times as long to complete a determination as he should and is then not certain of the result; nor is one wanted who wastes time in inconclusive literature searches.

THE NEED OF FOREIGN LANGUAGES

Chemical investigation is carried on all over the world and is, therefore, published in many languages, but in the early days of science, England, France, and Germany took the lead in investigation and particularly in the founding of journals for the publication of research. In addition to this, the wide dissemination of the languages of these countries aided them in coming to be recognized as the languages of science. If anything is published in one of these languages, it is regarded as published to the world and everyone is held responsible for knowing it. This distinction is partly shared by Italian and Russian. A considerable amount of chemical research is published in Italian, and it is desirable to be able to read this language. However, with a knowledge of Latin and French, and with the aid of a dictionary, one can get the substance of an occasional Italian article. Within recent years, Russian has risen to second place with 16% of chemical publications. A reading knowledge of Russian is desirable, and many chemists have taken up its study. The situation is eased by the fact that a number of journals and many articles are available in English translation. Russian publications are discussed in chapter 17.

Over half of the chemical articles of the world are published in English. In view of this fact, many chemists have relaxed their study of foreign languages, depending on *Chemical Abstracts* for what they cannot get in English. This is unwise, as it puts them at a disadvantage in competition with better linguists.

At the time I was a graduate student (1894 to 1898), about 75% of the articles that I had to read were in German. I found that a good reading knowledge of German, which I was fortunate in having, enabled me to get along easier than some who had had more chemistry but had to stumble along with a dictionary.

To succeed as a chemist one needs English, German, and French at least, and to make any speed in searching chemical literature, one must handle these three languages with facility. An extremely small proportion of what is published in one of these three languages is ever translated into the others. If one wants the information, one must go and get it in the original publication.

LEARNING FOREIGN LANGUAGES

The young chemist is sometimes appalled when he is told that he will have to acquire facility in German and French. It simply must be done. It can be done and it is not as serious a task as it appears at first sight, since one must needs only read these languages, which is quite a different thing from having to speak or write them. Furthermore, scientific articles are usually written in simple, direct style and they are comparatively easy to understand. The fact that many scientific terms appear in various languages with little change in form is of great assistance to the beginner.

To acquire the desired reading knowledge of one of these languages, it is best to start with a short course in the rudiments of grammar, but one can get on with a comparatively limited amount of this, as the subjunctive mood, future perfect tense, and other complexities are rare in scientific writing. Irregular verbs give little trouble, as one rarely meets any of their parts except third person singular and plural, present and past tenses. Of course a thorough knowledge of French and German grammar and an acquaintance with the masterpieces of poetry, drama, and fiction are desirable attainments, but these are not necessary for the chemist whose task is to extract a number of facts from a straightforward scientific article.

Given a modicum of grammar, facility in reading is to be acquired by extensive reading, and the more extensive the better. It is best to lay aside the dictionary and read rapidly without translating. At first one gets only a glimmer of an idea now and then, and may read a page without finding what it is all about, but as one reads and reads one gets more and more of the meaning; strange words look less strange and their meaning is guessed from the context. Words learned in this way stick better than those gotten from the dictionary, though it is always safe to verify guessed-at meanings by reference to the dictionary. It is advantageous to start with German or French articles on subjects with which we are familiar. Thus it is easy to get the meaning of an article on benzoic acid, since we know in advance approximately what the author should say about it. All organic chemists have to look up items in *Beilstein*. There is little difficulty in doing this, since the formulae and figures help tell the story.

Early in the process, one must quit translating into English and must go directly from the foreign word to the object or action which it represents. As the eyes read the French or German the mind should be filled with the images suggested and not be cluttered up with English words. To translate, one must change the order of French nouns and adjectives and must go to the end of a long German sentence to pick up the verb; one must get the meaning of the sentence and then search for English words to express that meaning. Supposing that the reader knows all of the words, it takes about three times as long to translate it as it does to get the meaning directly. The chemist has thousands of pages to search through and cannot afford the extra time required by translating. Much assistance may be obtained from several books that have been written to aid the student in acquiring the necessary knowledge of French and German.[3]

---

[3] George E. Condoyannis, *Scientific German*, New York, Wiley, 1957.

Hans Eichner and Hans Hein, *Reading German for Scientists*, New York, Wiley, 1959.

One must learn to skim in foreign languages as well as in English. It frequently happens that only a few paragraphs, or perhaps only a sentence or two, in a long article are pertinent to the particular object of the search. Two things are required: 1. rapidity in skimming through what does not concern the matter in hand and 2. certainty in spotting the things that may be of service. Much time is wasted if we read every word of a fifty-page article to find a single fact, but it is disastrous if there are two facts in the article that are of great importance to us and we miss one of them.

CAUTION IN READING

The reader must be cautioned against accepting as accurate every statement simply because it is printed in a book. Sometimes errors are copied from one book into another. This is not to suggest dishonesty, but rather to point out that all of us are fallible. Articles published many years ago have to be read in the light of theories then current. I have been impressed with the inaccuracies in physical data in compiling property tables for my book: *Organic Chemistry of Bivalent Sulfur*.

H. H. Neville and W. E. Yuill, *Translation from German for Chemists*, New York, Interscience, 1959.

Austin M. Patterson, *A German-English Dictionary for Chemists*, 3rd Edition, New York, Wiley, 1950.

William N. Locke, *Scientific French*, New York, Wiley, 1957.

Austin M. Patterson, *A French-English Dictionary for Chemists*, 2nd Edition, New York, Wiley, 1954.

16. Primary publications

INTRODUCTION

Primary publications are those in which new information is given to the public for the first time. Of these, journals occupy first place. Along with them must be put dissertations.

Patents rival journals as sources of information, whose newness is certified and whose importance is claimed.

In addition to these, new information is frequently found, mixed with old, in books and bulletins.

CHEMICAL JOURNALS

Most of the results of investigations appear as articles in the journals, some of which contain nothing else, while others have editorials, reports of meetings, and other material. It is possible to get the bulk of what has been found out about any subject from the journals, but books may be of great assistance

247

as summaries and particularly as guides to the journals. The student should learn to make the best possible use of both.

By reading the journals, the student sees science in the making and observes how one fact is added to another as bricks are laid in a wall, though in science the structure is never finished nor does it grow according to blueprints previously prepared.

The current journals keep us abreast of the chemical thought of the time, of the latest discoveries in the laboratories, and of the newest developments in plant processes. The chemist who does not read them is like a blind man at the movies. The student should cultivate the habit of reading them. Of course he cannot read all of the journals that are published even if he has access to them, but he can browse through several, at least reading the articles which appeal to him most. It is advantageous for a chemist to join the chemical society of his own country as early as possible in his career, for then its journals come to his own study table where they are constantly in his sight so that he can pick them up a few minutes at a time each day. To be sure the research chemist spends a large part of his time searching the literature for things that bear directly on his own problem and necessarily so, but he cannot afford so to narrow himself as to see only one small segment of chemistry. The man of one idea has not a whole idea, for his one idea is incomplete without its relations to other ideas: The zenith is related to the whole horizon. One must read broadly of many things in order to think deeply on one. The research chemist must read everything about his own field but cannot afford to neglect the rest of chemical literature. It is remarkable how much light is thrown on a problem from distant sources: One can hardly read a piece of investigation of any sort without finding something that suggests an idea about one's own problem.

By reading the old journals, we come in contact with the masters of experimentation and of reasoning who have gone before. Their results may have been superseded by more modern observations, but they have laid the foundations of the science of today and they have much to teach us as to methods of thinking and working. The young artist spends much of his time copying the productions of the painters of centuries ago or of sculptors of ancient Greece, so the young chemist must study the masterpieces of investigation for inspiration and guidance. In the old journals, we have the works of these ancient worthies told in their own words, and in the reading of them there is great reward.

KINDS OF JOURNALS

There are many kinds of chemical journals, some containing only records of investigations in pure science, others being filled chiefly with trade news and touching upon investigations only in so far as they have a practical bearing. There are journals that devote themselves exclusively to chemistry and there are others which include several sciencies. Journals of physics, geology, and other sciences frequently publish articles of more or less interest to chemists.

The young chemist should get acquainted with the chief journals in pure and applied chemistry. He should know how they are arranged and indexed.

For a thorough discussion of journals, their character and content, reference should be made to Crane, Patterson, and Marr.[1] They give a list of some 700 important journals with some information about each.

Reference should also be made to Melon's book on chemical literature.[2]

PUBLICATIONS OF SOCIETIES

The most important journals are those published by the chemical societies of the various countries. A large membership enables a society to publish a bulky journal at moderate cost to the individual member. Many independent journals have been merged into the society organs or their publication taken over by the societies.

---

[1] E. J. Crane, A. M. Patterson, and E. B. Marr, *A Guide to the Literature of Chemistry,* 2nd Ed., New York, John Wiley & Sons, 1957, pp. 64-157.

[2] M. G. Melon, *Chemical Publications—Their Nature and Use,* 3rd Edition, New York, McGraw-Hill, 1958.

The publication of journals is usually the chief function of societies, though the organization and growth of the great national societies have aided greatly in the diffusion of scientific knowledge and the general betterment of the position of the chemical profession. Self-interest and loyalty to the science should impel every chemist to join at least one chemical society. Patriotism and the possibility of attending meetings make it natural to begin with the national society of one's own country. Societies representing some application of chemistry make a strong appeal to those engaged in that particular line, as the meetings afford contact with others having kindred interests, and the publications contain information bearing directly on their daily problems. The general society with its broader outlook and more varied contacts should come first, and the specialized society should follow closely. Membership in one or more foreign societies also is valuable.

The United States boasts the largest chemical society in the world and, what is more surprising, claims the first two devoted to chemistry exclusively, the Chemical Society of Philadelphia founded by James Woodhouse in 1792 and continuing seventeen years, and the Columbian Chemical Society started in the same city in 1811 under the patronage of Thomas Jefferson. These societies, however, left no footprints on the sands of chemical time, since they published no journals.

The importance of the societies in bringing in the era of modern science as well as many interesting facts about society journals and about other chemical publications may be gathered from a presidential address by Professor Noyes[3] from which the following paragraphs are quoted:

> Through the middle ages and at their close, the alchemists and iatrochemists had no journals or organized methods of publication. Their researches, if we can dignify their random experiments by such a name, were published in books, usually in the Latin language. Many of the alchemists used mystical symbols and expressions and some of their writings were designed rather to conceal than to reveal their knowledge—an art which has not been altogether lost in the writing of German and sometimes of other patents.

[3] W. A. Noyes, *J. Amer. Chem. Soc.* **42**, 2099 (1920).

It is very significant and interesting for us as a Society to recall that the beginning of a different and better form of publication had its origin in the organization of national societies, about the middle of the seventeenth century. Between 1650 and 1670 such societies were begun in London, Vienna, Florence, and Paris. The Royal Society, which grew from the union of small scientific societies in Oxford and London has been, perhaps, the most effective of the group, in its influence on the growth of science. The meeting of small groups of kindred spirits in these societies gave an opportunity for the announcement of new results and for the exchange of ideas on scientific topics which was most useful, not only in the dissemination of new knowledge, but perhaps still more in that growth of ideas which comes from the action of keen minds on each other. We miss something of this very valuable side of society life in the large meetings of the present time. It is better represented, now, by the discussions among small groups in our laboratories.

The publication of the *Philosophical Transactions of the Royal Society,* begun in 1665, represents a new function of the Society which became of vastly greater importance than the scientific meetings. It would be difficult to overestimate the value of those *Transactions* in their effect on the growth of science. In their pages is to be found the first notice of the microscopic organisms which we now call bacteria. There, too, we find an account of the epoch-making discoveries of Davy and of Faraday and of others who did some of the fundamental work of the nineteenth century.

The publication of the *Comptes rendus* in France was begun in 1776, the year of our American Independence. Like *Transactions of the Royal Society,* it publishes articles in many different lines of science. In other respects the policies of the two journals are very radically different. The Royal Society aims to publish papers which are the finished product, frequently of years of work, and publication has often been long delayed. Publication in the *Comptes rendus* is prompt, but the papers are very brief and frequently lack details which are essential to make them useful. Both kinds of publication are desirable, but for the permanent growth of our science and for the future, publication of the form used in the *Transactions* is much more valuable.

As far as I can learn, the first journal devoted to chemistry apart from other sciences was Crell's *Chemische Annalen,* which began as the *Chemisches Journal* in 1778. The oldest chemical journal which has had a continuous existence is the *Annales de chimie,* which was begun in 1789, the year of the French Revolution, by de Morveau, Lavoisier, Berthollet, de Fourcroy, and four others, less well known. The subtitle of the journal was "Recueil de memoires concernant de chimie et les arts qui en dependent." In the introduction, the value of chemistry for the arts is emphasized, also the purpose of making new work in chemistry, wherever undertaken, available to all. Another object was, undoubtedly, to give untrammelled expression to the new ideas advocated by Lavoisier at a time when the *Journal de physique* was still controlled by adherents of the "phlogiston" theory. This journal must have been one of the factors which made Paris a chief center for the development of chemistry for fifty years following. Four volumes were published the first year, at 12 francs each. Volume 18 was published in July 1793, and we find in it some signatures on blue paper, a reflection, doubtless, of the troublous times when it was printed, for that was the beginning of The Terror. After that there is a hiatus for four years and Volume 19 appeared in 1797 "Par les Citoyens Guyton, Monge, Berthollet, etc." We miss the name of Lavoisier, who was executed in 1794. In resuming publication, the editors explain the interruption by saying that it was because of the necessity of busying themselves with the defense of the Republic, the events of the Revolution, and the public occupations and functions of the authors. In 1816, the second series of the journal was commenced under the name *Annales de chimie et de physique*. The ninth series began in 1914, once more under the original name *Annales de chimie*. The other part of the ninth series is published as *Annales de physique*.

A second journal of very great importance was founded in 1832 under the name *Annalen der Pharmacie*. The editors were Brandes, Lorenz, Geiger, and Liebig. Volume 25, published in 1838, bears the names of Dumas of Paris, Graham of London, and Liebig, evidently an attempt to make the journal international. Apparently this did not prove successful, for with volume 41, four years later, we find only the names of Wöhler and Liebig. In 1840 the name was changed from *Annalen der Pharmacie* to *Annalen der Chemie und Pharmacie,* and this name continued till the death of Liebig in 1873. In 1874 we find the name which is still retained, Justus Liebig's *Annalen der Chemie*. Through the middle of the nineteenth century the *Annalen* was doubtless more valuable than any other journal for the development of chemistry. It remains one of our most valuable journals, but its relative value has decreased for three reasons —the growth of the journals of national societies, the estab-

lishment of special journals for various fields, and the fact
that it has become exclusively a journal of organic chemistry.

Silliman's Journal, which later became the *American Journal of Science,* was organized in 1818. This has published some chemical articles throughout its history, but
when Professor Remsen and others began the intensive study
of organic chemistry in the seventies, they did not find that
journal a very suitable medium of publication. This led to
the establishment of the *American Chemical Journal* in 1879.
For the following thirty years that journal contributed
much toward the development of chemistry in America and
to the recognition of the work of American chemists abroad.
During that period, it was more often quoted than any
other American journal. In 1913, we had the good fortune
to incorporate it in our own *Journal.*

Just as it was in England that the first scientific
journal, the *Philosophical Transactions,* appeared, so it was
in England, again, that the first representative of the group
of journals which has become the most important of all, was
published. The *Quarterly Journal* of the Chemical Society
of London began in 1847. (The Chemical Society had published previously, however, the '*Memoirs and Proceedings,*'
Volumes I to III, 1841-43, 1843-5, 1845-7, containing original
papers and some abstracts.) It was followed by the *Bulletin
de la Société chimique de Paris* in 1864, the *Berichte der
deutschen chemischen Gesellschaft* in 1868, the *Gazzetta
chimica italiana* in 1871, and our own *Journal of the American Chemical Society* in 1876. These journals fulfill, more
nearly than any others, the function of the older volumes
of the *Annalen* in furnishing their readers with an account
of researches from all fields of chemistry. I believe we are
justified in thinking our own *Journal* performs this function
more fully than any other journal published at the present
time. In these days of intense specialization, it is very important for us to retain some knowledge of fields remote from
our own. President Remsen once told me that in his student
days he read the older volumes of the *Annalen* till he was
familiar, in a general way, with all of the important researches recorded in them. Even as late as the eighties, we
heard of chemists who read the *Berichte* from cover to cover,
and I am sure that some of those who did so gained a breadth
of view that is too rare today. I should consider it a very
great misfortune, especially for our younger men, if there
were any important branch of chemistry which was not occasionally represented by papers in our *Journal.*

An interesting account of the difficulties encountered by the *Journal of the American Chemical Society* in its
early years and of its later phenomenal growth was given by
Dr. Lamb[4] in his address on the reception of the Nichols Medal.
He was editor of the Journal from 1918 through 1949 and must
be given much credit for its development.

The following authoritative account of the development of the publication program of the American Chemical
Society was written at my request by Dr. Alden H. Emery, Secretary of the Society.

The chemical profession is fortunate. In no other
scientific field is the literature so extensive or so well organized. A large share of the credit for this situation belongs to
the American Chemical Society whose comprehensive and
voluminous publishing program is second to none in the
world.

As one looks at the list of current periodicals, it is
difficult to realize that all but two can trace their ancestry
directly to the 132 pages published in two numbers of the
"Proceedings" in 1876. Today we have JOURNAL OF THE
AMERICAN CHEMICAL SOCIETY, CHEMICAL ABSTRACTS, INDUSTRIAL
AND ENGINEERING CHEMISTRY, ANALYTICAL CHEMISTRY, JOUR-
NAL OF ORGANIC CHEMISTRY, JOURNAL OF PHYSICAL CHEMISTRY,
JOURNAL OF AGRICULTURAL AND FOOD CHEMISTRY, JOURNAL OF
CHEMICAL AND ENGINEERING DATA, AND CHEMICAL AND EN-
GINEERING NEWS. In 1959, they published a total of nearly
38,000 editorial pages.

The development of this publication program may
be considered as indicative of the growth of chemical research
and technology in this country. The *Proceedings of the American Chemical Society* became *Journal of the American
Chemical Society* in 1879. Abstracts of the chemical literature
were first published in *Journal of the American Chemical
Society* in 1902. By 1907 the concept of abstracting and indexing the chemical literature of the world had been approved,
and *Chemical Abstracts* was started. Meanwhile applied
chemistry had come of age and was demanding a publication outlet suitable to its needs in place of inclusion in
Journal of the American Chemical Society. The result was
Industrial and Engineering Chemistry, first published in
1908. By 1923, the *American Chemical Society* had become
of sufficient size and diversity so that it generated news as

⁴ A. B. Lamb, *Chem. Eng. News* **21**, 365 (1943).

distinct from purely scientific papers and items. Consequently *The News Edition* (of *Industrial and Engineering Chemistry*) was made a separate entity. In 1929, a further diversification appeared desirable and *The Analytical Edition* of *Industrial and Engineering Chemistry* came into being. In 1940, *The News Edition* was made an independent publication; in 1942, it adopted its present name *Chemical and Engineering News;* and in 1947, it became a weekly.

Meanwhile analytical chemistry continued to grow and diversify with the result that *The Analytical Edition,* renamed *Analytical Chemistry,* started its independent career in 1948. Last in this group, and illustrative of the rapidly growing importance of chemistry in the field, is *Journal of Agricultural and Food Chemistry,* first issued in 1953.

The JOURNAL OF CHEMICAL AND ENGINEERING DATA began publication in 1959, succeeding an experimental CHEMICAL AND ENGINEERING DATA SERIES produced by the editors of the applied journals. In 1960, INDUSTRIAL AND ENGINEERING CHEMISTRY was issued in two separate editions—Domestic and International—further to expand its services.

During this period, areas of specialization developed in "pure" chemistry almost as extensively as in the applied areas. The *Journal of the American Chemical Society* continued publication as a "horizontal" journal covering physical, inorganic, organic, and biological chemistry. This has been done partly because of the overlapping nature of these areas and, partly, in order that readers, through one journal, may keep in touch with important developments in all fields of fundamental chemistry.

The two journals which do not stem from the *Proceedings, Journal of Physical Chemistry* and *Journal of Organic Chemistry,* have made possible a more comprehensive coverage of these fields than would have been possible with *Journal of the American Chemical Society* alone. They illustrate one phase of ACS publication policy, namely, that of meeting expanding publication needs as rapidly as feasible. In line with this policy, the appearance of other journals can be expected.

Serving a different area from those publications named, the Society launched in January 1960 a JOURNAL OF CHEMICAL DOCUMENTATION. To serve those who want information on new chemical developments promptly, CHEMICAL TITLES, a permuted index of titles of articles in the current literature, was offered on a subscription basis in 1960. Experimental issues were circulated in 1959.

A few high lights will serve to illustrate the magnitude of this publishing operation. In 1883, the first year for which a report is available, the total cost of *Journal of the American Chemical Society* (the only Society publication) was $373.20. In 1959, publication costs for all ACS publications were very nearly $6,500,000.

The growth of the chemical publication field as a whole has been equally amazing. In 1959, *Chemical Abstracts* published 125,395 abstracts of papers and patents. This contrasts with the 7,975 published in 1907, the date of the first volume of this noted abstract journal.

Membership growth in recent years has continued without a break and at a fairly steady rate. This was not true in earlier years as the following table shows.

Membership of the American Chemical Society

Year	Number
1880	303
1885	255
1890	238
1895	903
1900	1,715
1905	2,919
1910	5,081
1915	7,417
1920	15,582
1925	14,381
1930	18,206
1935	17,541
1940	25,414
1945	43,075
1950	63,349
1955	75,223
1959	88,806

Striking as these figures are, they have been exceeded by the growth of chemistry and chemical technology. The American Chemical Society has not yet attained its full potential in either membership or services.

The following account of the German Chemical Society and of its publications was written at my request by Dr. Rudolf Wolf, Secretary of the Society.

The end of the War and the resultant political division of Germany had the following effects on the chemical scientific societies of Germany: In the Federal Republic of Germany was founded in September 1946 the Gesellschaft deutscher Chemiker as the bearer of the tradition of the former deutsche chemische Gesellschaft (founded 1866) and of the former Verein deutscher Chemiker (founded 1886). Within the sphere of its activity it has taken over all the tasks of the two earlier organizations in fostering chemical science and investigation and the advancement of chemistry and chemists. The Gesellschaft deutscher Chemiker has over 11,000 members. Every two years, it holds meetings of chemists. In its thirty-three local sections, addresses are delivered throughout the year. Eight divisions promote special fields of chemistry, especially applied chemistry. Problems in the development of scientifically trained youths, shortening the hours of study, and other questions of vocation and standing are also a part of the activities of the Gesellschaft deutscher Chemiker.

The publication of scientific literature is a major task of Gesellschaft deutscher Chemiker. Until the end of the War, in 1945, the deutsche chemische Gesellschaft sponsored and published the following scientific literature: *Berichte der deutschen chemischen Gesellschaft, Chemisches Zentralblatt, Gmelin's Handbuch der anorganischen Chemie,* and *Beilstein's Handbuch der organischen Chemie.* The Verein deutscher Chemiker issued until the end of the War the journals: *Angewandte Chemie* and *Chemische Technik.*

In the postwar period, there have been the following developments in chemical publications: Gmelin-Institut für anorganischen Chemie und Grenzgebiete in der Max Planck Gesellschaft zur Förderung der Wissenschaften publishes *Gmelin's Handbuch der anorganischen Chemie. Beilstein's Handbuch der organischen Chemie* is published by the Beilstein Institut, a public foundation, through the Springer Verlag. The Gesellschaft deutscher Chemiker publishes the following journals: *Angewandte Chemie,* 72nd year in 1960, *Chemische Berichte,* 93rd year in 1960 (formerly *Berichte der deutschen chemischen Gesellschaft*), *Chemie-Ingenieur-Technik,* 32nd year in 1960 (published jointly by the Verein deutscher Ingenieure and DECHEMA), *Chemisches Zentralblatt,* 131st year in 1960 (published jointly by the Deutsche Akademie der Wissenschaften in Berlin, the Akademie der Wissenschaften in Göttingen, and the Chemische Gesellschaft in Deutsche Demokratische Republik and *Nachrichten aus Chemie und Technik,* Volume

8 in 1960. The divisions of the Gesellschaft deutscher Chemiker publish their own communications or have chosen the journals in their more closely related fields as their organs. *Justus Liebig's Annalen der Chemie,* Vol. 634 in 1960, is not published by the Gesellschaft deutscher Chemiker, but by Professor Richard Kuhn, Heidelberg. The journal is the property of Verlag Chemie, G.m.b.H., Weinheim (Bergstrasse).

PATENTS

In bulk and in importance, patents constitute a large segment of chemical literature. They are primary publications, and if the information contained in them has been published previously, it is because the examiner has been asleep, and examiners seldom doze during working hours. My own experience is that prior publications are seldom missed by the examiner.

The number of chemical patents listed in *Chemical Abstracts* for 1959 is about 25,000, which is about four times the number of pages in the *Journal of the American Chemical Society* for the same year.

There is no way of estimating the cost of obtaining the information disclosed in the 10,000 United States chemical patents, but it must represent a considerable part of the hundreds of millions spent on research.

Taking out a patent on the results of your research is like registering the title to property you have purchased. Patents are vital to industrial progress. You would not spend thousands building a house on a lot unless you were assured of a clear title; a corporation cannot afford to invest millions in developing a new product of which it does not have exclusive ownership.

Academic chemists cannot afford to overlook the vast amount of information contained in patents, only a small part of which is otherwise published. Many patents disclose new reactions which may be adapted to other uses, while others describe the preparation of new compounds which may be starting points for syntheses. Almost every patent may suggest something to an alert mind. Sometimes it is possible to extract from the disclosure valuable hints which are not covered by the claims. Anything not actually claimed is donated to the public.

What is said in the following paragraphs relates specifically to United States patents. As Dr. Schmitz points out,[5] the interval between time of application and time of issue in foreign countries is much shorter than in this country; in Belgium, two months, never more than six. Patent applications are published in some countries; in some, patents are issued as filed with little or no examination as to originality.

In reading any document, we should consider its nature, the purpose for which it was written, and the integrity of the writer. A patent is a contract in which the inventor conveys to the public certain information in return for the exclusive use of the same for a period of seventeen years. In a reputable store, the goods offered are genuine and the prices asked are fair. As a rule, the patents in which the leading American corporations are concerned may well be taken at face value, as being based on actual experiments and frankly disclosed. This is as it should be, but it does not have to be this way and it is not always this way. There is more than a suspicion that the only experimental work behind some patents consists in bringing a stick of graphite into intermittent contact with a sheet of cellulose. It is possible for a chemist who has a good imagination and a stout lead pencil to write up a plausible patent that will pass the Examiner. This is permitted by the rules of the game. The Examiner insists on novelty, but asks no questions as to the experiments. An experienced chemist can think up a way, or possibly several ways, for preparing a desired compound. As the date of application is important, he may write up one or more of these and send them in without waiting for experimental verification, or he may make a few test-tube experiments. If the method described proves to be good, he has a valid patent; if it does not work, he just has a patent. I secured two patents on electronic organs with no other equipment than a slide rule and a lead pencil. This was admitted in an interview with the Examiner. These patents have expired without being tried out. I am sure

[5] N. S. Schmitz, *Chem. Eng. News,* **36,** 82 (1958).

that they will work, if someone will take the trouble to test them.

At the present time research is largely done in corporation laboratories. When a chemist digs up something which appears to be important, he passes the information on to the Patent Department where the application is written up by those who know how.

The process claimed is described in such a convincing manner that it is made to appear as a great discovery, far superior to anything known previously and leaving no room for further improvement.

A patent is designed to ward off competitors, not to help them; and some have considered it high art to write the specifications so that a competitor will waste time and money getting the process to work and then find that what he has done is covered in the patent. Much is gained if a competitor can be put on a cold trail.

Patents may be written with the deliberate intention of misleading the reader. Success in carrying out an organic reaction may depend on close attention to some apparently insignificant detail. This detail may be omitted in the disclosure or put in so that it will not attract attention. "Caveat emptor" should be written on some patents.

Often equations are written for the reactions that are supposed to take place. A display of chemical knowledge is impressive but adds nothing to the value of the patent. It is always possible that the chemist might be mistaken as to what really takes place. The patent is in no way dependent on the accuracy of his ideas, and would still be good if his theory should be found to be wrong. A patent for making "dephlogistigated marine acid," if it actually produced chlorine, would be valid. A patent is to be read for the operations described rather than for the theories expounded. It covers a series of operations and what results from them. If the laboratory dish washer takes so much of something, mixes it with so much of something else, treats the mixture in a certain way, and gets a valuable product, he has all that is required for a patent, provided it has not been anticipated and provided he can describe the operations and identify the starting materials as well as the product so that his work can be repeated. The probability of a dish washer getting a valuable product in this way is remote, but if he does, it is all right. A knowledge of chemistry is useful in directing one to probable lines of experimenting. A knowledge of geology is an efficient aid in locating minerals, but productive mines have been found by ignorant people.

A patent consists of two parts: the "specification," as the disclosure is called, and the claims. The disclosure is what John Doe offers to the public as compensation for what he asks in the claims. As the scope of the claims is limited by the breadth of the disclosure, this is made as broad as possible. Considerable latitude is allowed in stating the reaction conditions. Thus if the reaction has been found to go satisfactorily at 100° it is safe to assume that it would go at somewhat higher and lower temperatures. A range of 50 to 200° might be mentioned. It is considered fair and proper to include compounds to which it is reasonably certain that it would apply. It is damaging to the patent if the disclosure is stretched too far. In writing it, one is in a quandary as to how far to generalize. It is hard to prove a negative; it is difficult to be sure that the reaction does not go at all. I have had difficulty getting results when trying to make compounds according to directions given in patents, but the same has happened with directions found in the journals. It is known that organic reactions are tricky. It is customary to give several typical examples of the operation of the process claimed. It should not be difficult to repeat these. The disclosure is like a sealed bid in that it cannot be altered after the application is filed. An exception is made for clerical errors.

The claims are what the applicant asks in return for his disclosure. Naturally he asks for more than he expects to get. If an applicant should get all he asked for, he would be quite unhappy about not having asked for more. The first claim, which is as broad as possible, is followed by progressively narrower ones. The claims are fought over by the applicant's attorney and the examiner, who starts by rejecting all claims except possibly one or two narrow ones. Of course, he says that there is nothing new in the process and cites several references that anticipate it. They argue over each claim, and when one is rejected a new one is substituted for it, changing just a few words. The claims in the patent as issued may be quite different from the original. Any anticipations that may be proved against it operate to limit the claims. Of course, if the anticipations are too serious, the whole case is thrown out.

BULLETINS

Bulletins there are in great numbers and in wide variety. Many of them contain first-hand scientific information, while others are devoted to practical subjects. The largest producers are the Departments of the United States Government. Some of these issue long series of bulletins. Usually each bulletin treats of a single subject. In this respect, they differ markedly from journals, each number of which contains articles on many subjects. Even when they form a series, bulletins are issued more or less irregularly. Lists of bulletins published by the Departments may be obtained and single numbers can be purchased. The information given in these bulletins is authoritative.

Many chemical manufacturers put out bulletins on their products, particularly on new additions to their lists. Some of these bulletins are elaborate and filled with information. Naturally the emphasis is on the properties and reactions that suggest commercial uses for the compounds. These bulletins make exciting reading for the research minded. They are sent free to all who ask.

DISSERTATIONS

The articles in the chemical journals have been discussed as primary publications. Eighty years ago, most of the research that was done was done by candidates for the doctor's degree and was later published as journal articles. The dissertations were actually preprimary. When the requirements for that degree were formulated by Johns Hopkins University, a prime item was the publication of the dissertation and the donation of one hundred copies to the university for distribution to other universities. Other American universities adopted this regulation. A hundred copies was supposed to be sufficient for all probable demands. This regulation was adapted from the German. The Johns Hopkins Chemistry Library contains hundreds of dissertations acquired by exchange with foreign as well as with American universities, which still continues. These dissertations are cataloged. What is said of this library applies to a greater or lesser extent to other university libraries. The system of exchange has run into difficulties with the multiplication of institutions awarding the doctor's degree and of the number of dissertations. The publication requirement was frequently met by publishing the material in a journal and having title page, acknowledgments, etc., added to make a dissertation. In some cases, the student gave his promise to publish and never did. The originals of all dissertations are on file in the libraries of the institutions granting them, where they may be consulted. They are not available for interlibrary exchange.

Lists of dissertations accepted by American universities have been published by the Government Printing Office, Washington, D.C. (from 1913 to 1940), and by the Association of Research Libraries (since 1934). They are being issued currently by University Microfilms, Ann Arbor, Michigan.

Many dissertations are published as microfilms. Since 1938, doctoral dissertations have been published by University Microfilms. Over 40,000 have been published (up to 1960) with the cooperation of ninety-eight universities. A 600-word abstract of each, written by the author, is published in *Dissertation Abstracts,* which is issued annually. Chemistry is only one of the many fields covered.

UNPUBLISHED INFORMATION

Sources of unpublished information, such as company reports, and papers read at scientific meetings, are discussed by Miss Stephens in the new edition of the American Chemical Society's *Advances* No. 4, 1961.

17.

■ Soviet chemical literature

BY JULIAN F. SMITH
Professor of Chemistry, Lenoir Rhyne College

BACKGROUND

Czarist Russia, lagging far behind Western Europe in outgrowing feudalism and serfdom, had a low literacy level and a wide gap between the illiterate serf class and the wealthy, educated aristocrats. Lacking a large literate middle class, its chemical literature was scanty in quantity though sometimes brilliant in quality. Illustrious names occasionally drew the attention of the outside world, among them Mendeleev (the periodic table), Beilstein (organic chemistry handbook), Chichibabin (organic synthesis) and Ostromyslenskii (isoprene and rubber).

The foremost chemical publication was *Journal of the Russian Physical Chemical Society,* continued in Soviet Russia as two journals, one for physics and the other for chemistry. It was approximately contemporaneous with *Berichte der deutschen chemischen Gesellschaft* (now *Chemische Berichte*). Students of

265

chemistry were not numerous, and tended to study abroad. As a result, there was no great proliferation of textbooks. Chemical books and dissertations achieved extensive outside circulation only when the author's fame stimulated a demand for translations.

As in all Europe prior to the industrial revolution, motivation for scientific research was still limited to the questing few who had the means and leisure to seek answers, or such a driving urge to investigate that they found or created opportunities. In the USSR, after the October (1917) revolution, the spread of such motivation through the populace was slow, but took a sharp upturn after the decline due to World War II.

Quantitatively the Russian language is now second to English in output of chemical books, periodicals, and separates, such as dissertations and bulletins. Patents fall far short of second rank; so does sales-promotion literature, a medium not extensively used where industry is 100% nationalized.

The Soviet Union now proclaims the conquest of illiteracy and takes pride in having 116 languages within its borders. Its Lenin State Library, staking out a claim (not undisputed) to be the largest in the world, has millions of items and is a repository for publications from the USSR and satellite nations. It is an exchange center through which current Soviet publications flow to all parts of the world in return for publications from recipient nations. This goes on without much attention to temperature fluctuations in the cold war. Although the United States Patent Office and the Soviet Patent Office did not come to a working exchange until 1959, the Library of Congress had then had years of Soviet exchange relations, as had also a few universities.

Qualitatively, Soviet chemical literature is much harder to assess. Before the first artificial satellite startled the world in 1957, many American chemists excused their inattention to Soviet literature by dismissing it as not worth reading. American and European post-sputnik alarmists shuddered at the lag behind Soviet science. The two extremes are equally ridiculous. Numerical assays are impossible; we can only say that our science is ahead in some areas, Soviet science in others. Progress achieved per man-hour or per dollar or per ruble cannot be compared, but Brooks[1] estimated the science effort expended in the United States, the USSR, and some other nations (U.S. first rank, USSR second).

Quality of publications can be compared in several respects. Soviet publications long ranked low in quality of paper, printing, binding, bibliographic citations, and English summaries. Paper, printing, and binding are now comparable with Western products. Bibliographic citations, once full of misprints and neglected bibliographic errors, gave little attention to non-Soviet sources. Errata lists, which then included the name of the erring proofreader, seemed almost to ignore reference lists. Now they are shorter, proofreaders retain their anonymity, and fewer misprints seem to be escaping. Linguistically, English summaries terminating periodical articles still leave much to be desired. But after a wave of economy or nationalism abolished them for a few years, their return is welcomed because they are helpful. Doubtless they rate better than would Russian summaries if they were provided by American authors or editors.

The number of non-Soviet references cited by Soviet authors has substantially increased. Presumably the seeming inattention of former years stemmed from lack of ready access to foreign current literature, rather than from lack of interest or from national pride. The flow of foreign publications into the USSR increased greatly in the 1950's, for reasons to be discussed.

Security regulations for control of militarily significant information withhold designated items until they are declassified. Presumably they have about the same effect on scientific literature wherever they exist. All Soviet research is a responsibility of government (USSR, an autonomous republic or a local unit), whereas in America, the connection with government is often only through a grant of funds or a contract. Soviet security control may, therefore, be tighter than in America; but the belief, once common, that the USSR systematically prevents export of published scientific information apparently had no firmer basis than that the Soviet incentive to export was weak.

---

[1] Benjamin T. Brooks, "Current Research Efforts in the United States, Russia and Other Countries," *J. Chem. Ed.* **35,** 468-469 (1958).

The Soviet economy was and is centered on fast expansion; in the competition between capital goods and consumer products, the output of science publications was orphaned somewhere in the middle. Press runs were intentionally small, sometimes too scanty even for the domestic demand, but never secret. The number of copies (Tirazh) is always printed at the end of a publication, e.g., each issue of a periodical. Soviet science, also largely self-centered, had not yet acquired a strong urge for wide dissemination of science records in either direction (export or import).

While incentive was weak, Soviet authorities made no active effort to encourage export of scientific publications, but there were channels all along for those who sought and found them. The slow rise of desire for interchange of information received a mighty impetus in and after 1952, when the Council of Ministers and Akademiya Nauk (Academy of Sciences, AN) jointly established *Vsesoyuznyi Institut Nauchnoi i Tekhnicheskoi Informatsii* (All-Union Institute of Scientific and Technical Information, VINITI). Publication of comprehensive world-combing abstract journals, a new venture in Soviet science, was commenced by VINITI in 1953. This enterprise, with related services requiring thousands of scientists for full- or part-time abstracting and other duties, multiplied many-fold the Soviet demand for non-Soviet science publications. The soaring rise of Sputnik I brought a soaring rise in Western demand for Soviet literature, preferably *not* in Russian. Fortunately several groups (in Government, among professional societies, and professional translators) had sensed the need even though they did not anticipate sputniks. So English-speaking scientists were not caught with no source of help.

Some information on the structure of Soviet science is needed for understanding the rising Soviet desire for interchange of information. Chemists wishing to utilize Soviet literature need some pointers on sources, whether original or in translation. It remains to consider these two topics in turn.

SOVIET SCIENCE

Academic research in the USSR is conducted partly in small specialized schools, but mainly in more than thirty state universities in the sixteen autonomous republics. Every university has a number of research institutes.

Ministries (Agriculture, Health, Mines, Trade, etc.) of the USSR or of an autonomous republic perform much research, largely through laboratories or institutes responsible directly to the ministry, but partly also in the laboratories of state-owned plants or refineries. Learned academies (the USSR has five) are responsible for much research, some academic, some with direct academy affiliations. As in other nations, election as an academician is a high honor. After the AN the academies having the greatest range of chemical interests are those of medicine and agriculture.

Autonomous republics have their own academies and ministries, much as do states in the United States. By far the largest Soviet republic in area, population, and research activity is *Rossiĭskaya Sovetskaya Federativnaya Sotsialisticheskaya Respublika* (RSFSR), covering much of European and Asiatic Russia. Moscow, its capital, and Leningrad are the chief research centers in the USSR, and RSFSR has numerous small centers. Next in research activity is *Ukrainskaya Sovetskaya Sotsialisticheskaya Respublika* (USSR, different from SSSR, the Russian abbreviation for Soviet Union). Its capital, Kiev, has numerous research institutes. Kharkov, Lvov, and Odessa are also important centers.

Research in medicine and biology is most readily located through *Public Health Service Publication No. 587*.[2] It lists 739 institutions, many having a score or more of affiliated institutes or laboratories. The Ministry of Health supports much of this research; most of the remainder is academic. Among subject areas with much chemical interest, the Publication lists 112 under microbiology, 104 under public health, 66 under biochem-

---

[2] "Directory of Medical and Biological Research Institutes of the USSR." *Publication No. 587, U.S. Public Health Service* (National Institutes of Health), Washington, 1958.

istry, and 64 under pharmacology. In public health, 15 of the 104 are in Moscow, 8 in Leningrad, 5 in Kiev, and 4 in Kharkov; the other 72 are in fifteen of the sixteen republics.

As examples, the N.I. Pirogov Medical Institute in Odessa is an agency of the Ukrainian Ministry of Health, it has three faculties, twenty-two departments and ten clinics. The Institute of Nutrition, Moscow, an affiliate of *Akademiya Meditsinskikh Nauk* (Academy of Medical Sciences, AMN), has two departments, six divisions, twelve laboratories and one clinic. Far out in Siberia, in the less familiar city of Yakutsk, AN maintains an Institute of Biology (three divisions and one laboratory), and AMN supports an Institute of Tuberculosis.

Another directory of research activities, with broad coverage of the physical sciences, is issued bimonthly by the Library of Congress.[3]

Soviet Chemical Literature

As in Western nations, Soviet chemical publications are mostly in one of these groups: periodicals, textbooks, reference works, monographs, dissertations, bulletins, instruction manuals, and patents. Many publications are translated from other languages into Russian, sometimes with and sometimes without acknowledgment. Soviet copyright law, as in Czarist Russia, does not regard translation from or into Russian as a copyright infringement. Compensating authors of translated foreign books is not customary, but at least one American author who protested to a Soviet publishing house received a royalty check.

As elsewhere, Soviet chemical periodicals tend to emphasize either theoretical or applied chemistry. Applied chemistry journals often resemble English-language trade journals without chatty news items or personal news notes. Chemical process industries have their journals, petroleum, food products, and metallurgy are prominent among them. Advertising is not uncommon, much of it from Western European makers of equip-

---

[3] *Scientific Research Institutes of the USSR,* Lexicographic and Terminology Section, Air Information Div., Library of Congress, Washington. Bimonthly from February 1960. Over 500 entries.

ment; but there is no such phenomenon as a trade journal which depends, as in America, on advertising as a major source of income.

The Soviet Patent Office emphasizes that its output (patents and certificates of invention) is approaching 150,000 since its first grant in 1924, mostly to Soviet inventors, whereas the Czarist Patent Office granted only 36,078 patents (82% of foreign origin) from 1803 to 1917. But as compared with the United States, British, French, and West German patent offices the Soviet output is numerically small. In proportion of chemical patents to the total number there are no radical differences. The Soviet patent system is well described by M. Hoseh;[4] a different aspect is discussed by H. F. Clesner.[5]

Soviet Information Service

Incentive for study of foreign chemical literature was greatly sharpened in the USSR by Referativnyi Zhurnal (Abstract Journal, RZh), initiated by VINITI in 1953 for world-wide coverage. It is published in fifteen subject sections (increased from thirteen since 1958 by adding *Mining* and *Industrial Economics*), and so is comparable in range with the summation of numerous English-language abstract journals.

The sections of major chemical interest are *Khimiya* (Chemistry, RZh:Kh) and *Biokhimiya* (RZh:B). Editorial policy (limited to some extent by practical considerations) is to abstract an article in as many different subject sections as its interests warrant. Sometimes the same abstract is repeated in each, but sometimes the same article is assigned to different abstractors for abstracts slanted according to subject-section interests.

Though *Chemical Abstracts* (CA) rejects separate issue of subject parts to subscribers with specific interests, as economically impracticable, RZh:Kh accepts separate subscriptions to its *General and Inorganic, Organic, Inorganic Technology, Organic Technology,* and *Macromolecules* subsections.

---

[4] M. Hoseh, "The USSR Patent System," *Patent, Trademark and Copyright J.* 4, 220-232 (Fall, 1960).

[5] Herschel F. Clesner, "Coordinated Soviet Effort to Promote and Apply Major Inventions," *Patent, Trademark and Copyright J.* 4, 212-219 (Fall, 1960).

Under this plan, VINITI finds subscribers divided in about the ratio 3:2 of whole to partial subscriptions. Economic feasibility has different standards in America and in the USSR.

For world coverage, RZh (all fifteen sections) reviews about 15,000 periodicals (about 3,000 from Soviet sources) from ninety-five nations in sixty-five languages. This is a rise from about 8,000 periodicals (about 1,000 of Soviet origin) in 1955. Shortly before World War II, the annual issues of *Periodica USSR* listed about 900 titles, including nontechnical periodicals and newspapers. For chemistry, CA reviews about 8,000 journals from eighty-five nations in over fifty languages.

During this rapid growth in world coverage, RZh spent so much of its energy on publishing that it ignored subject indexing. As compared with the indexing standards of CA this is a drastic deficiency, to which RZh editors are alert. The first indexes to appear were for authors only; subject indexes to a few RZh sections followed, and more are in progress. Current volumes are being indexed first, but indexes of prior years are also in preparation.

In addition to abstracting, VINITI also publishes *Ekspress Informatsiya,* a fast service for current awareness in fifty subject sections (raised from forty-eight in 1960). Each section (e.g., *Food Industries, Heat Engineering, Transportation*) disseminates annually, in forty-eight issues, selected translations or long abstracts from newly received non-Soviet periodicals (about 2100, largely from the United States). Press runs for an issue are about 3,000 to 5,000 copies. The Council of Ministers operates a similar service for new Soviet literature. Three *Ekspress Informatsiya* series (*Automation, Electronics, Physics*) are issued in English translation by International Physical Index, Inc., New York City.

There is no known plan in Europe or America for a full English-language issue of any section of RZh. So many of the abstracts are from English-language sources that such an effort would be wasteful. There are, however, some translations of abstracts taken by RZh from Soviet, satellite, and Chinese sources. Notable examples are from RZh:Kh, issued by United States

Joint Publications Research Service, New York and Washington; and RZh:Metallurgiya, under the auspices of *Acta Metallurgica,* New York City.

In subject coverage, RZh, backed by AN, treads lightly in medicine and agriculture, which have their own academies. In 1958, AMN organized its Institute of Medical, Scientific, and Technical Information, and established a medical abstract journal (four subject sections in 1959). Functions of VINITI, other than RZh, include:

1. A series of monographs, *Itogi Nauki* (Advances in Science), somewhat comparable to *Advances in Chemistry,* published at intervals by the American Chemical Society.

2. Photocopying service, on a fee basis, for items in VINITI files (extending back to 1953).

3. Translation service, full fee paid by the first customer and a nominal charge by later purchasers. Lists of translations are issued, somewhat as in America and Great Britain as mentioned later.

4. Research, considered an important function although VINITI is so largely an operating organization. Much of the effort is devoted to operating techniques and equipment, with emphasis on mechanized information handling; and the VINITI staff carefully studies its own objectives. Thus VINITI has much in common with the Center for Documentation and Communication Research (Western Reserve University, Cleveland). Documentation is not the central topic here, but is intimately related to efficient utilization of the literature. A guide to fuller information on current activities is issued by the National Science Foundation.[6]

Mechanical language-to-language translation is a documentation problem now receiving much attention. Among Soviet research centers active in this area are Institute of Linguistics, Leningrad (AN); Institute of Precision Mechanics and Computer Technique, Moscow (AN); V. A. Steklov Mathematics Institute, Moscow (AN); First Moscow State Pedagogical Insti-

---

[6] *Current Research and Development in Scientific Documentation,* Semiannual. National Science Foundation, Washington. No. 7, November 1960.

tute for Foreign Languages, headquarters of the Society for
Machine Translation; and Experimental Laboratory for Machine
Translation, A. A. Zhdanov State University, Leningrad. Similar
lists, at least as impressive, can be compiled for Western Europe
and the United States, but this topic is also eccentric here. Fuller
information is provided by the National Science Foundation.[6]

Russians study English in elementary and secondary
schools, and most Soviet chemists can glean some information
from chemical literature in English. In the reverse direction, most
American chemists glean only bewilderment. While American
interest in Soviet advances grew after 1945 and ballooned after
the first sputnik, commercial translators began in the late 1940's
to offer whole issues of Soviet journals in English. Government
agencies and scientific societies took a hand and the number of
operating projects grew. Some which possess chemical significance
are listed in the next section.

LITERATURE SOURCES AND SERVICES

The first Soviet periodical offered in cover-to-cover
translation was *Zhurnal obshchei khimii* (Journal of General
Chemistry), successor to the chemical portion of the old *Journal
of the Russian Physical Chemical Society*. The translation is by
Consultants Bureau, New York. The same firm followed up in
1950 with *Zhurnal prikladnoi khimii* (Journal of Applied Chemistry) and has since added numerous others, mostly on chemistry
or biology.

Scientific societies, encouraged by grants of funds
from the National Science Foundation, undertook similar enterprises during the 1950's. Among them are American Institute of
Physics, American Institute of Biological Societies, and Instru-
ment Society of America. Government agencies taking an active
part include Library of Congress,[7] National Institutes of Health,[2]

---

[7] *Monthly List of Russian Accessions*, Library of Congress, Washington,
1948-. Tables of contents of journals, and titles of separates, in English.

Office of Technical Services,[8,9] Central Intelligence Agency,[10] and Atomic Energy Commission.[11]

Among its other functions, the Office of Technical Services (OTS) guides searchers to locations of available translations (from many languages), whether held in its own collection from government sources (United States and foreign), or in the Special Libraries Association Translation Center (nongovernment sources) at the John Crerar Library in Chicago, or at one of several depository libraries in other cities. The two collections together have more than 50,000 translations. In 1957, the Library of Congress transferred its collection of translated Russian documents to the SLA Translation Center. At the end of 1958, this Center discontinued its *Translation Monthly* by transfer of the function to OTS, which in January 1959 began the publication of its *Technical Translations.*[9]

Comparable efforts in Great Britain overlap to some extent with American work, but there is a helpful degree of coordination. British and American enterprises together raised the total number of Soviet journals available in cover-to-cover translation to eighty-seven in 1960.[12] Some, not duplicated in America, are sponsored by the Department of Scientific and Industrial Research (DSIR) in London, mainly through its affiliated research institutes. Other DSIR enterprises include current tables of contents,[13] and a Lending Library Unit (LLU) which collaborates

[8] *Current Review of the Soviet Technical Press,* OTS, Washington. Weekly. Fast-service abstracts.

[9] *Technical Translations.* Semimonthly, 1959-. OTS, Washington. Subscriptions (from Superintendent of Documents, Washington) $12.00 per year. Lists new translations from various languages into English. The first issue of each volume lists all cover-to-cover translations of Soviet periodicals into English.

[10] *Scientific Information Report,* Central Intelligence Agency, Washington; distributed by OTS. $28.00 per year. Abstracts from current Soviet block and Chinese publications.

[11] Translation Series, Atomic Energy Commission, Washington. Irregular. Selected items obtainable from OTS at designated prices.

[12] Russian Technical Literature. Irregular, 1960-. European Productivity Agency (Organization for European Economic Cooperation), Paris. Information and articles about sources, translations, etc.

[13] *Translated Contents of Russian Periodicals.* Monthly, 1949-. DSIR, London.

with ASLIB (Association of Special Libraries and Information Bureaux), although their published lists are separate.[14,15]

English-language service on Soviet patents comes largely from England. Pergamon Press (which also has an office in New York) translates *Byulletin izobretenii* (the Soviet patent gazette) cover-to-cover. Technical Information Co., London, abstracts current Soviet patents and certificates of invention.[16]

The Royal Society, through its Abstracting Services Consultative Committee, has helped to systematize transliteration from Cyrillic to Latin alphabets.[17]

Academic dissertations are important sources of information. Those from Soviet universities are listed in the Soviet National Bibliography, received in the Library of Congress and in a few other American libraries. For recent years, the semi-annual list issued by the Lenin State Library (Moscow) is nearly complete[18] and facilitates tracing of individual dissertations. Many universities issue lists of their own dissertations; the University of Moscow has a collective list (1934 to 1954), published in 1956. For older Soviet dissertations, some bibliographies are cited by the Library of Congress.[19]

Problems of Soviet technical literature are also matters of concern in Continental Europe. The situation is summarized by Mrs. Vibeke Ammundsen.[20] Functions of VINITI were described in English[21] in an invited paper by its director.

[14] *LLU Translation Bulletin*. Monthly, 1959-. Lending Library Unit, DSIR, London. Selected translations from Russian, and list of translations from many sources.

[15] *ASLIB Commonwealth Index of Unpublished Translations*. ASLIB, London. Translations from various languages, and their availability.

[16] *Russian Patents Gazette*. Semimonthly, 1959-. Technical Information Co., London. Abstracts of patents and certificates of invention.

[17] H. S. Bushell, *Transliteration of Russian, Serbian, and Bulgarian for Bibliographical Purposes*, Royal Society, London, 1953.

[18] Doctoral Dissertations Received by the Lenin State Library. Semiannual, 1957-. Lenin State Library, Moscow. In Russian.

[19] *Guide to Soviet Bibliographies*, Library of Congress, Washington, 1950. Academic dissertations, pp. 27-28.

[20] Vibeke Ammundsen, "Accessibility of Russian Scientific and Technical Literature in Western Nations," *Ingeniøren* **67**, 317-326 (1958). In Danish. A condensed, annotated translation by Julian F. Smith was issued in August 1958 as *National Bureau of Standards Rept. No. 6115*.

[21] D. Yu. Panov, "Institute of Scientific Information of the Academy of Sciences of the USSR," *J. Documentation* **12**, 94-100 (1956).

A guide to Soviet translations then available appeared in 1956.[22]

The geographic spread and varied sponsorship of projects for more effective utilization of Soviet scientific literature show that many people in many nations consider the effort and expense worth while. For background and factual material not brought out in this brief survey, see Hoseh.[23] For current awareness Consultants Bureau[24] issues translated tables of contents of more than eighty Soviet journals available in English translation. Bibliographies on special topics are compiled in various organizations, e.g., on field emission.[25] These are generally entered in appropriate indexes or source lists. The language barrier seems less formidable now than a decade ago. Instruction in Russian is widespread, and student enrollment is high. Crashing the language barrier, still the most effective way to surmount it, is no longer the only way; but study of Russian is still advisable for research chemists.

Locating Sources and Translations

Requests for information, and orders for items listed as available, may be sent to:

1. SLA Translation Center, John Crerar Library, 86 N. Randolph St., Chicago 1, Illinois.
2. Office of Technical Services, Washington 25, D.C.
3. ASLIB, 3 Belgrave Square, London SW1 (for British sources and translations).

To ascertain what Soviet journals are now being translated cover-to-cover (including British enterprises), *Techni-*

---

[22] Elizabeth Byerley, "Translations from the Russian: A Guide to Sources," *Rev. Documentation* **23**, 33-41 (No. 2, 1956).

[23] M. Hoseh, Scientific and Technical Literature of the USSR. I. Publications and Publishers. II. Facts and Figures. III. Distribution and Availability; *J. Chem. Ed.* **33**, 397-402, **34**, 182-185, 235-238 (1956, 1957).

[24] "Soviet Science in Translation: A Monthly Preview of Soviet Research," Consultants Bureau, New York City. $25.00 per year. Tables of contents, in advance of publication, for more than 80 cover-to-cover translations of Russian periodicals.

[25] T. W. Marton and Ralph Klein, *Soviet Research in Field Electron and Ion Emission*, 1955-1959: An Annotated Bibliography. *Tech. Note 75*, National Bureau of Standards, Washington, October, 1960.

cal Translations may be consulted. Twice yearly (first issue of each volume) the current complete list is printed, with information as to source and availability. As new ones appear, they are listed in current issues. Each issue also serves for current awareness as to new items, e.g., translations of single documents.

Most of the references cited here are available in large reference libraries and can be borrowed by any library through interlibrary loan relations. For items abstracted in CA, and too new for the translation centers, CA can sometimes give source information but should not be queried if any known source indicates the probability that a translation will be forthcoming.

Some Pertinent Publications

Irving S. Bengelsdorf, "Teaching Scientific Russian: An Experiment in Educational Television," *J. Chem. Ed.* **37,** 211-213 (1960).

E. J. Crane and Karl F. Heumann, "CA Measures a Nation's Research," *Chem. Eng. News* **36,** 64-66 (August 4, 1958).

Raymond Ewell, "Education and Research in Soviet Russia," *Chem. Eng. News* **36,** 66-70 (April 14, 1958).

Ian F. Finlay, "Some Aspects of Technical Translation," *J. Chem. Ed.* **35,** 519-521 (1958).

Eva Lou Fisher, "Sokrashcheniya (Abbreviations) for Bibliographic Search," *Special Libraries* **49,** 365-370 (1958). Russian abbreviations, their full terms, and English equivalents.

Albert G. Guy, "Sources of Metallurgical Literature in the Soviet Union," *Special Libraries* **51,** 532-536 (1960).

A. F. Hubbell et al., *Russian-English Scientific and Technical Dictionaries: A Survey,* Committee for Russian-English Technical Dictionaries, New York University, 1960.

Alexander King, "Scientific and Technical Information from Russia," *Russian Tech. Literature* **1,** 5-8 (No. 1, February 1960).

Karol Maichel, "Soviet Scientific Abstracting Journals," *Special Libraries* **50,** 398-402 (1959).

James W. Perry, *Scientific Russian,* Interscience Publishers, New York City, 1951.

Alexander Rosenberg, *Russian Abbreviations: A Selective List,* 2nd Ed., 1957. Reference Dept. Library of Congress, Washington, D. C.

Thomas J. Whitby, "Expanding Network of Engineering Libraries in the Soviet Union," *Special Libraries* **51**, 537-539 (1960).

Thomas J. Whitby, "Slavica: USSR: Science," *Quarterly J. Acquisitions* (Library of Congress) **17**, 128-143 (No. 2, February 1960). The Slavica: USSR series reviews accessions at intervals; technology has its turn in 1961.

"Abstracts and Patents in the USSR," *Chem. Eng. News* **36**, 26 (September 22, 1958).

"Key to Soviet Science," *Chem. Eng. News* **36**, 112-113 (January 6, 1958).

Polytechnical Dictionaries, Engineers Joint Council, New York City, 1960.

18. Secondary publications

INTRODUCTION

The primary publications are the journals which contain the facts of chemistry as they are dug out by their discoverers. Raw materials from field or mine must be more or less manufactured before they enter into commerce. The facts of chemistry must be gathered, sorted, stored, and worked over before they are used. Abstract journals and bibliographies locate and index them, while reviews and compendiums assemble and arrange them. On these ordered facts are built our systems and theories, and certain of them are selected to be put into textbooks for the instruction of chemists to be.

These publications, which are concerned with the presentation of material that has already been published, may be called secondary publications. This does not mean that they are of secondary importance, for they are indispensable to the student and to the research chemist.

With the growth of chemistry, its division and sub-division into numerous fields, and the rapid expansion of these, with the increase in number and variety of contributions published by the ever-growing host of investigators, the task of searching all the journals has become too great for the individual. Dr. J. P. Nash, director for Lockheed's missile and space division, estimates that sixty million pages of scientific reports will be published during 1960.[1] What is impossible for one soldier is easy for a disciplined army.

ABSTRACT JOURNALS [2]

It is only in comparatively recent years that abstracts have been completely segregated into special journals except in the *Zentralblatt*. In the earlier times, nearly all chemical journals carried some sort of digest or review of articles published outside of their own pages, particularly those from other countries, each aiming to keep its readers informed as to the progress of chemistry as a whole. There was no uniformity; sometimes an important article would be translated and published almost entirely, while only a few extracts would be made from others, the majority going unnoticed. There was no attempt to make the service comprehensive; each editor presented such a selection as he thought would interest his readers. The task of reading, digesting, and abstracting chemical literature has been taken over by the great national societies.

CHEMICAL ABSTRACTS

In 1907, the American Chemical Society began the publication of *Chemical Abstracts*. This is the most extensive and inclusive abstract journal ever published. In addition to covering the strictly chemical journals, it goes into those of the bordering sciences and even into trade journals in search of any and

---

[1] J. P. Nash, *Chem & Eng. News*, June 20, 1960, p. 47.

[2] Thanks are due to Dr. G. Nathan Reed for some of the items included in this chapter. Others have been drawn from the book: *A Guide to the Literature of Chemistry, 2nd Edition*, by Crane, Patterson, and Marr, New York, John Wiley & Sons, 1957.

every sort of new chemical information. After the combing process is completed, the editors check up the articles they have gathered with those noticed in the other abstract journals, and if they find that they have missed an article, it is promptly abstracted either directly or through the foreign abstract. This is done, of course, by arrangement with the other journals. *Chemical Abstracts* excels all others as an index and guide to chemical information, whether it is found in the regular chemical journals or tucked away in some place where no one would ever think of looking for it. A vast deal of information is brought together which is not strictly chemical, but which is apt to be of service to chemists. Patents of all countries are abstracted in so far as they relate to chemistry, no partiality being shown to American patents.

According to subject matter, the abstracts are divided into thirty-three sections, each cared for by an assistant editor and abstractors particularly interested in that line. It is the policy of *Chemical Abstracts* to make use of a large number of part-time abstractors because of the desire to get papers into the hands of specialists in the subjects involved. To make a good abstract one needs to be trained in abstracting as well as thoroughly familiar with the paper and the subject which it covers. The abstract journal which utilizes only a limited number of abstractors has the advantage that its abstractors are likely to be more experienced as abstractors, but has the disadvantage that many abstracts are bound to be made by individuals who are not in a position to appreciate fully all the points brought out in the paper nor to evaluate them properly. Special efforts in training abstractors have been made so as to minimize the disadvantage of having a larger number of abstractors.

Of the total effort which goes into the making of *Chemical Abstracts* approximately half is expended on indexing, all of which is done by professionals. For every 1000 words in the abstracts there are about 700 in the indexes.

There have been from the first annual author and subject indexes. A formula index was added in 1920 (Volume 14), and a numerical patent index in 1935 (Volume 29). Four decennial author and subject indexes have been published and the fifth is now appearing. There is a cumulative formula index to volumes 14 to 40 (1920 to 1946). The numerical patent index for volumes 1 to 30 was published by Edwards Brothers and one for volumes 31 to 40 by the Society.

Chemical Abstracts is produced by an editor, 19 associate editors, and 35 assistant editors and advisers, aided by the part-time work of 50 section editors and about 1,500 abstractors. It covers over 7,000 periodicals, chemical patents, and a wide variety of occasional publications, in short, practically everything printed which might contain information of interest to chemists. In 1954, fifty new journals were noted.

According to Dr. Emery,[3] a comprehensive abstracting and indexing service is an international undertaking. *Chemical Abstracts* covers papers appearing in 85 countries, has abstractors residing in 34 of these (74 in Japan), and is widely distributed outside of the United States (about one-fourth of its subscribers). Corrected proofs of important journals are distributed by air mail so that they are received about two months before regular delivery. There is close cooperation between editors of abstract journals.

To provide more prompt information, a new publication is being started. *Chemical Titles* will help to speed the dissemination of chemical literature. It will publish and index the contents of 550 leading journals of pure and applied chemistry, no later than twenty-one days after the journals are received in Columbus, Ohio. The new publication is the first regular application of an automatic indexing system worked out by the International Business Machine Corporation.[4]

The rapid expansion of *Chemical Abstracts* is shown in the following table. The figures are for single years, ten years apart. For the later years columns are counted as pages.

It is a curious fact that, while the authors and abstracts increased many fold, the number of patents has not. They show a decrease for the war years and little difference between volumes 31 and 51. The *Fifth Decennial Index* (1947 to 1956) will contain 543,064 abstracts of papers and 104,249 of patents, with

---

[3] Alden H. Emery, *Chem. Eng. News*, February 3, 1958, p. 90.
[4] *Chem. Eng. News*, April 4, 1960, p. 27.

The Expansion of Chemical Abstracts

Volume Number	Number of Pages		Number of Authors	Number of Patents	
	of Abstracts	of Subject Index		United States	Foreign
1	3074	202	8800		
11	3470	298	12300		
21	4098	774	25800		
31	8996	839	47000	7600	12200
41	7818	923	38300	4300	4000
51	18706	2593	102000	8300	9500

authors, subjects, formulae, patent numbers, and organic rings. It will be published in nineteen volumes.

CHEMISCHES ZENTRALBLATT

This is the oldest abstract journal devoted exclusively to chemistry. Up to the founding of *Chemical Abstracts,* it was the one outstanding source of general information for the chemists of the world. It has continued to grow in size and importance, but it is now only one of several great abstract journals.

The *Chemisches Zentralblatt,* until 1897 spelled *Centralblatt* and commonly designated by *C.,* has been a great factor in the development of chemistry. It was begun in 1830 as the *Pharmaceutisches Centralblatt,* and became *Chemisch-Pharmaceutisches Centralblatt,* in 1850 and assumed its present name in 1856. Till 1892 it was issued as one volume a year, but was then divided into two: I January to June, and II July to December, each with its own indexes. It has a volume number but is always referred to by the year thus: C. 1910, I, 254, or C. 1912, II, 459. Indexing at half-year intervals is convenient if we are interested in obtaining the most recent information, but is troublesome when it comes to going through back years. There are collective indexes for four-year periods since 1897, which reduce the labor of a search covering a long period of time.

The *Zentralblatt* at first covered only German chemical patents thoroughly, but later added those from other countries. For many years there were numerical indexes for German patents only, but later similar indexes for other countries were included. In looking for a patent in the numerical index, it must be remembered that German patents are not issued in the same order in which they are numbered, so D.R.P. 369,127 may be abstracted in the first half of a given year and 369,111 in the second half, while 369,145 may have been granted earlier and gotten into the abstracts for the preceding year. Therefore, a German patent of a given number must be searched for not only in the volume which contains the bulk of the numbers near it but also in one or two volumes earlier and later.

Starting with 1919, the *Zentralblatt* for a year is divided into four parts instead of two. These are designated I, II, III, and IV. Parts I and III contain abstracts of "scientific" and II and IV of technical publications. Parts I and II are issued together, though paged separately and cover the period January to June as it did formerly. These are separated in binding, but are indexed together. Parts III and IV cover the latter half of the year in the same way. A reference on atomic energy C. 1920, III, 464 is to the scientific section, last half of year 1920.

Until 1919, *Chemisches Zentralblatt* covered only pure chemistry, with scant attention to work from outside of Germany. In that year it took over the abstracts section of *Angewandte Chemie* and began complete coverage of all branches of chemistry.

BRITISH ABSTRACTS

In Great Britain, the situation is different from what it is in America. There are two great societies, the Chemical Society and the Society of Chemical Industry. They have amicably divided the field, the one taking pure chemistry and the other its industrial applications, including chemical patents. The *Journal of the Chemical Society* has published abstracts since 1871. From 1871 to 1877 the first part of each monthly issue was devoted to original papers and the second to abstracts. These were paged consecutively and bound together. The annual index made no distinction between original articles and abstracts. Starting with 1878, the two sections, though issued together, have been paged independently and segregated in binding, the odd-numbered volume being designated "transactions" and the even "abstracts." The two volumes are indexed independently. Starting with 1916, the abstracts have been further divided into part 1, "organic," and part 2, "inorganic," the two being paged independently and usually bound separately, but having a common index. There are cumulative indexes for 1841 to 1872, 1873 to 1882, 1883 to 1892, 1893 to 1902, 1903 to 1912, and 1913 to 1922.

In the *Journal of the Society of Chemical Industry* for a time the abstracts were not segregated. They occupied a large part of the publication since its beginning in 1882 and have been extremely important to anyone looking up a technical subject. For this period one may well begin one's investigations with this journal.

Starting with volume 37 (1918), the material presented has been segregated into "review," "transactions," and "abstracts" which are paged independently. One index covers all three parts, the letters R, T, and A being added to the page numbers. Starting with volume 42 (1923), the "review" is replaced by a new section called "chemistry and industry," published weekly.

Beginning with volume 20 (1901), there is appended to the index a numerical list of English patents abstracted with page references; and from volume 35 (1916), there are similar lists for United States, German, and French patents.

In 1926, the abstracts of the two journals were merged in *British Chemical Abstracts,* which, temporarily under different names, continued to the present. Pure and applied chemistry, including patents of all countries, are covered, though not quite so extensively as in *Chemical Abstracts.*

GERMAN ABSTRACTS

The *Chemisches Zentralblatt* has been mentioned as devoted exclusively to abstracts. *Liebig's Annalen,* like all early chemical journals, contained notes on chemical work in other countries.

The *Berichte* of the German Chemical Society carried abstracts till 1897 when the Society acquired the *Chemisches*

Centralblatt. The abstracts in the *Berichte* are called *Referate* and are paged separately and usually bound separately, but with the same volume number as the original articles. A reference to *Ber.* **25,** 897 (1892) would be to an original article, but *Ber.,* **25,** 429R (1892) designates an abstract and is to be found in the *Referate* section.

Angewandte Chemie, formerly called *Zeitschrift für angewandte Chemie,* like its British counterpart, the *Journal of the Society of Chemical Industry,* contained an extensive section of abstracts on official chemistry, including patents, until it was merged with *Chemisches Centralblatt.*

FRENCH ABSTRACTS

Up to 1933, the *Bulletin de la société chimique de France* published original papers in the odd-numbered volumes, and abstracts in the even. After 1933, the *Bulletin* was divided and the abstract section continued as *Bulletin de la société chimique de France, Documentation.*

BEILSTEIN

Attention has already been called to the fact that chemistry is one of the most thoroughly indexed branches of human knowledge. Of all the divisions of chemistry, organic is the most splendidly systematized and catalogued. This is largely due to the efforts of two men who have left massive monuments to their painstaking labors in chemical literature. These men are Beilstein and Richter, a Russian and a German. Both of them were overwhelmed by the multitudes of organic compounds turned out in later years, and both had to resign their tasks in favor of the German Chemical Society with its larger resources. Both of them covered the whole field of organic chemistry and arranged its myriads of compounds in orderly fashion so that each may be located, but their systems are entirely different. Each work is valuable and each supplements the other.

F. K. Beilstein was born in Petrograd in 1838,[5]

---

[5] Paul Jacobson, *Z. angew. Chem.,* **33,** I, 178 (1920).

studied with Wöhler and also in France. He returned to Russia and was Professor of Chemistry in the University of Petrograd for forty years, from 1866 to his death. He began to index organic compounds for his own use and printed his *Handbuch der organischen Chemie,* known to chemists as '*Beilstein,*' in 1881 to 1883 in two volumes. The second edition was issued in three volumes in 1886 to 1890, and the third, aggregating 6635 pages, appeared in 1893 to 1899. Supplements to these four volumes adding 4047 pages and an index volume of 441 pages came out in 1901 to 1906.

Beilstein prepared the first two editions unaided and had one assistant on the third.

The fourth edition describes all organic compounds of ascertained structure known up to December 31, 1909, the same closing date as Richter's *Lexikon der Kohlenstoffverbindungen,* now discontinued, which contains 144,150 compounds. Thus we may credit the same number to Beilstein. For each compound listed, there are given name, structural formula, preparation, available data as to melting and boiling points, density, and refractive index. For the more important compounds, several methods of preparation may be given along with the principal reactions. The space allotted to a single compound varies from a couple of lines to several pages, in keeping with its importance. Thus ethanol requires nineteen pages, while tridecanol gets only three lines.

The compounds, which are divided into systems, are arranged in logical order, starting with the simple hydrocarbons and ending with the most complex compounds. Users are advised to learn the system, but only its broad outlines are necessary. Each volume covers a class of compounds which are arranged systematically so that a trained organic chemist can find a desired compound without the aid of the index. However, the index gets you there quicker.

There will never be a fifth edition; instead, new information is cared for by supplements, one to each volume. The first supplement covers the period 1910 to 1920, and the second 1920 to 1930. The third will extend from 1930 to 1950. The rapid growth of chemistry is evidenced by the fact that the first ten-year supplement to volume I contains 492 pages and the second, 941 compared to 982 in the main volume. An important development of American research in organic chemistry was the reproduction of *Beilstein* by the photo-offset process in 1942 under the Alien Property Act. The price of $568 (now $850) for the complete fourth edition with all of the first supplement and six of the second, made it available to a large number of smaller institutions that were unable to pay the German price of about $2300. I know what this meant to several institutions which I visited at about that time.

SOME OTHER ORGANIC REFERENCE BOOKS

Elsevier's *Encyclopaedia of Organic Chemistry,* New York-Amsterdam, Elsevier Publishing Co., Inc.

Grignard's *Traité de chimie organique.*

Meyer and Jacobson: *Lehrbuch der organischen Chemie,* Leipzig, Verlag von Veit and Co.

Heilbron: *Dictionary of Organic Compounds,* London, Eyre and Spottiswoode, 1953.

Groggins: *Unit Processes in Organic Syntheses,* 5th Edition, New York, McGraw-Hill, 1958.

Gilman: *Organic Chemistry,* Volumes I to IV, New York, Wiley, 1943-1953.

Roger Adams, Editor: *Organic Reactions* (a series started in 1942; volume 10 published in 1959), New York, Wiley.

Patterson and Capell: *The Ring Index,* New York, Reinhold, 1940.

Reid: *Organic Chemistry of Bivalent Sulfur* (five volumes; four published up to 1961), New York, Chemical Publishing Co.

SOME INORGANIC REFERENCE BOOKS

Gmelin's *Handbuch der anorganischen Chemie,* continued as Gmelin-Kraut,[6] Berlin, Verlag Chemie, the eighth edition of which is now in progress, will be the most complete treatise in its field.

Mellor: *Comprehensive Treatise on Inorganic and Theoretical Chemistry,* London, Longmans, Green and Co.

---

[6] *Chem. Eng. News,* March 28, 1960, p. 96.

Pascal: *Traité de chimie minérale,* Paris, Masson et Cie.
Abegg: *Handbuch der anorganischen Chemie,* Leipzig, Verlag von S. Hirzel.
Dammer: *Handbuch der anorganischen Chemie,* Stuttgart, F. Enke.
Moissan: *Traité de chimie minérale,* Paris, Masson et Cie.
Jacobson and Hampel: *Encyclopedia of Chemical Reactions,* 8 volumes, New York, Reinhold, 1946-1959.
Hückel: *Structural Chemistry of Inorganic Compounds,* New York-Amsterdam, Elsevier Publishing Co., Inc.

REVIEWS

A review brings together the facts in a certain area of chemistry and presents them as an organized whole. It is of great service to anyone interested in that particular field. Reviews are of many kinds, but may be divided into two general classes: annual reviews, which cover progress in certain related areas within a period of time, and topical reviews, each of which gives a complete story of the history and development of a reaction or group of compounds.

In 1821, Berzelius began his great *Jahresbericht* which continued till 1847 and was in its day of immense service to investigators. It is still an important source of information on topics of that period, particularly since the originals which are quoted are frequently not accessible. It was published in Swedish and also in German.

Annual reports on the progress of chemistry, issued by the Chemical Society, are of service to those wishing to keep informed on the advances of chemistry as a whole. The annual reports of the Society of Chemical Industry on the progress of applied chemistry give a general view of technical advances.

Two examples of topical reviews are given.

Ahren's Sammlung, full name *Sammlung chemischer und chemischtechnischer Vorträge,* is a series of comprehensive articles on special topics in chemistry. Each of these is a brief monograph written by an expert in the particular line, frequently by the man who has done the most important part of the work

that is described. There are abundant references to the original
literature.

Chemical Reviews, sponsored by the American
Chemical Society, publishes reviews on special topics, which are
issued bimonthly and bound in annual volumes.

MONOGRAPHS

These resemble reviews as to treatment, but are
larger and more elaborate. A monograph may run to a thousand
pages or more, and is published as a book which may or may not
belong to a series. Two important series are mentioned: *Die
chemische Analyse,* published by Enke, Stuttgart, of which 45
volumes have appeared, and the series sponsored by the American
Chemical Society, published by Reinhold Publishing Co. of New
York, of which 145 have appeared.

BOOKS

"Of the making of books there is no end" was said
nearly nineteen hundred years ago and is still true. Journals have
come into vogue in recent times, but books have been the deposi-
tories of information for thousands of years. All that we know
about alchemy, the precursor of chemistry, we have had to learn
from books. Ancient books recorded a vast deal of information
that has been incorporated into present-day organized science.
As late as fifty years ago, our pharmacopeia contained a pre-
ponderance of natural products as drugs, many of which had
come down from antiquity.

Monographs and reviews have been mentioned, but
these make up only a small fraction of the books that are being
published which are of interest to chemists. *Chemical Abstracts*
lists 1926 as being published in 1954. Counting only 260 pages
per book these come to half a million pages, all of which contain
more or less valuable information. Journals are the prime sources,
but books can be most helpful and should not be disregarded.

Books go back for thousands of years, while journals are only recent.

Only a few books are abstracted by *Chemical Abstracts,* and a few are reviewed in the journals; for the rest we have to rely on the titles, which do not always tell us much.

19. Searching the chemical literature

INTRODUCTION

Looking for something? Just turn to the yellow pages in the telephone book and you will find everything from accessories to zippers. You just pick up your telephone and order anything you want. It is just that simple. There is, however, a limit to the things that can be gotten in this way.

If you go to New York City and want to meet your friend, Bill Totempole, you might stand at a corner of Times Square until he happens to pass by. I met a friend on 42nd Street, and another on a street in Oberammergau. On a trip to Australia, my son met the only man he knew on that continent on a street in Brisbane. This is an uncertain way to make contact with friends. As Eastman says: "There must be a better way." A more effective way to get hold of your friend, Bill, would be to look him up in the telephone book and dial his number.

If you want to get in touch with any of the 144,150

organic compounds known January 1, 1920, all you have to do is to look in the index to *Beilstein,* which is about as quick as finding Bill's number in the directory.

The classification and indexing of the vast accumulation of chemical information are more nearly complete than in any other branch of human knowledge. But to use these efficiently requires training.

For a thorough discussion of searching chemical literature, reference should be made to the authoritative book by Crane, Patterson, and Marr, and to the papers from a symposium on searching chemical literature.[1]

Searches differ in size and in kind, depending on the sort of information desired and on its importance. If you want to know the melting point of benzoic acid, you look it up in a handbook which requires only a minute or two. You can find a method for making benzoyl chloride in *Beilstein* in about ten minutes; but if you are interested in the best method to make it, you may need several hours of careful research. If you believe you have a new and more efficient way of manufacturing it and are thinking of applying for a patent on it, the search will have to be far more thorough. In an important case, the research may take many months. An undiscovered bit of information in the prior art may wreck a manufacturing process like a bomb in the baggage on an airplane. Finding out a great deal about any topic is easy; finding everything that has been published about it is quite another matter.

Searching is a game in which there are no rules; you play it as you please. It is catch as catch can with no holds barred. There are some places where you should look, but none where you should not. You just have to keep on looking, anywhere, everywhere. Searching requires persistence in following up clues, imagination to think up odd places in which to look, and a broad knowledge of chemistry so as to be able to recognize the object of search even if disguised under some other name.

---

[1] Crane, Patterson, and Marr, *A Guide to the Literature of Chemistry,* New York, John Wiley & Sons, 1957. "Symposium on Searching the Chemical Literature," Division of Chemical Literature, Detroit meeting, April 1950. Published in *Advances in Chemistry,* Series No. 4, by the American Chemical Society.

How you hunt depends on the game you are after; for uranium you take a Geiger counter; for foxes you take a dog; for skunks you do not need the dog.

Since you cannot possibly scan the millions of pages of technical literature that are coming out, you have to rely on abstract journals and books to direct you to the most likely locations to explore.

When beginning a search on any topic, it is desirable to consult any available books that may contain information bearing directly or indirectly on the subject. This gives a general view of the field and may furnish some specific information.

INDEXES

The desired information is scattered through the abstract journals but the searcher must know how to find it. The index is the door, so to speak, by which we enter these storehouses of information. It is easy to say to one, "Look in the index," but it is quite another matter to use an index efficiently.

The following is taken from an address by the chief indexer of them all.[2] The statements made years ago are still true.

The making of indexes is an art in itself, involving more than a comprehensive knowledge of the general subject being covered, and the use of indexes is no less an art. . . . Conscious effort to become a good index user will repay any scientist . . . Index searching is a neglected art and yet one of much importance . . . An index must be accurate, complete, sufficiently precise in the information supplied, and so planned and arranged as to be convenient to use.

To illustrate a kind of scattering of entries which may result from word indexing, let us consider a series of article titles as follows: 'An Apparatus for the Determination of Carbon Dioxide,' 'A New Absorption Apparatus,' 'Apparatus for Use in the Analysis of Baking Powder,' 'An Improved Potash Bulb,' and 'Flue-Gas Analysis.' Word index would no doubt contain an entry under the heading 'Carbon dioxide' for the first title, one under 'Absorption ap-

[2] E. J. Crane in *J. Ind. Eng. Chem.* **14**, 901 (1922); used by permission of the author.

paratus' for the second, under 'Baking powder' for the third, under 'Potash bulb' for the fourth, and one under 'Flue gas' for the fifth, and probably no others. These entries seem reasonable enough if the titles are considered separately without thought of the others. And yet the articles may all be descriptive of the same sort of apparatus. As a matter of fact, all these titles might conceivably be used for the same article; if the author happened to be working on baking powder or on flue-gas analysis when he conceived the idea for his novel piece of apparatus, or had it in mind particularly for one purpose or the other, he might choose one of the more specific titles for his article rather than one of the more general ones. . . . Cross references play an important role in subject indexing and in the use of subject indexes. . . . Literature searching is a dignified pursuit, and it cannot with impunity be assigned to a lower level than that of the laboratory side of problems, as far as the attention it receives is concerned.

If the searcher were to separate his subject into its essential parts and then to consult the literature on each factor, he would find considerable information which he otherwise would miss. Even though some index headings to which to turn, perhaps the more important ones, may be brought to mind without ingenuity, the completeness of a search may be marred by a failure properly to analyze the problem . . . With a given heading in mind, it is well to cudgel one's brain for synonymous words and phrases to try, as well as for variously related subjects, and it is advisable to try these even though entries as expected are found in the first place to which one has turned. Words or phrases with an opposite meaning to the one in mind may serve as subject headings under which desired entries may be found. For example, the searcher interested in viscosity may find significant entries under the heading 'Fluidity' in addition to those under 'Viscosity.'

Suppose one were interested in looking up all possible references on vitamins. The first place to which to turn naturally would be the heading 'Vitamins' in the indexes to the various references sources to be used. This would rarely, if ever, be far enough to go. If only one of the indexes contained 'see also' cross references, these might be helpful in the use of the other indexes. This playing of one index against another, so to speak, is always a possible means of helping out. Cross references should be looked for.

To be complete, Dr. Crane advises looking also under the following headings: "Foods," "Diet," "Feeding Experiments," "Nu-

trition," "Plant Nutrition," "Plants," "Auximones," "Diseases,"
"Avitaminosis," "Polished Rice," "Fat-soluble A," "Water-soluble
B," and in the earlier literature "Nutramines," "Bios," and
"Oryzanin."

The following comments and rules are given by
Dr. Smith:[3]

> Searchers need not become expert indexers of chem-
> ical literature, but the better they understand indexers' prob-
> lems and answers, the shorter the path to information needed
> from an index. Through all the maze of word, formula, num-
> ber, and punch-position lanes for placing and retrieving in-
> formation, the searcher must choose his starting point and
> his path. If he chooses wisely in a well-indexed area, his
> search turns up all pertinent information entered in the
> system. If he knows how well the system covers the field, he
> has a fair estimate of how near his search comes to totality.
> Successful searching demands a balanced blend of training,
> experience, and the faculty known as horse sense.
> Start with exact definitions of coverage in time, sub-
> ject matter, and sources. Find out where prior searchers
> stopped (on all three counts), and start there. Slant the whole
> job to the basic purpose (background, critical review, read-
> ing list, anticipation, interference, infringement, state of the
> art, etc.). Reserve bulldog tenacity for 'must' assignments; on
> all ordinary jobs, abandon any line of inquiry when yield
> value drops below operating cost, and close the project when
> the results are reasonably adequate.

When the possibilities of one plan of searching appear to be exhausted, it is well to try a new approach; the few new
references turned up may include something of value. Two additional approaches are suggested.

AUTHOR INDEX

It may not appear that one searching for information on a particular subject would have any use for the author
index, but an individual who writes an article or takes out a
patent in some field is apt to repeat the offense and may well be

[3] Julian F. Smith, in "Searching the Chemical Literature," *Advances in Chemistry Series No. 4*, American Chemical Society, 1951, pp. 19-23.

watched for several years thereafter. After finding a considerable number of articles or patents on the subject in hand, it is well to make a list of the authors concerned and look them up in the name indexes for some years covering the period of their probable activity. This can be done rapidly if the names are arranged in alphabetical order, as then one can follow the index right through. The references found are scanned for possible bearing on the problem in hand. This method is particularly useful as an aid in patent searches, since patents are made as broad as possible and their titles frequently do not suggest many of the processes which they are intended to cover or which they may be later stretched so as to cover. It has the merit of turning up more recent references.

CHAIN LETTER SYSTEM

If Smith writes to five friends advising them to buy his cough drops and asking each of them to write to five and each of these to five and so on for eleven times, 61,035,155 people or about as many of the people of the United States who may be supposed to have coughs at one time will receive letters, provided everyone writes. If one reads an article on a topic, one usually finds more than five references to the work of others along the same line. These are looked up and new references obtained from each, and so on back. A surprisingly full literature review of a subject may be made in this way, and this method should never be neglected in making a search, though it is to be regarded as supplemental. A weakness of this plan is that the references multiply as one goes backward in the years, while as a matter of fact the number of articles appearing is increasing from year to year; thus one locates only a small proportion of recent articles.

When the index method is employed, it is best to begin with the last index, work backward from year to year, and add to the references thus found all those in the articles as they are looked up. As each article is abstracted, references to other articles may be added to the abstract to be checked off as they are looked up. All the references, primary, secondary, tertiary, and so on, may be written down. As they are looked up, they are checked off, the important ones being abstracted in the notebook or on cards. Some time may be saved by placing all references to one journal on one sheet of paper and those to another journal on another, and then looking up all those in a given journal in succession, rather than running from one part of the library to the other.

The same methods apply to the search for patents on a given subject. Patents are abstracted and indexed by *Chemical Abstracts* along with articles. A more comprehensive treatment of patent searches is given in chapter 20.

FORMULA INDEXES

For looking up particular compounds in *Chemical Abstracts* or in *Beilstein,* formula indexes are convenient.

In the telephone directory, the subscribers' names are arranged alphabetically so that you know just where to find any particular person's name. If you do find it, you know exactly how to locate him. In the formula index, all known compounds are arranged in a certain order, there being one and only one place for each compound. When you find it in the index you are told exactly where to find it in *Beilstein* or in *Chemical Abstracts.* Two or more isomers have the identical empirical formula, but you can select the one you want. In the Baltimore telephone directory, the name William Smith appears nine times. You have to identify your friend by his street address.

Formula indexes have been adapted to chemical compounds in general, but are more commonly used for organic compounds to which the present discussion will be limited. Two systems are in use, the American, suggested by Professor Hill, and the German system.

In the dictionary we have several words starting with ab, abacus, abbess, abdicate, and abscond. These are arranged alphabetically according to the third letter. In the American system, starting with compounds which contain hydrogen as well as carbon, we have: $CHBr_3$, $CHCl_3$, CHF_3, CHI_3, and CHN, which are arranged alphabetically according to the third element. Later on we find CH_2Br_2, CH_2Cl_2, and CH_2O, followed by CH_3Br, CH_3Cl, etc. The compounds are arranged in the order of the number of carbon atoms and then according to the number of hydrogens, and then according to those containing a third element alphabetically.

In the German system, used in *Richter* and in the first formula index to *Beilstein,* the compounds are divided into classes according to the number of different kinds of atoms in addition to carbon. Hydrocarbons are in class I. Thus CH_4 and $C_{10}H_{22}$ are in class I, $CHCl_3$ would be in class II, and CH_2BrCl would be in class III. There is another difference. Thus oxygen, the most common element next to carbon and hydrogen, in organic compounds, is given preferential treatment and CH_2O comes before CH_2Br_2, in spite of the fact that O follows Br in the alphabet. The order would be reversed in the American system. Nitrogen comes next to oxygen. The less common elements are arranged alphabetically.

If a compound is to be looked up in a formula index, its empirical formula must be written according to the system of the index. If we wish to look up *p*-chlorobenzamide in *Beilstein* we write it C_7H_7ONCl, while to find it in *Chemical Abstracts* we write it C_7H_7ClNO.

A SIMPLE EXAMPLE

If a student wants to make tridecyl benzoate, he will need to know:

1. Whether it has been made.
2. How to make it.
3. Its probable properties.

To answer the first question he writes the empirical formula and looks it up in the formula index to *Beilstein*. If it is not there, he can assume that it had not been made up to January 1, 1920. From there on, reliance must be put on *Chemical Abstracts*. The cumulative formula indexes up to volume 40 save time; for the rest, use has to be made of the decennial subject indexes. Since the compound which is to be made is an ester, it is helpful to read the chapter on esterification in *Groggins' Unit Processes* to get background. Then it is desirable to look up the preparation of benzoic esters, particularly those of higher-weight alcohols. As tridecanol is a scarce alcohol, methods which require small quantities of materials must be considered. The isolation and purification of a product are as important as its preparation. The methods to be used for the isolation and purification of the compound to be made can be adapted from those that have been used for closely analogous compounds. When the compound is finally prepared, its physical properties should be checked by comparison with those of homologs. Of all properties, the melting point is the most important, since it is the most characteristic and the most sensitive to the presence of impurities. If the compound is what it should be, its melting point should fit into the pattern obtained by plotting others of the series.

SEARCHING DISSERTATIONS

In chapter 16, dissertations have been discussed as primary sources of chemical information. Some of this appears in chemical journals and some as microfilms, but much of it is difficult to obtain. The problem of obtaining information from dissertations is discussed by Crane, Patterson and Marr in their book,[1] which has been mentioned earlier in this chapter.

SEARCHING GOVERNMENT PUBLICATIONS

Government publications have been mentioned in a previous chapter as primary sources of information. There is no simple way of searching the enormous amount of scientific and practical information that they contain. The methods that are available are discussed by Crane, Patterson and Marr,[1] pp. 183-98, to which reference should be made.

RECORDING INFORMATION

The immediate product of a search of the *C.A.* subject index is an accumulation of *C.A.* references. It is desirable to write each of these on a card. Each reference is looked up and the reference to the original, journal, volume, page, and the author's name, added. Then the salient facts from the abstracts are written on the lower part of the card. When this has been done for all of the cards, the originals are consulted as far as practicable for further information which is entered on the card. If necessary, one or more additional cards are used. Additional references uncovered in this process are written on other cards to be looked up and added to the collection. On each card is written the main subject and a subdivision. This is the first stage. These cards, when properly filled out, constitute the material from which an article or report is to be written.

For writing the report, the cards are sorted according to the main subjects and to their subdivisions. These groups and subgroups of cards are arranged according to the outline that has been adopted. Writing the report from logically arranged cards becomes a comparatively simple matter. There will, of course, be much checking and rechecking to insure the incorporation of all of the material and some shifting of cards.

My five volume book: *Organic Chemistry of Bivalent Sulfur,*[4] was written entirely from cards. Many references were collected in the course of several investigations. Where practicable, the originals were read and abstracted on cards. Later on I went through, item by item, certain sections of each number of *C.A.,* writing down column numbers of sulfur references. Then a card was written for each as outlined here. The cards were then divided into broad classes, mercaptans, sulfides, mercaptals, etc. The mercaptan cards were sorted into occurrence, preparation, reactions, etc. The cards in each subgroup were arranged in logical order and the chapter written directly from them. Some 40,000 cards were used in this way. At the end, the cards for each chapter were alphabetized for the bibliography. This looks simple, but actually it required many years of part-time work. It could not have been accomplished but for the capable assistance of Dr. Jane Dick Meyer.

---

[4] New York, Chemical Publishing Co.

HANDLING REFERENCE CARDS

Just how reference cards are to be handled depends on their number and the purposes that they are to serve. Individuals have their preferences as to size of cards and how they are to be handled. Small collections can be sorted by hand as desired. When the number of cards in a collection reaches into the thousands, hand sorting becomes tedious. Punched cards and mechanical sorting are being developed for handling this situation. Perfection is yet to be attained, but substantial progress is being made.

This is not the place for a detailed description of punched cards and their uses, but the principle can be stated briefly. Holes are punched in numerically designated positions. A code has to be established, assigning numbers to the various groups or atoms that may be present in a compound. Physical and pharmacological properties may be handled similarly. In the never-ending search for chemical agents for various purposes, many thousands of compounds have been prepared and tested, 14,000 tested as antimalarials have been catalogued. Suppose 5,000 compounds, tested as pesticides, have been put on punched cards. By running these through the machine all compounds containing sulfur or chlorine, for example, or all those effective against certain insects, can be sorted out.

For use in limited searches, in which not more than 500 compounds are involved, cards having marginal holes can be purchased. By means of a long needle one can lift out cards which carry compounds with selected characteristics.

I can dial the number of any one of the many thousands of telephone subscribers in Baltimore within ten seconds. Behind this quick service is an immense amount of labor, installing the telephones, running thousands of miles of wire, constructing dialing mechanisms, and printing directories. The machine sorting of 14,000 cards requires only a few seconds, but it took Wiselogel many months to code that number of possible antimalarials and put them on punched cards.

The development of machine sorting has been traced in editorial reports[5] in *Chemical & Engineering News*. Dyson of England has been a leader in devising codes, one of which is known by his name.

Another approach to the problem is described.[6] The Dow coding system uses high-speed computers. One reel of magnetic tape can store more than 25,000 coded structures of average complexity. The structures of 1,000,000 compounds can be stored on tape reels occupying less than 30 inches of shelf space. A thousand organic compounds can be searched in two to fifteen seconds.

One coding system uses 332 structural elements to which are assigned three-digit numbers.[6] It is claimed that this code is able to supply an unequivocal representation of the compounds, and is simple to learn and to apply.

[5] *Chem. Eng. News,* **32,** 866 (1954); **33,** 2838 (1955).
[6] Ascher Opler and Ted R. Norton, *Chem. Eng. News,* **34,** 2812-6 (1956).

20. Patent searches

INTRODUCTION

A chemist working on a technical problem must, of course, take into account all patents in the field. It is obviously poor business to spend time and money elaborating a process which has been covered by patents belonging to other people. An exact knowledge of the patents in a particular field is necessary to avoid infringing them and is good insurance against the possibility of unfair prosecution. The investigator in pure chemistry is not in fear of legal penalties in case he trespasses on a field covered by a patent but is bound by the scientific code to give credit due for ideas and data wherever published, so he must be able to search patents as well as articles.

The modern abstract journals treat patents as any other publication, abstracting, classifying, and indexing them so that the chemist frequently does not need to go further; but when a thorough search is to be made, it must be based on the patents themselves. An abstract of a patent is not the patent either in science or in law. A fortune may hang on the wording of a sentence: A patent supposed to be worth millions may be invalidated by the unearthing of a statement or claim in a prior patent.

PATENT SEARCHING OUTSIDE
OF THE PATENT OFFICE

BY ROBERT CALVERT, PH.D.
Patent Attorney[1]

IMPORTANCE OF PATENTS AS LITERATURE

The chemist will find a source of abundant, valuable, and concise information in patents, particularly in United States patents. These are now being issued at the rate of about 52,500 a year, not counting design or reissue patents. Patents of all classes, as bound by the Government, make 262 large volumes a year. In processing these patents and also the applications that become abandoned, the Government spends just over twenty million dollars a year. The cost to the patent owners is much larger, the research basis for a single patent application by a corporation often amounting to several thousand dollars or more. The results from these expenditures are available to the chemist. They should be utilized.

At the time of publication, patents as a class are considered the most nearly up to date of all chemical literature. This is true especially for developments that promise to be of commercial value, such as those of primary concern to the great industrial laboratories. Such organizations will ordinarily apply for patent or patents on important inventions almost as soon as a plateau has been reached in the research and several years before the publication of details in the technical journals. Perkin Medal addresses and the like, inspiring as they are, are frequently

---

[1] Author of *Patent Practice and Management*.

interesting and personalized accounts of what has been largely described in patents several years before. Even in the case of atomic energy, when the patents now applied for finally break through the necessary secrecy bar and appear in volume, it will no doubt be evident that the Government has utilized this method of publication almost exclusively for the details of an extremely large number of patentable discoveries in this field.

A second advantage of patents as literature is the fact that they are written by professional writers. For example, whereas the chemist may report the use for a special purpose of sulfuric acid, the patent covering the new application will state the general properties required in the acid to be used and list three or more alternatives. The patent will or should follow this general procedure for each class of materials used, then give the proportions and the ranges within which the invention is workable, conditions of operation, and limits also to those conditions, such as temperature, pressure, and time or the end point to which the reaction is carried. Examples then illustrate the invention. Seldom is so much useful information of a chemical nature presented in an original communication in such short space as in a well-written chemical patent.

AVAILABILITY OF PATENTS

The Patent Office "Search Room" has the millions of United States patents carefully classified and separated into trays arranged numerically to correspond to an index number for each subject. This index number is shown in the *Manual of Classification of the United States Patent Office.*

Since relatively few chemists ever go to this search room, they must either rely upon professional searchers or do the searching for patents elsewhere.

The literature available locally to chemists for searching patents and the manner of obtaining a patent search without the chemist himself going to Washington are discussed here, the actual searching of the patent files in Washington being the subject of the following section.

SPECIAL PATENT SERVICES

Ordering patents in advance from the United States Patent Office is probably the most effective manner of keeping informed on United States patents in a given field. One interested in a particular subject may locate the class and subclass numbers of the subject in the *Manual of Classification* or determine the numbers through his patent attorney. Then he may place with the Patent Office the order for patents in that subclass as they issue.

The principal rules relating to this service are, in effect, as follows:

The Patent Office charges a yearly service fee for selecting patents as they issue weekly. This fee is payable at the beginning of each fiscal year (July 1) and is computed as follows: $1.00 for the entry of the order for one subclass and 10¢ for each additional subclass.

The Office requires that a deposit of funds be credited to an account, to pay for the cost of copies of patents at 25¢ each as they issue and are mailed. The amount of this deposit is computed in accordance with the activity of the subclass ordered.

If it should be found that the number of patents received is so large as to make the cost objectionable, too few of the patents forwarded are of direct interest, or the wrong subclass has been ordered, then the service may be discontinued by simply cancelling the order.

Abstracts of patents issued abroad may be obtained through the Technical Information Company, Chancery House, Chancery Lane, London W. C. 2, England. Thus the abstracts of the British patent application, as published for possible opposition proceedings in the fields of chemistry and chemical engineering, may be obtained on a weekly basis for a fee. A firm in the plastics industry, for instance, may take this service, clip all the abstracts that seem to be of interest to its research or other departments, paste these on backing sheets, and then photostat and distribute the sheets.

The same English firm, for an annual fee, supplies abstracts in English, also on a weekly basis, of German applications at the same stage, i.e., laid open to inspection. This particular service is in reality an English translation of what is called the *German Patents Gazette*.

Other organizations make available abstracts in certain fields of chemical research. Thus *British Plastics Abstracts* also can be obtained for an annual fee. The separate abstracts so supplied are understood to number close to 5,000 a year. They relate to patents and also journal articles on plastics in major countries, including the United States.

ENCYCLOPEDIAS

Many important patents are shown in Kirk and Othmer's, *Encyclopedia of Chemical Technology*,[2] in the bibliographies at the ends of the major sections of that admirable work. A test made with "Amino Resins and Plastics," selected as a representative title, shows reference in Kirk and Othmer to 41 journal articles and 43 patents. Ordering those of these patents which are of direct interest from the United States Patent Office would bring much late and useful information. Since each patent now has, at its end, a list of the references cited by the Patent Office during the prosecution of the application to the stage of issuance as a patent, the patents obtained would supply a list of additional patents or other art of probable interest.

CHEMICAL ABSTRACTS

Another convenient source of patent references is the *Chemical Abstracts*. In the case of the representative title selected for the present test, a recent annual index of *Chemical Abstracts* shows 26 references during the year to journal articles and 24 to patents, under the headings "Aminoplasts" and "Urea (and Melamine) Condensation Products with HCHO."

[2] New York, Interscience Publishers, 1947-56.

ANNUAL INDEX OF PATENTS

The *Annual Index of Patents,* published and sold by the United States Government Printing Office, is less satisfactory in searching patent subject matter than might be supposed. The difficulty arises from titles for patents that are not sufficiently specific for index purposes. It will be recalled that many patents formerly were entitled as broadly as "Composition of Matter." While such nonsignificant titles are now resisted in the Patent Office, the custom still remains with the inventors of choosing titles carelessly. This makes for unsatisfactory indexing, especially since the Patent Office hesitates to change titles unnecessarily or to select index words that might infer a more narrow scope of inventions than the inventors had intended. It should not be surprising, therefore, that a recent *Annual Index of Patents* showed under the test titles "Aminoplasts," etc., only 5 patents that could be identified from the most probable entries in the index. This is only 5/24ths of the number located in *Chemical Abstracts* for the same year on the same subject. It should be noted, however, that the *Abstracts* include both United States and foreign patents.

The Official Gazette of the United States Patent Office

The *Gazette* is free of this difficulty. A chemist examining the titles in the weekly issues will note abstracts of possible interest to him. By reading the claim or claims that follow the title for each patent, he will see quickly whether or not the patent is one that he should order.

The *Gazette* is useful, in fact, not only in keeping a research group informed, but also in stimulating thought and imagination. For this reason, most research laboratories employing six or more chemists are justified in subscribing to the *Gazette* ($30.00 a year) and assigning to one member of the group the glancing through the chemical section of the *Gazette* each week. There he will find usually about two hundred chemical patents (235 in a late issue) reviewed weekly. The separation of the abstracts by classes, into "General and Mechanical," "Chemical," and "Electrical," saves much time for the specialized worker who formerly was obliged to hunt through five hundred to a thousand entries each week, to discover the much smaller number relating strictly to chemistry.

In reading the *Gazette,* it is well to remember that the claims selected for publication are the ones considered to be broad and representative.

The *Gazette* shows for each patent the total number of claims that the patent contains, regardless of the number published in the *Gazette.*

Although very satisfactory in keeping the chemist informed week by week of the trend of research and of work of direct interest to him, the *Gazette* is unsatisfactory, or at the best inconvenient, for reviewing at any one time the patents issued on a given subject over a long period of time. It is unsatisfactory for this purpose even when used in connection with the *Annual Index of Patents,* in view of the indexing difficulties described.

For information on chemical patents, issued during the last quarter of the past century and the first quarter of this, reference should be made to Friedländer's *Fortschritte der Teerfarbenfabrikation* (Advances in the Manufacture of Coal-Tar Dyes).[3] The name stems from the fact that the great German chemical industry was centered almost entirely on the manufacture of dyes from coal-tar derivatives. However, patents on organic compounds other than dyes were also included and ample coverage was given to German chemical patents, with scant attention to those from other countries.

The importance of Friedländer declined with the rise of abstract journals.

ATTORNEYS' SEARCHES

Patent searches ordered through attorneys are a common means of being informed as to the state of the patent art on a specific matter. A request for such a search is ordinarily forwarded by the attorney to some professional searcher known

---

[3] Berlin, Julius Springer Verlag, 1877 to 1942 (25 volumes).

to make a business of searching the classified patent files for clients. The searcher is usually so selected as to be highly experienced in the chemical or other art to which the search relates. He first locates the index number and in many cases several numbers that may apply. Then he looks through the trays of patents classified under the selected numbers. Often he searches several classes. He orders for the client those patents that seem to him to be of interest.

Searches can be made in a few hours or a few weeks. Because of competitive rates, most searches to show patentability of an invention are very brief. A thorough search, such as one relating to patent infringement or patent validity, however, may reach a $1,000 or more in cost. It is well, therefore, to make clear to the attorney the approximate extent of the search you wish unless he knows from past association what you want.

Regardless of the extent of the search, only a search that finds what it seeks is conclusive. A negative result cannot be accepted with finality as showing that what was not found does not really exist. Further searching might reveal it.

PATENT SEARCHING IN THE PATENT OFFICE
BY W. W. AMMEN [4]

WHEN SHOULD PATENTS BE EXAMINED?

The answer to this question must depend especially on the nature of the matter under investigation.

1. Is it purely scientific and academic, without practical phases or possibilities to bring it into the vision of inventors?

2. Has the industry involved resorted much to patents?

In many industries, every slightest variation of practice is marked by a patent, while textbooks, and the technical literature as a whole, deal rather with generalities, or with shop

---

[4] Late of the Philadelphia Patent Bar. Brought up to date by John R. Milburn, patent attorney.

practice, etc. In other industries, the case is just the reverse. They keep important processes and improvements secret. In such industries, relatively little is ever patented and only meager outlines of actual practice find their way into print at all.

COUNTRIES AND PERIODS

Here a background of general and historical knowledge regarding the broad subject involved in the search often affords valuable guidance. No chemist is likely to overlook Germany where dyestuffs are involved; but he also needs to know something of dates at which certain classes of dyes came into use. Likewise, one interested in vacuum tubes or in some classes of electrolytic apparatus may overlook an important field or waste much time if not adequately informed as to the use of vacuum tube or electrolytic detectors in wireless telegraphy.

Besides such special points arising out of the particular subject matter under investigation, certain more general considerations are helpful.

On inventions that are patented at all, applications are generally filed earliest in the country of the inventor's residence. A very large majority of all inventions are made in the progressive industrial countries: Austria, England, France, Germany, and the United States: to a less extent, Switzerland, the Scandinavian countries, Italy, Canada, and Japan; also Belgium, Holland, and Australia. However, most inventions of any practical value that are patented in *any* country are usually eventually patented in one or more of the five more important ones first mentioned.

Good searching facilities are available in this country for American, British, German, French, Austrian, Swiss, Swedish, Danish, and Norwegian patents. After these have been examined with reasonable thoroughness, the labor of covering other countries becomes so much greater in proportion to the diminished chance of finding a reference as to be well nigh prohibitive—unless, of course, peculiar circumstances point to some particular country's patents as being especially promising.

More or less frequently, the searcher will find a

relevant patent in some country other than that of the patentee. It is then often desirable to examine the indexes of patentees issued by that inventor's own country, to see whether he has not patented the invention at home. The reason for this is twofold: 1. The home patent may sometimes contain descriptive matter that is omitted from the patents taken out in other countries; and 2. its date may be earlier.

It is frequently useful also, to know something about the practice of issuing patents in various countries. In England, for example, all applications on which patents are not granted within a certain time are thrown open to public inspection. In most of the important countries, patents are granted only after an examination for novelty, which necessarily consumes more or less time, and may result in more or less change of the specifications. In France, however, the specification regularly issues just as filed with the application; and in Belgium, the specification so issues with extreme and invariable promptitude, in fact, only about one month after the application there.

Therefore, some concerns have agencies in these countries to watch and send them copies of all patents along certain lines as soon as made public, in order to know at the earliest moment what patents they must ultimately expect to see granted in the countries where they have important interests.

In this connection, it is desirable to refer briefly to the *International Convention for the Protection of Industrial Property,* an agreement to which most of the countries mentioned are parties. Under this agreement, a patent application filed in any of the countries adhering to it, by a citizen of *any* adhering country has the same effect as if filed on the date of the *first* application filed by the same applicant (or his assignor) in any *other* adhering country. This means that, in case of several applications for the same invention, preference is given to the one with earliest filing date in *any* "convention country."

This right of priority, however, is subject to one important limitation. It exists only in favor of applications filed *within one year* after the first in a convention country. Thus we rarely find a patentee with patents for which the applications spread over more than a year; for otherwise the later patents would generally be void. This limitation greatly reduces the period to be covered in running down all patents issued under the right of one inventor to a particular invention. It does *not,* however, of course, preclude the existence of *other* patents on a like invention under the right of some *other* inventor. However, by minor modifications, one patent may be strung out into a series covering a number of years.

FACILITIES FOR PATENT SEARCHING

A great many libraries in this country have substantially complete sets of United States patents, and a smaller number have sets of the patents of various foreign countries, such as British, French, German, etc. German patents are rare in this country. In most or all cases, such sets are simply bound in numerical order for convenient reference, so that it is really impracticable to use them for searching. In the United States Patent Office at Washington, however, sets of American, British, German, Austrian, Swiss, Swedish, Danish, Norwegian, and French patents are available classified nearly according to the official classifications of the country of origin. Generally speaking, it is on the whole rather preferable to search them about in the order of their enumeration here. The French is given as last because the classification is unsatisfactory and a search in them is often very time-consuming and tedious.

Anyone starting his first search in the Patent Office at Washington will find the clerk who sits in and directs the search room most able, willing, helpful, and all but a walking encyclopedia of information as to files of patents to be searched.

LOCATION OF FACILITIES

In the "Classification Division," you will find a numerical list giving the official classification of all United States Patents in the "Revised Classes," and of a considerable number of those of other countries.

In the *Search Room,* which is open until 9 o'clock each day through Friday without any charge for the time after

5 o'clock, and until 12:30 P.M. on Saturdays, but not at all on Sundays or holidays, there is:

1. a complete set of United States patents, arranged according to the official classification, and extensively cross-referenced

2. a complete set of the *Official Gazette*

Bound volumes of United States patents, arranged in numerical order, are located in the *Search Room* and the *Scientific Library*. Bound volumes of foreign patents are in the stacks adjoining the *Scientific Library*.

In the *Attorney's Room,* which is part of the *Search Room* but with another clerk in charge, the application for any United States patent may be ordered down from the files and examined. This is not only useful in determining the scope of the "claims" of a patent, but also in finding the references the Patent Office cited as bearing on its subject matter. Often these references extend to features not contained in the claims as issued. Files may be obtained here within about one hour for patents of higher number than No. 2,050,000; the older ones require two days as they are stored elsewhere.

In the various *Examining Divisions,* there are duplicate classified sets of the United States patents in the classes over which each has jurisdiction in reference to applications for United States patents; also foreign patents relating to the subjects handled in the division, *classified more or less according to the United States official classification.*

In addition, various examiners (especially in the chemical divisions) have "unofficial" cross references, digests of particular subjects along lines different from those of the official classification, or have the official subclasses further subdivided for their own convenience. Permission to examine such material can generally be secured, and may result in shortening the search or putting one on the track of references one might not find otherwise, and of classes one might not think of investigating otherwise.

The *Scientific Library,* adjacent to the *Search Room* also closes at 5 o'clock and is not open on Saturday.

This room houses, besides the official classification

of the German Patent Office and its index, mentioned previously, the official *Classification of the British Patent Office,* and a small booklet published by the British Patent Office containing (in English) the official classification of the remaining six of the nine countries mentioned before, and one or two others.

As to all of these, it may be said generally that the British, French, German, and Swiss classifications differ greatly from those of the United States and from one another; the Swedish, Danish, and Norwegian patents are arranged according to the German scheme, but with less subdivision; and the Austrian is also much like the German, but with some minor modifications.

In the *Scientific Library,* you will find also periodical publications of most of the patent offices of the world corresponding more or less to the *Official Gazette* of the United States Patent Office and to the indexes in the *Annual Report of the Commissioner of Patents,* etc. These are sometimes useful in ascertaining the exact dates of issue, publication or "sealing," etc., of foreign patents, or in running down patents in various other countries corresponding to one of interest, or in determining whether or not a particular patent is still in force; also in ascertaining the native classification of a particular patent.

Besides the classified sets of British, German, Austrian, Swiss, Swedish, Danish, Norwegian, and French patents, there are *numerically* arranged sets of these and of the patents of several other countries. These are useful not only for general reference, but also in finding the native official classification of patents known to relate to the subject under investigation—for the patents of most foreign countries bear the official classification as part of the title at the head of the specification.

Of all patents the British are, perhaps, the easiest and most satisfactory to search, especially as so many inventions made elsewhere are patented in England. Not only is the classification exceedingly good, but the search is carried out on an excellent system of abridgments, so that it proceeds more rapidly than if the patents themselves had to be examined. Instead of being subdivided, each class is provided with periodic sets of *index headings,* which bring together cognate patents of the period on almost every conceivable basis of similarity. Indeed, this feature is equivalent to a number of independent classifications rolled together, with thorough cross-referencing thrown in. The system appears to have been applied to all the patents regardless of the division into main classes, as well as within each class. Its only drawback is that in recent years the number of patents to be looked up under any heading tends to be tediously large, so that where the feature sought for can be picked out in a drawing, at least, it is often quicker to go through a class page by page.

As the searcher will quickly find, the numbering of the older British patents starts afresh each year, the numbers being those of the applications as originally filed. In 1916, however, the continuous system of numbers used in most other countries was adopted also in England, starting at 100,000.

The present system of British abridgments begins with the year 1855. There are abridgments prior to this, but differently classified, and intrinsically much inferior. In many cases, of course, it is not necessary to look at them; but occasionally it may be found well worth while.

After the British, the German patents are the most satisfactory to search. The classification is good and the subdivision has been carried to the point where the number of patents in a final subclass is generally small, so that subclasses can often be searched in a very short time. The German set in the United States Patent Office begins with 1892, almost coinciding with the period of our more modern industrial development.

The Austrian, Swiss, and the Scandinavian countries' patents are very much on a par, but the ultimate divisions to be searched are larger than in the German classification and the likelihood of a reference not duplicated or paralleled elsewhere is generally small.

The French patents are exceedingly unsatisfactory to search. The classification is cumbersome and unscientific.

PROCEDURE RECOMMENDED FOR PATENT SEARCHES

While everyone will naturally develop his own procedure with experience and vary it according to peculiar circumstances of particular cases, for the beginner, who feels at a loss where to start, the following suggestions may not come amiss.

1. If you know of any patents closely relevant to your subject, it is well to ascertain their classification in their native patent systems. This will serve as a starting point in examining the classifications. If the closeness of such preknown references to the points on which the search is being made seems to show that the best existing references will probably be found there, it may be well to search such subclasses at once. In this way one gains a certain perspective, as well as a standard of comparison for references to be examined later. Both of these lines of orientation are useful in determining what further portions of the classified patent sets should be examined.

2. Examine the *United States Manual of Classification*. Besides looking in its subject index under such terms as may naturally suggest themselves, it is always advisable to go over the list of main classes and to examine the subclass lists of all main classes that seem likely to contain relevant matter.

3. Confer with the *Search Room Examiner*.

Approaching the matter from these angles, it is only a question of interpreting the class and subclass titles and understanding the general scheme of classification (explained in the front of the *Manual*) to make sure, at least, of not overlooking any possibly relevant subclasses. At the risk of repeating what is stated in the *Manual*, we advise here that the searcher note for first examination the subclasses with the most specific titles that might embrace relevant material, marking those with broader and more-inclusive titles to be looked at later.

In determining what subclasses to examine, it is necessary, of course, to consider such possibilities as the following in reference to the essentials of the ideas sought:

a. Their application to uses other than that particularly sought, or under more or less different conditions.

b. Their use in various combinations with other instrumentalities, or outside of any combination.

c. Their possibilities in reference to the several components of the idea sought, especially in cases where the idea sought is an improvement in one component of some old combination.

If, after exhausting the apparent possibilities of the *Manual*, no promising subclasses are found, or the number to be examined seems too large, it may be worth while to ascertain from the *Manual* which of the *Examining Divisions* of the Patent Office has the classes that seem most relevant, and consult some of the Examiners. Otherwise, it is usually advisable to postpone such consultation to a later stage of the search. It may be added that the classification of chemical subjects is very unsatisfactory and difficult to understand; it has recently been receiving considerable attention from the *Classification Division*.

4. Having arrived at an apparently complete program of subclasses, proceed with the actual examination of the United States patents in the *Search Room*, taking the various subclasses in the order of promise.

The reasons for starting with United States patents are, first, the advantage of "breaking in" on a subject in a familiar language with the possibility of expert assistance and, second, the saving in cost, since United States patents are sold at 25 cents each as compared with about 30 cents *a sheet* for photostats of foreign patents. It is wasteful to order extensive foreign references if equally good are to be found among United States patents. When there is plenty of time, foreign patents can be obtained more cheaply from the governments that issue them.

READING UNITED STATES PATENTS

In examining the United States patents, one is usually justified in relying on a rather rigorously enforced rule of the Patent Office that everything described in a specification which admits of illustration in drawings *must* be so illustrated. Whenever the thing sought falls within this rule, much time is saved by looking primarily at the patent drawings, referring to the reading matter only when one is at a loss to understand the drawings. In this connection, it should be noted that the published *Rules of Practice* of the United States Patent Office contain charts of symbols for the use of draftsmen in making patent drawings, and that these rules can be had gratis. In chemical patents, unfortunately, illustration by drawing is often impossible, and the searcher must read the printed text, which makes the work much slower. Even so, however, it is rarely necessary to read it through from beginning to end in order to determine whether the patent is of interest. Usually reading the first and last claims is sufficient.

When the text, the so-called *specification,* must be referred to, it helps to know the usual arrangement of such documents, foreign as well as domestic:

a. The heading, including the title of the invention patented.

b. An explanation of the general nature or objects of the invention.

c. A brief explanation of the figures if there are any.

d. A specific, detailed description of one or more ways of embodying and carrying out the invention in practice. In the case of a machine or other apparatus of any complexity, this often concludes with an explanation of its operation. Reading "Example 1" is usually enlightening.

e. One or more "claims" defining concisely the invention that the patent is granted to cover, in its various aspects and phases of breadth and of subject matter.

Where the patent has no drawings, or the point sought for is such that it cannot be illustrated, the title of the invention is first noted. If this does not seem to definitely preclude relevance, one naturally reads the general explanation of the invention or a few of the claims. If these neither indicate nor seem absolutely to preclude relevance, one skims over the detailed description. If, however, the claims show some connection with the general subject of the search, it will not do to rely on the fact that they do not involve the particular points sought; for many matters of which no trace appears in the claims may be dealt with in the description.

In each subclass that has been revised by the *Classification Division* should be found a "search card," bearing the definition of that subclass and references to such other classes and subclasses as may contain relevant material. Where applicable to the problem in hand, these references should, of course, be incorporated in the searcher's program.

In working in the *Search Room,* it is well to bear in mind that the material is handled many times over by a great number of people in the course of a year, so that copies of patents become misplaced or even lost and may remain so for some time before the mischance is discovered and rectified by those in charge. It will not do to rely much on the dates marked on the bundles composing a subclass, and still less on the supposedly chronological arrangement of the patents in each bundle. In cases where great thoroughness is desired, it is even advisable to review in the *Examining Division* such subclasses as have proved potentially relevant. This review will proceed much faster than the initial search and, in addition to affording a check on both the searcher's vigilance and *Search-Room* files, it gives the now better-oriented searcher a clearer perspective of the subject, with a chance to pick up references whose full bearing may not have been apparent before.

5. The examination of United States patents in the *Search Room* completed, including any extensions of the original program suggested by the actual search, consultation with the Examiners or Assistant Examiners in charge of the various classes covered is fairly in order. By postponing such consultation to this stage of the search, the searcher gains the advantage of being able to weigh the general value of the advice received and to judge its applicability to his case. Also, he knows better what to ask about. He can tell where he has searched, show his best finds, and ask whether the Examiner knows of better references, or can suggest other subclasses. Time in travel about the office can be saved, of course, by making this consultation the occasion for looking at the Examiners' sets of domestic patents (if it is desired to make such a review as suggested before), cross references, foreign patents, etc.

Almost universally, the Examiners and the other employees of the Patent Office will be found courteous and obliging in their attention to inquiries to a degree quite surprising in view of their own onerous work of examining some 80,000 fresh patent applications filed each year. It is also a source of satisfaction to the searcher to know that he can communicate to them freely the specific subject of his quest without apprehension of its going further.

6. Before considering the examination of United States patents complete, one should, of course, make a point of ascertaining definitely that no new classes or subclasses of interest to him have been created by the *Classification Division* since its latest bulletin. For this purpose, the head of the *Search Room* may be consulted, and also the *Classification Division*. Occasionally, it may seem desirable to consult the Examiner of Classification himself to make sure that no possible field of search has been overlooked.

7. The next step is naturally to examine foreign patents in the *Scientific Library*.

It may naturally be asked why this is worth while, seeing that the *Examining Divisions* have the like material classified according to the *Manual?* Or else why look at the Examiners' sets at all?

In the first place, there is a great advantage in covering the patented "art" from the different points of view of several different classifications, since each classification may take cognizance of some feature of a patent that may have been overlooked or disregarded in another. Moreover, it is to be expected that the patents of each country will be dealt with most carefully by the patent office that granted them.

In the second place, it is a fact that the files of foreign patents in the *Examining Divisions* of the United States Patent Office are by no means so reliable as the files of United States patents. Instead of being attended to by the *Classification Division,* the foreign patents are classified by the Assistant Examiners in charge of the various classes and subclasses, who are seldom familiar with all the languages involved, and have not the time to read the patents through carefully anyhow. When, moreover, the United States classification is changed, and classes or subclasses are transferred from one *Examining Division* to another, the foreign patents are liable to receive very imperfect attention. As a consequence, the files of some very recently revised classes contain scarcely any foreign patents at all.

However, the Examiners' foreign files afford at least *some* chance at the patents of certain countries not classified for searching in the *Scientific Library*.

Experience shows that, in the long run, each way of searching the foreign patents will reveal material not discovered in the other way. Where only *one* way can be afforded, the search in the *Scientific Library* is to be favored as on the whole likely to be the more complete. It has also the advantage that one always has the drawings and text of each patent together before him. However, the search in the Examiner's files, where the text is often filed away separately, can usually be carried through more rapidly.

8. The final step is naturally to run down any leads or "loose ends" of the previous work, such as examining the application files of the nearest United States patents found and the records of any interferences in which they may have been involved. On occasion, copies of the application files of foreign patents may also be ordered from the patent offices of the various countries.

It is usually worth while to examine the technical literature at large for published articles by patentees of closely allied processes.

9. As a check, or in case of necessity, as a substitute, reference should be made to published bibliographies.

GERMAN PATENT PUBLICATIONS

German patent publications and their use are well described by Dr. Jessop.[5]

In most cases, it is a difficult and tedious task to find the specification data of a German patent unless one is familiar with the method of procedure.

The German patent system differs from the United States patent system, in that the German patents are not published in the *Auszüge aus den Patentschriften* (Abstracts of Patent Specifications corresponding to the *United States Patent Office Gazette*) in chronological order, but are distributed, according to their subjects, among various classes

---

[5] Earl N. Jessop, *Ind. Eng. Chem.*, **8**, 1053 (1916). Quoted by permission.

and subclasses. There are approximately 380 classes and subclasses which include many and varied subjects, such as *Sprengstoffe* (Explosives), *Photographie* (Photography), *Tabak, Zigarren, Zigaretten* (Tobacco, Cigars, Cigarettes), etc., with appropriate subclasses. The class especially interesting to chemists is Class 12, *Chemische Apparate und Prozesse* (Chemical Apparatus and Processes). There are numerous subclasses (denoted by letters) to Class 12, *e.g.*, Class 12d, *Klaren, Scheiden, Filtrieren* (Clarification, Separation, Filtration), Class 12h, *Allgemeine elektrochemische Verfahren und Apparate* (General Electrochemical Processes and Apparatus), etc.

Thus the patents are placed in the particular class to which they belong, regardless of a chronological arrangement of numbers, and present a rather confused appearance; e.g., Patent No. 266,863 is followed by Patent No. 267,138.

Corresponding to the Index to the *United States Patent Office Gazette* is the *Verzeichnis erteilter Patente* (Index of Patents Granted), which is the proper starting point in a search for a patent.

There are five sections to the *Verzeichnis* (Index), as follows:

(1) *Chronologische Uebersicht der Patente* (Chronological List of Patents), a chronological list of the patent numbers, followed by the number and letter, showing in which class the patent has been placed.

(2) *Systematische Uebersicht der Patente* (Systematic List of Patents), a chronological list of classes and subclasses, with the patents as they have been distributed, including the patent number, title of patent, date, and a page reference to the *Auszüge* (Abstracts).

(3) *Alphabetisches Namenverzeichnis der Patentinhaber* (Alphabetical Name Index of Patentees) gives the names of patentee, number of patent, class, and a page reference to the above class from which can be obtained the data desired.

(4) *Alphabetisches Sachverzeichnis* (Alphabetical Subject Index) indexes the patents according to subjects and gives the patent number, class, and a page reference to section 2 above. This list gives no names.

(5) *Verzeichnis der Patente* (Index of Patents):

(a) *Nach Patentklassen geordnet* (Arranged according to classes).

(b) *Nach Patentnummern geordnet* (Arranged according to numbers).

This list gives all patents which are in effect at that

date, but gives only the patent numbers. In (b) the patent numbers are given, and after them are the class numbers and letters given in parentheses.

The only index given in the *Auszüge* (Abstracts) is the chronological list of classes and subclasses, with the patents included in them.

With this preliminary information, the method of procedure, which is comparatively simple, is as follows: There are three possible starting points, *viz.*:

I. Patent Number. II. Name of Patentee. III. Subject of Patent.

I. If the number of the patent is known, . . . *first . . . find . . . the year . . . the patent was published.*

Then look in either the first or last table in the *Verzeichnis* (Index) for that year—where the patent numbers are arranged consecutively and a class number will be found following the patent number. Then look under that class in the *Systematische Uebersicht* (Systematic List) and here will be found the patent number, name of patentee, title of patent, date, and a page reference to the *Auszüge* (Abstracts) for the same year. On this page in the *Auszüge* (Abstracts) will be found a short abstract of the patent (such as appears in the *United States Patent Office Gazette*).

II. If only the name of the patentee is known, look in *Alphabetisches Namenverzeichnis der Patentinhaber* (Alphabetical Name Index of Patentees) and there will be found the patent number, class number, and a page reference to *Systematische Uebersicht* (Systematic List). From this point the procedure is the same as in I.

III. If only the subject of the patent is known, look in *Alphabetisches Sachverzeichnis* (Alphabetical Subject Index) and there will be found the patent number, class number, and a page reference to *Systematische Uebersicht* (Systematic List), but no names are given in this section. From this point the method is the same as before.

If neither the number of the patent nor the name of the patentee were known, but only the subject, the patent could be located by looking under *Wasserstoff* (Hydrogen) in the *Alphabetische Sachverzeichnis* (Alphabetical Subject Index), where there would be given the patent number, class, etc., and from this the patent could be traced as explained above.

21. ∎ Literature chemists

INTRODUCTION

Once upon a time—in the early part of the nineteenth century—
there was not much chemistry being discovered, and so there was
little difficulty in keeping up with it. Priestley, Scheele, and
Lavoisier devoted only their spare time to chemistry, yet it is
probable that they kept up with practically all that was going
on, either by reading the few publications of their time, or by
personal correspondence. Berzelius packed all the chemistry that
was being produced into his *Jahresbericht* from 1817 to 1847.
Liebig edited the *Annalen* and read all that was published in
chemistry besides engaging actively in research. For his first edition Beilstein assembled all the organic compounds that were
known, classified them, and catalogued their properties with full
references. Remsen founded and edited the *American Chemical
Journal,* while writing chemistry texts and conducting research on
a scale new to America.

With the enormous growth of chemical publications, editing has become a full-time job for many chemists. As mentioned in chapter 18, *Chemical Abstracts* employs more than 50 in the central office and 1500 part-time abstractors. "C.A. workers have often spoken of their work as being more like going to college in many ways. Whether these workers have B.A., M.A., or Ph.D. degrees (there is work for all three kinds) to start, they sometimes claim that they rapidly learn enough more chemistry as to deserve a C.A. degree as significant as any of the others." [1]

The other journals of the American Chemical Society require the services of many more chemists. The same is true of numerous other chemical publications. There is now a Society of Technical Writers and Editors which includes many chemists.

In industrial research organizations, the increasing need of keeping up with the ever-growing amount of chemical literature has shifted many chemists from the laboratory to the library. According to Dr. Hilty of Union Carbide, literature research costs from one third to one half as much as laboratory research.[2]

The publication of the bulletins, which are issued in large numbers by Government departments, requires the services of many chemists. There are many literature consultants who make searches, large or small, for any who may need them. Patent searches give chemists much employment. Altogether we have a host of chemists who handle books and journals rather than chemicals. Chemical literature has become a recognized profession. There is now a Division of Chemical Literature of the American Chemical Society, having about a thousand members and holding regular sessions.

TRAINING OF A LITERATURE CHEMIST

A symposium on the "Training of a Literature Chemist" was held at the Cincinnati meeting of the American Chemical Society in March, 1955, and the papers were published as *Advances in Chemistry Series No. 17* in June 1956. It is gen-

---

[1] Advertisement, *Chem. Eng. News*, January 25, 1960, p. 23, Part II.
[2] Don C. Hilty, *Chem. Eng. News*, February 24, 1958, p. 104.

erally agreed that the literature chemist should have thorough
training in a variety of lines, which, curiously enough, do not
include the handling of chemical literature; he can learn that
on the job. There are no schools that give the M.S. or Ph.D.
degree in literature searching. The emphasis is put on a broad
and thorough knowledge of chemistry. Wayne State University,
after acquiring the Kresge-Hooker Scientific Library, experimented with a doctoral curriculum in chemical literature, but
shifted the emphasis back to chemistry.

"Them that has, gits."

This is an axiom that Euclid missed. Those who
have acquired much knowledge are likely to get more. Only a
chemist can grasp the significance of an item in a chemical
journal.

If a man is not a chemist, putting him in a chair in
the library does not make him a literature chemist. Put a chemist
in that chair and he goes to work; as he works he will acquire
more proficiency and work more effectively. As a matter of fact,
most literature chemists started out in other lines. Some instruction in the handling of chemical literature is given to nearly all
chemistry majors. All through this book emphasis has been put
on the necessity of a chemist being adept at handling books as
well as apparatus. In a book, *Introduction to Organic Research*,[3]
which I wrote many years ago, I devoted six of the eighteen
chapters to chemical literature.

The purpose of this chapter is to present literature
chemistry as an honorable and rewarding career. As in other fields
of chemical endeavor, there are difficulties, sometimes long
stretches of dreary climbing, but ability and industry bring appropriate rewards.

INFORMATION GROUP

In every research organization, there must be one or
more employees whose special function is to secure information

---

[3] E. Emmet Reid, *Introduction to Organic Research*, New York, D. Van
Nostrand, 1924.

about what has been done in the past and what is going on at the present time. We will call this the information group. It will grow in size and its functions will multiply as the organization grows in size and in complexity. We may begin with the technical librarian whose activities have been described by Miss Shorb and Dr. Beck, long with Hercules Powder Co.[4]

They include: 1. reference work, 2. abstracting and indexing, and 3. bibliographical work; sometimes, 4. patent searching, 5. translating, and 6. editing and writing are under the auspices of the technical library, and sometimes they are done by members of other units of a company.

A librarian has been facetiously defined as a person who needs a profound knowledge of what is on the cover of a book. But a reference librarian is quite a different person, one who knows how to find answers to questions by knowing the contents of books. The question in a chemical library may concern a property of one substance, such as the solubility of nitroglycerin in water at a given temperature, or it may be what plasticizers are compatible with a new resin. But in the life of a reference librarian there are also lighter questions, as that of an earnest Ph.D. who hurried up to the desk and asked the young woman there, "What did I come in here for?"

The first essential qualification for successful reference work is to know everything about the collection. What is in it, and how to use it. This involves considerable knowledge of chemical nomenclature, the peculiar arrangements of indexes of chemical compounds and properties, and some knowledge of other languages. If the collection includes not only the usual library tools of published material, but also technical correspondence, patents, research reports, and trade catalogs, the knowledge and versatility needed are multiplied. The reference librarian must also know what is in neighboring libraries and how to bring it to her own clientele.

The multitudinous activities of the information group may be divided into getting past knowledge and keeping up with present developments. When a chemist is assigned to a new project, he needs to dig up information about previous work bearing on his problem. Finding an article, particularly one that is in some obscure place, may take hours, while reading it may

---

[4] Lura Shorb and Lewis W. Beck, *J. Chem. Ed.* **21**, 315 (1944).

require only a few minutes. The literature expert is quicker at finding articles and may locate some that the researcher would miss. However, the research chemist must do his own reading and thinking on the most important articles. He must learn not only the facts stated in an article, but must get the thinking back of them and see implications that touch his work.

Here is an illustration from my own experience. While reading in one of Clemmensen's articles about the reduction of acetophenone to ethylbenzene by amalgamated zinc, I came across a little note in fine print stating that if the reduction were not strong enough some styrene might be formed. It so happened that I had just been reducing cinnamic acid to hydrocinnamic acid by the clumsy sodium amalgam method. Clemmensen had said nothing about the reduction of an unsaturate, but his note implied that styrene could be reduced, and if styrene, why not cinnamic acid. In short order I had all of the hydrocinnamic acid that I wanted. The joke was on Clemmensen. Many years later I found out that he had been given the problem of making hydrocinnamic acid, and the ketone reduction was incidental. I would have missed the significance of that little note if I had not then needed just that information.

When a new line of manufacture is contemplated a "paper project" may be set up. This is a request for the information group to acquire all available information relative to the proposed manufacture, the availability and cost of starting materials, manufacturing costs, probable market, etc.

The patent situation must receive "first aid" treatment. All of this information is to be added to any which can be found in the company's files in order to give management a basis for a decision as to whether or not to go ahead.

It is desirable that the literature chemists keep in touch with the originator of the project and report unexpected findings. An advertisement in a trade journal of a competing product or the issuing of a patent on an analogous process might change the entire course of the investigation or even terminate it. There is the old story of a genealogist being employed to dig up a man's family history and then being paid a larger amount to forget what he found.

The information group is charged with keeping up with current developments. A large research organization may subscribe to 900 journals. In any issue of one of these there may be items affecting the corporation's interests. The group must scan every issue of every one of these journals to pick up all such items. To do this quickly takes experience and skill. It also requires a comprehensive knowledge of all the lines in which the corporation may have interests. This may cover a lot of territory. To catch the less obvious implications of the new knowledge keen insight is needed. They must know the problems on which each chemist is working. A journal containing an item touching the work of Dr. X. is marked and sent to him. All items of possible interest to anyone in the organization are abstracted briefly and put in the weekly abstract bulletin.

Along with the journals come hundreds of patents which must be examined. Any one of these may cut into some investigation that is being carried on. The members of the information group do not have to be patent experts, but they must know enough about patents to spot any that cut close to the corporation's interests. These and new patents that appear to be of interest are noted in the weekly bulletin. Corporations usually have standing orders with the Patent Office for all patents of certain classes, which are mailed as fast as they are issued.

Of course, all research organizations subscribe to *Chemical Abstracts* and use it, but they rely on the information group to secure the information before it appears in *C.A.*, to slant the abstracts more specifically to company interests, and to track down sources (even advertisements) not covered by *C.A.*

QUALIFICATIONS OF A LITERATURE CHEMIST

The qualifications, activities, and opportunities of literature chemists are well stated by Dr. Perry.[5] They are summed up by Dr. Longnecker as follows:[6]

What we want, primarily, are research scientists who have some postdoctoral laboratory experience but are

---

[5] J. W. Perry, *Chem. Eng. News*, **28**, 4530 (1950).
[6] H. C. Longnecker, *J. Chem. Ed.* **33**, 633 (1956).

not "wedded" to the bench; who have as broad a scientific training and background as possible; who are interested in a wide range of subjects; who have a flair for writing and generally have the gift of clear expression; and who wish to work with literature and not in a laboratory, but on equal terms with laboratory and clinical associates. Beyond this, the literature scientist has an excellent opportunity to come up with new ideas. As compared to the bench man, whose readings may be rather specific, the literature scientist is exposed to a wide spectrum of information. Thus, with a realization that the key to the solution to many problems may lie buried in the literature, he is in a most advantageous position to secure new ideas. It is, therefore, not surprising that in the past few years, our science information department has produced a fairly steady flow of ideas on new products and improvements in methods for research and development screening.

As is well stated by Dr. Longnecker, the literature chemist has many opportunities to get suggestions for research in the course of his reading. This happens only when he is research minded and also has a considerable knowledge of the particular field. Things stick only where there is something to which they can stick. As stated by Dr. Perry, it requires much tact to get them across. I knew a chemist who was always thinking up better ways for his fellow chemists to do things. He was really brilliant, but the corporation found that they could get on without him. Conversely some laboratories expect from literature chemists, quite as much as from laboratory investigators, suggestions gleaned from or inspired by their reading. Suggestion forms, subject to customary confidential precautions, are issued to literature chemists as to other chemists.

RESEARCH RECORDS

In chapter 14, emphasis has been placed on the great value of the records of past research which are deposited in a company's library. All of these must be so indexed and filed that the information in them can be made available when needed. The information group must know how to secure from the reports of past research all information needed for present projects. In patent interferences, laboratory note books of the two contestants are compared, page by page, to establish dates and details of experiments. In one patent suit, in which I was a witness, old calendars were produced to verify the days of the week on which the experiments were performed. Some laboratories, under the urging of their patent attorneys, have each day's laboratory records signed by the experimenter and witnessed, each signature being dated, for possible future use as evidence. Storage of microfilm copies is not uncommon as a precaution against loss of records.

LANGUAGE REQUIREMENTS

The language requirements for members of the information group are high. Foreign languages must be read with facility. One must know a language well enough to be able to scan a page and pick out items without reading it line by line. Every information group must have someone who can read Russian and read it easily.

TRANSLATIONS

For one reason or another, many articles have to be translated. This is particularly true of Russian articles. Cooperation has been established to lighten this burden. Information on how to locate translations of Russian articles is given at the end of chapter 17.

22. ∎ Reporting results

INTRODUCTION

At the Baltimore meeting of the American Chemical Society in 1908, I heard a speaker tell a story of how a crusty old manufacturer, who did not believe in technical education, was shown his error. A young graduate applied for a position. As a sort of a dare and also to show the young fellow how his time had been wasted in school, the old chap told him to go into the plant for the afternoon and steal the process if he could. He did so and later spent the evening in writing up a description of the process, handing it the next morning to the manufacturer, who was horrified that his treasured secret process had been found out and so astonished at the insight of the young graduate that he hired him on the spot, "and they lived happily ever after." A second speaker said that the part of the story about unravelling the process seemed reasonable enough, but that a technical graduate could write it up so that it could be understood was unbelievable

337

to him. He slandered chemists, saying that there are some among
them who can write, but the proportion of those who can express themselves clearly and forcefully is sadly small. There are
men who have excellent ideas and can do splendid work but will
always hold subordinate positions because they lack the ability
to present their results.

MARKETING KNOWLEDGE

Every business has two ends: producing and selling.
It may be true that "if you can make something better than anyone else, the world will make a path to your door," but it may
take the world a long time to find out about the product and
still longer to locate your door. Modern business has decided to
hasten the wearing of the path by judicious advertising of the
product and erecting signboards along the way to the proper
door. Millions upon millions of dollars are spent in advertising
and, if it is well done, the more that is spent this way the greater
the profit to the manufacturer and the less the cost of the product
to the public. Some go to the extreme of trying to market a
mediocre product by superlative advertising, and fail because no
one buys a second time. Success comes when a strictly first-class
product is properly introduced to those who need it.

It is well recognized that the chemical profession
does not occupy the position it should because chemistry has not
been "sold" to the public. If we are convinced that we have
something that the world needs, it is for us to inform the world
of that fact; we can hardly expect the lawyers, doctors, and
preachers to do it for us. If they do eventually discover us and
sing our praises, many of us by that time may be too old to
enjoy the music.

The success of the great fruit-raising industry of
California has been due to cooperative marketing associations.
Oranges on the trees are pretty to look at, but those that are
delivered in sound condition and in attractive form to the consumer in the East are the ones that pay for the orchards. Perhaps
sometime a great organizer like those who gathered together the
fruit growers and the tobacco raisers and made them wealthy

will take hold of us chemists and market our product for us, but until then we must do it ourselves.

THE IMPORTANCE OF REPORTS

Chemists of every sort are called upon to present their results either orally or in writing and should see that their findings do not fail of their purpose through faulty presentation. If the results may be published, they must be put into such form that they shall meet the requirements of the editors of the journals and shall produce the desired effect on the reader. The plant chemist must write his monthly reports or must sum up his investigations so that they are properly put on record and reach the desired persons. If he has an idea which he wishes to investigate, he usually has to write it up and present it in order to get an appropriation for the experimental work. The consulting chemist gets money for solving some problem and he must present his findings so that they will be of the utmost service to his client. The form of presentation may be different in these different cases, but the necessity of making clear and forceful statements is common to all.

The university man writes for fellow chemists and has the great advantage of having readers who understand technical language and who can appreciate his results. The plant chemist is under the double necessity of recording his results so fully and clearly that his successors in the laboratory can repeat his experiments, and of translating his conclusions into such language as will be understood by the executives or directors of the company who may be nontechnical businessmen. The consulting chemist must direct the technical men who are to carry out his recommendations and must give the proper impression to the businessmen or bankers who have to decide whether or not to go ahead with the enterprise.

The researcher who publishes his results but fails to present them adequately discounts his own labors. The plant operative who spills half of the product on the floor or lets it go out dirty or in soiled packages will soon be replaced. He is not as bad as the plant chemist who fails to report his experiments or who writes them up so poorly that the proper conclusions cannot be drawn. A restaurant advertises: "the value is on the platter," and so it is; for the diner does not ransack the kitchen. The consulting chemist must realize that the value must be in the report, for it is the report that is handed the client in exchange for his check.

To put the process in chemical terms: Suppose a process employs expensive chemicals and troublesome processes, yet is so worked out that each step is under perfect control and the successive operations give maximum yields right up to the end, but in the final isolation of the product, a faulty still or leaky filterpress wastes half of the product. The plant would soon suspend operations. Reporting a chemical investigation corresponds to separating and boxing up the factory product.

According to Tingle[1] one should treat one's own results with respect:

> Authors should remember that the simple act of publication constitutes, in itself, an invitation to the world to give due credit and honor for the work which is described in their papers. A chemist is, presumably, not likely to underrate the value of his own work; if *he* does not consider it worthy of clear and accurate description, he has no right to expect that busy people will take the time and trouble to acquaint themselves with his results, no matter how important they may be.

Bauer has several things to say about publication:[2]

> I think it may be taken as almost axiomatic that whatever is worthy of investigation should be made known in some effective manner, so as to reach without question those concerned. It should be noted that it is as important to make research work known as it is to do it.

Professor Lamb, who edited the *Journal of the American Chemical Society* for many years, wrote:[3]

> Science progresses by the joint efforts of many workers, each building on the achievements of his predecessors. New discoveries, when published, can shed new light on

---

[1] J. B. Tingle, *Science*, **26**, 627 (1907).
[2] Bauer, *Chem. News*, **100**, 62 (1909).
[3] *Chem. Eng. News*, **27**, 2842 (1949).

thousands of unsolved problems; from a single such discovery, hundreds of new machines or new drugs or a deeper insight into our surroundings may result. On the other hand, new discoveries that remain undisclosed might almost as well not have been made. The prompt and widespread communication of new findings is essential particularly to fellow scientists who can appreciate and use them. Publication is the lifeblood of science!

Doctor Bennett put emphasis on reports:[4]

"Actions speak louder than words," but words have to be used to report actions. The scientist and engineer must explain orally or in writing the significance of their work. The usefulness of research results is partially determined by the clearness and the accuracy of their presentation to interested professional groups . . .
. . . 'the report' constitutes the only visible product of many scientific investigations.

Dr. Gray maintains that reports should be understandable and tells how to make them so.[5]

The writing of scientific papers and reports has been discussed in books.[6] A very practical book on writing technical papers has appeared recently.[7]

In an elaborate and most useful book on graphic methods of presentation, which every chemist should study, Brinton makes some strong statements about presenting ideas and conclusions. Anyone who has had much experience must agree that he is not far wrong.[8]

After a person has collected data and studied a proposition with great care so that his own mind is made up as to the best solution for the problem, he is apt to feel that his work is about completed. Usually, however, when his own mind is made up, his task is only half done. The larger

[4] *Chem. Eng. News*, **26**, 2435 (1948).

[5] D. E. Gray, *J. Chem. Ed.* **25**, 226-8 (1948).

[6] W. Paul Jones, *Writing Scientific Papers and Reports*. Dubuque, Iowa, William C. Brown, 1946.
Siegfried Mandel, Editor, *Writing in Industry*, New York, Plenum Press, Inc. (Reviewed by Saul Herner in *Chem. Eng. News*, May 23, 1960, p. 72.)

[7] Fieser and Fieser, *Style Guide for Chemists*, New York, Reinhold, 1960.

[8] Willard C. Brinton, *Graphic Methods for Presenting Facts*, New York, The Engineering Magazine Co., 1919, pp. 1 and 2.

and more difficult part of the work is to convince the minds
of others that the proposed solution is the best one—that
all the recommendations are really necessary.

Though accurate data and real facts are valuable,
when it comes to getting results, the manner of presentation
is ordinarily more important than the facts themselves. The
foundation of an edifice is of vast importance. Still, it is not
the foundation but the structure built on the foundation
which gives the result for which the whole work is planned.
In many of these cases the attitude of the person presenting
the matter seems to be that the facts will speak for themselves and that they need little or no assistance. Ordinarily,
facts do not speak for themselves. When they do speak for
themselves, the wrong conclusions are often drawn from
them.

Looking at things as they are, we do not always
find elegant English and lucid logic in our articles, as the following, which appeared in a prominent chemical journal, will illustrate:

"By varying the time factor at constant temperature
and pressure, the recovered oil differed in constitution from the
starting oil and from each other widely . . . Due to the time
factor at constant temperature of 700°C and 150 lb. pressure,
the initial oil had changed from a paraffine oil to a mixture
of . . ." This blames a great deal on the innocent time factor.

In recognition of the importance of good writing,
technical schools are featuring courses on English literature and
composition.

THE SOURCE OF THE DIFFICULTY

The present-day tendency toward specialization has
gone too far, and many students are allowed to spend their time
in college and even in high school on the subjects that they like
best without due regard to a well-rounded development. Those
who are fond of science frequently neglect languages. Happy are
those who are not dwarfed by so doing.

Of course, it cannot be expected that a student who
is brilliant in science will be equally good in a number of other
lines, but a certain amount—and not a small amount either—

of training in English is necessary to success as a chemist. If we
are fortunate enough to have it, well and good, otherwise we must
set about obtaining it.

            Doctor Florence E. Wall regards the ability to use
English as essential:[9]

> . . . the fact still remains that ability in the use of
> good English, both oral and written, is still one of the best
> assets that the well-trained chemist can offer. . . . If a tech-
> nically trained man, presumably educated, cannot spell cor-
> rectly or use good grammar (and many university graduates
> cannot), it is frequently difficult to convince others that he
> is qualified professionally.

         Every chemist should read the books by Tyndall
as examples of scientific writing at its best.

IMPROVING OUR ENGLISH

         Numerous aids are offered us by correspondence
schools and by intensively advertised courses in forceful English.
These may help, but the only things that can be relied upon are
determination and hard work.

         Benjamin Franklin tells us in his autobiography
how he found himself at a disadvantage in an argument with a
friend because his friend had a better command of words and
could present the weaker arguments so forcefully that they appeared to be the stronger. He determined then and there to rid
himself of that handicap. A volume of the *Spectator* came into
his hands. He says:

> I bought it, read it over and over, and was much
> delighted with it. I thought the writing excellent, and wished
> if possible to imitate it. With this view I took some of the
> papers, and making short hints of the sentiments in each
> sentence, laid them by for a few days, and then without
> looking at the book, tried to complete the papers again, by
> expressing each hinted sentiment at length, and as fully as
> it had been expressed before, in any suitable words that
> should come to hand. Then I compared my *Spectator* with

[9] *J. Chem. Ed.*, **20**, 580 (1943).

the original, discovered some of my faults and corrected them.

He turned some of the articles into verse and then back into prose which he compared with the originals. Later on he would note down all the ideas in an article, jumble them up, then arrange them and put them into form.

Franklin's method should appeal to the chemist. It is much like mixing a pound of pure benzoic acid with sand and then trying to recover and purify it. He could test his product almost as one would weigh the recovered benzoic acid and take its melting point. Expressing Franklin's experience in an equation we have:

$$W_p + Q_i = W_e$$

in which W_p is any poor writer and W_e an excellent one. Q_i stands for intelligent work. It is the work term that balks the most of us. Franklin's method may be used on chemical articles.

Translating has been recommended as a useful exercise in improving our English. For the chemist who must study French and German for other purposes, there is a double advantage. We have in the German article certain definite ideas which must be put into English. We can keep going over our translation till we are sure that every idea has been fully expressed. The benefit will be lost if we stop with a sloppy so-called translation which but for being couched in English words sounds like the German. Only ideas must be brought over into the translation and they must be so expressed in idiomatic English that no trace of the original is left and the reader cannot tell whether it came from French or from German.

It is useful to take a poem and turn it into prose or to rewrite a piece of prose in a different style.

REPORTS AND CHEMICALS

If we are selling benzoic acid in pound packages, we inspect our acid before shipping. We may find the weight short, or we may find trash mixed with the product, or its melting point may be low. There is no use paying freight two ways and losing a customer. We should inspect our writings. They may be short weight; we have not said all we wanted to say. In filling an order, the items are checked over and over to see that nothing is left out. It is a good thing before starting to write an article, or even a letter, to list the things that must go into it and then check over the list when we have finished writing.

Slang expressions and irrelevant statements mar a report in very much the same way as trash or shavings do our benzoic acid. We must adjust our packing operations so as to keep such things out.

If we find the quality of our benzoic acid is low, we repurify it till it is fully up to standard. We must be as rigid with our writings and not let them leave our hands till they are up to specifications. We may experiment with our writings and test them as objectively as we do the benzoic acid. It is advisable to get someone not familiar with the work described to read the report and study his reactions. If he does not get the idea, there is no use to call him stupid. Here is an experimentally ascertained fact: A man has read that report and failed to get the idea. It must be rewritten so that this cannot happen. Suppose he has to turn back and reread something in the first part to see its connection with something later on. The ideas should be put in such sequence that this would be unnecessary; the report should be rearranged.

Suppose that the reader has to stop and think a minute at one or two places before seeing the meaning. This is an experimental fact and shows that the writing is not clear. The writer is prone to say that, since the reader did get the idea, the report will pass. It is possible to drive a car on a muddy dirt road, but we do not usually find such roads thronged with motorists. A report must be so clearly written that it will be like a concrete road and not waste the time of those who have to go over it.

There are many little things, such as questionable expressions and doubtful constructions, which jar the reader as he goes along even though they do not hinder his progress materially. A hole in a concrete road will not prevent speedy driving, but it is hard on tires and machinery and must be eliminated. We must see that our writings are free from little imperfections.

QUALITIES OF STYLE REQUIRED

Simplicity, sincerity, and directness may be put first. A florid or pompous style is out of place, and high-sounding circumlocutions are to be shunned. Lincoln's Gettysburg address is regarded as a literary classic. It is as simple, as sincere, and as direct as anything that was ever penned and may well be taken as a model for scientific writing.

Accuracy is essential in our observations but goes for naught unless it is sustained by accuracy in our statements. No pains must be spared to insure a logical sequence in the presentation of our facts. When facts are logically arranged and accurately stated with simplicity, sincerity, and directness, we must have clearness and force, provided there *is* any force in the facts. If our facts have no force in them, we had better postpone our writing till we get some facts that have.

Fairness and moderation are virtues of the mind rather than of style, but they must watch over us and see that we do not write our historical introductions so as to minimize the achievements of our predecessors and that we are fair and moderate in drawing conclusions.

In recent times, with the high cost of printing and of paper and with a multitude of articles coming in, our journals have been in a difficult position. The editors have been forced to insist on brevity, and to elevate it to the position of the cardinal virtue. We may cut down an article so far that we destroy its vitals, thereby killing it, but dispensing with excess baggage is as beneficial to articles as it is to persons. It requires skill and much hard labor to condense twenty pages into ten without leaving out anything, but frequently the article is the better for it. There are many articles in the old journals that are so long and rambling that one forgets the first part before one finishes. Some of these would have made a deeper impression on chemists if their authors had been compelled to condense them. Succinctness is not an enemy to clearness, it is rather its ally.

If something can be said briefly, why waste words? One winter day, I was to visit the Hercules Experiment Station, five miles outside of Wilmington. I received a telegram which might have read: "Heavy snow, roads blocked, station closed, suggest postponement of visit." Instead it read: "Snowbound." I did not go that day. Solomon said, "He that hath knowledge spareth words."

HARD WRITING, EASY READING

Some writers have great facility and can turn out pages while others are toiling over a paragraph. Even the same author may write rapidly at one time and slowly at another according to mood. In writing, as in most things that are worth while, painstaking labor and patient plodding mingled with midnight oil bring the results. Gray labored years on the writing of his *Elegy*. As thousands of others have done for two centuries, I stood in the churchyard at Stokes Poges and thought over those lines. Under the inspiration of a moment, something excellent may be dashed off, but perspiration is more dependable than inspiration. Some writers maintain that they must write rapidly if they would give swing and style to their product. It is probably best to write as rapidly as one can, but nothing should be allowed to go out from the shop till it is as good as we can make it. An article may be written in an hour or two, but many gallons of midnight oil may be used in rewriting and polishing it.

Woodrow Wilson could pound out immortal documents on his typewriter, but for the most of us a pencil and scratch pad are the best tools. With these we can write and rewrite, scratch out and interline. We can look back over the pages and see whether we have repeated the same expression. We can cut off the top part of a page and paste it at the bottom, and move our sentences around till we get them in the proper order. That is the way I have always written anything intended for publication. Recently, however, my eyes have failed so that

I cannot see what I am writing and cannot read it to correct it, so I have taken up touch typing and am trying to learn a new way to compose. I think out what I have to say, type it, and have it read to me. If I do not like it, I type it again. The other day I typed five versions of a section and threw away all of them.

When one is dictating one often wonders whether a thing has been said explicitly enough and goes ahead and says it again without striking out the first. With pencil and paper one can go back and strengthen a doubtful statement. Of course it takes time to write and rewrite, but it is better to spend ten hours and produce a page that will be effective than to turn out ten pages that will fail.

The road which costs the most labor to build is the one on which it is easiest to ride.

WRITING A JOURNAL ARTICLE

The first thing to do is to lay out the article, i.e., to decide on its divisions and their order. Write one division at a time. Two plans are in use.

According to one plan the headings commonly used have been: 1. introduction, 2. historical, 3. theoretical, 4. materials, 5. apparatus, 6. methods of experimenting, 7. results, 8. discussion of results, 9. conclusions, 10. summary. Of course, some of these sections, particularly if they are short, may be combined. Thus "introduction" and "historical" or "materials" and "apparatus" or "discussion" and "conclusions" may be run together. In this arrangement, everything in the first part leads up to the "results" which are made to tell their full story and are then discussed and worked up into "conclusions," the "summary" being tacked on for the benefit of abstractors. This arrangement is the logical one and is the most satisfactory for those who are interested enough to read the whole article.

There are many who would like to know the new facts but who have not the time to go into all of the details as to how they were established, or to put it another way, suppose a chemist has the time to peruse ten complete articles, but would rather read the high lights of fifty. To save the trouble of looking at the end of the story to see how it all turned out, as we frequently do when we read detective stories, the conclusions are put at the beginning.

We then have an order like this: 1. introduction, 2. historical, 3. theoretical, 4. conclusions, 5. experimental, 6. summary. The "historical" and "theoretical" are made brief and lead directly to the "conclusions" under which heading all of the facts that have been ascertained are fully set forth. Thus the reader is told why the work was undertaken, gets its historical and theoretical background, and learns the facts quickly. If he is especially interested in the topic and wishes to repeat some of the experiments or doubts some of the conclusions, he delves into the "experimental."

In the "experimental" section, which is frequently printed in small type to save space in the journal, are put all of the other headings given in the first plan: "materials," "apparatus," "methods," and "results." Even historical details may be put here along with the experimental data. The usual summary is appended. An abstract of the article is frequently placed at the very beginning.

There is a strong tendency now to adopt the second arrangement as being the most suited to the busy reader. Even if this form is to be used in the journal, it is usually better for the chemist to write up his material in the order first given and then transpose the section containing the "conclusions."

A practical way to write is to select from the many well-written articles in the journals one on a similar line of investigation and adopt it as a model.

The arrangement and style of an article should be appropriate to the journal in which it is intended to publish it.

Drawings

Sketches of apparatus, diagrams and curves are required for many articles. Since in photographic reproductions drawings are reduced to the size appropriate to the journal, they may be made on any convenient scale. It must be remembered that when the drawing is reduced in size, the lines become correspondingly thinner.

WRITING INDUSTRIAL REPORTS

A large proportion of the chemists in this country are employed in the industries, many on research. Some of the larger companies are spending millions each year for research, while many smaller corporations are spending proportionate sums. In 1924, I estimated the amount spent annually in the United States at ten million dollars; now it runs into the hundreds of millions, and what is gotten in return is reports. All of the information garnered by the keen-eyed toilers in the laboratory must be recorded into these reports. It is from these reports that the executives draw their information as to what is possible, and on them they base their decisions as to what is best to undertake. These reports accumulated from year to year constitute the real assets of our industries, their most-active working capital. Reports are one of the most serious problems in any industrial organization.

A report differs from a journal article in that it is directed partly, at least, to businessmen who do not understand chemistry and also that the conclusions usually relate more or less to recommendations for spending money on plants or processes. There is not the demand for condensation that oppresses us in writing a journal article. There is rather a desire for completeness and insistence that no experimental details be left out.

The elaborateness of a report and its form depend, of course, on the subject matter and the purpose for which it is written. Each research organization has its preferences which should be regarded.

In many reports, a large part of the information is presented in tables of data; it is highly desirable that these are so constructed that the meaning of the data is evident.

Dr. Ethaline Cortelyou gives a list of useful rules for their construction.[10] Several of these are quoted below.

Many times the tables of data are the poorest part of a technical report . . . the scientist who collects the data is best equipped to design the tables.

[10] *J. Chem. Ed.* **31**, 590-3 (1954).

When four or more items of data are given, they should be presented in tabular form.

Even qualitative or descriptive comparisons and contrasts are more easily understood in table form. Every table should have a number and a title. The title should be brief, but it should clearly identify the information contained, with reference to the text. Columns and rows must have identifying headings. Units of measurement must be given. Usually, column or row headings are logical locations for units. Lack of such identification appears to be the most common failing of tables.

As is described by Dr. Tanberg, the complete industrial report must serve a number of purposes and is directed to several classes of readers. The executives, who handle finances, but who are not concerned with experimental details, must be given, briefly, but adequately, the facts as to the practicability and probable profit of the proposed process. The engineering group needs information on which to base plant designs. Whether or not the recommendations are adopted, the report must contain complete detailed information about all experimental work so that it may be duplicated by other chemists, either now or at some later time. Only a fraction of the processes worked out in the laboratory can be put into immediate operation; all investigations must be so reported that they can be taken up, even years later, or made the basis of further research. There should also be a literature section which serves as "first aid" to the patent department.

What follows is quoted from a paper by Dr. Tanberg,[11] a longtime director of the du Pont Experimental Station.

The report is divided into the following sections:

1. Introduction
2. Summary and conclusions
3. Experimental
4. Literature.

This particular arrangement is preferred because it makes easier the consideration of the report by those men

[11] *Suggestions Relative to the Preparation of Formal Reports,* by A. P. Tanberg, Director of Experimental Station, E. I. du Pont de Nemours and Co., written for guidance of the du Pont Company's chemists. Used by permission.

who are not interested in reading, or who do not have time
to read, the sections concerned with the details of the work
and the literature. The first two sections should always,
therefore, be written with the understanding that they should
cover the essential features and results of the investigation
without making necessary any reference to the other sections
of the report. Attention is called to the reason for this arrangement because chemists too often follow this same order
in *preparing* their reports, whereas it is undoubtedly easier
and more conducive to a well-rounded, concise report to
write the "Experimental" and "Literature" sections first and
the "Introduction" and "Summary and Conclusions" sections
last, and then rearrange the four sections in their proper
order.

The most important requirements of the first and
second sections are clearness and brevity; but care should
be taken that neither section is made brief by the omission
of essential facts. The important requirement of the third
section is that it shall cover all details of the experimental
work in such a way that any well-trained chemist will find
it possible by following the report to repeat the work and
to duplicate the results.

Before submitting a report, a chemist should try to
place himself in the position of a reader to whom the subject is entirely new in order to make sure that he has not
made use of such expressions, abbreviations, or symbols as
are intelligible only to those especially familiar with the
subject. Examples of such practices, such as the use of the
word 'soda' where caustic soda is meant, or the use of
'D.M.A.' for dimethylaniline, will readily occur to anyone
who has written or read chemical reports.

It is best to use ruled paper, and a good margin
should be left so that inserts may be made if necessary. If
any one of the sections or subdivisions of a section ends in
the middle of a page, start the next section on a new sheet
so that additional matter may be added if necessary. Suggestions of this kind, many of which are made here, if followed will result in a great decrease in the time at present
required to get out reports.

Introduction

The introduction should include statements as to
the object of the work and the reason for it, with a brief
explanation of the nature of the compound or process under
investigation, its origin, etc.; and the statements should be

made clear by chemical formulas or equations. Reference should be made in the introduction to previous reports on the same subject or to any report which has been found of assistance in the work. In many cases a description should be included of the 'prior art': that is, any previously published process which has been used as a basis for experiments described in the report.

Summary and Conclusions

This section should include a brief description of the process or processes investigated, a description of the conditions which are recommended as best, a brief statement as to why these conditions are selected and the general effect of a departure from these conditions, a statement of the results which may be expected by following the recommended conditions (including yields in percentage of the theoretical, quality of product, etc.), and the total cost of the materials required per pound of product based on a detailed estimate of this total cost which is included in the "Experimental" section. It may occasionally be necessary to include in this section some discussion of apparatus, especially when this phase of the subject has an influence on the selection of the method recommended.

Experimental

It is usually best to subdivide the "Experimental" section under the following headings, especially in reports of investigations along the lines of organic chemistry.

Apparatus

If the investigation is carried through the stage of semiworks-scale experiments, or if the report describes works operations, this subdivision is especially important. The apparatus should be described in detail so that it may be duplicated and operated at some future time, if it becomes necessary, by someone previously unfamiliar with the work. If the apparatus has been purchased, the name and address of the manufacturer should be given; if built at the Experimental Station, all details as to materials of construction, sizes, etc., should be included. Wherever possible, descriptions of apparatus should be accompanied by blueprints. If the investigation has been confined to laboratory work and the apparatus has been ordinary laboratory apparatus, a simple statement to this effect will ordinarily be sufficient, although such details as the type of column used in distillations, etc., should be included. If, as is often the case, the experiments have shown certain apparatus to be not altogether suitable, this point should be brought out and recommendations made for improving it.

The success or failure of experiments often depends on such details as the kind of gasket used in an autoclave, and, in general, no detail should be considered too insignificant to be included. It is easier to cut matter out of a report than to put it in.

Materials

Very often our investigations require certain materials which vary widely in quality or which are difficult to obtain. The subdivision on "Materials" should, therefore, include a description of all materials used as to purity, sources of supply, cost, etc. If it has been necessary to synthesize raw materials, the process used and the results obtained should be described. If the materials are ordinary, easily obtainable supplies, it is sufficient to state whether they were c.p., commercial, etc., or to give the melting points, boiling ranges, etc. If materials were purified before use, the process of purification should be described. If the investigation included experiments with different grades of the same material, the different grades should be described, and assigned brief names which may be set in the tables of numerical data included in the subdivision headed "Experimental Details."

Analyses and Tests

All tests and methods of analysis used in connection with the work should be carefully described or, if a standard method has been used, reference should be made to the book or journal in which a description of it may be easily found. The description of each method should be accompanied by some statement as to its merits or shortcomings.

Experimental Details

The numerical data recorded in connection with each experiment should be assembled as far as possible in tabular form. The tabulated data should include all conditions of the experiments, such as quality of materials (unless the quality of materials was the same in all the runs), the duration of runs, the temperatures used, the pressures (if the pressures varied), the yields in percentage of the theoretical, the conversions in percent (unless the main raw material is completely utilized), the quality of the product (express, if possible, in some simple manner, such as the melting point, boiling range, etc.), etc. It is usually advisable to include a column headed "Remarks," to be used in recording any unusual features of the experiments. It is just as important to include data with regard to experiments in which poor or negative results are obtained as it is to record successful experiments. If the laboratory notebooks have been properly kept, the same experiment numbers can be used in the final report so that reference can be made, if necessary, to the original record. It might be well to call attention here to the importance of carefully kept notebooks, not only from the standpoint of report writing, but from other standpoints of equal or even greater importance. Original records are often required in interference suits in patent cases, and granting of priority may depend entirely on whether the chemist has kept a clear, properly dated record of his experiments at the time they were carried out. A carelessly kept notebook is inexcusable, not only because it may mean an actual loss of valuable rights, but because it represents an actual waste of time in digging out the data for the purpose of preparing a report.

Tables

In making up tables of numerical data, use paper large enough so that the headings may be written without crowding and without using unusual abbreviations. If the tables cover more than one page, see that the headings on the several pages are identical and the columns are placed in the same order. Special care should be taken to make figures clear so that the tables may be copied by the stenographer without errors. Use decimals wherever possible instead of fractions, and under no circumstance use a decimal in one place and a fraction in another. If a certain figure consists of a fraction of a unit, as for example seventy-five hundredths of a percent, write it 0.75% and not .75%, in order to avoid mistakes in copying. Remember that ditto marks should not be used for repeating figures. Put the units, such as percent, grams, hours, etc., at the head of the columns, instead of repeating them after each figure. The proper abbreviation for "grams" is g; for "cubic centimeters," cc. Some of these points may not seem worthy of mention, but most of them are a constant source of trouble and annoyance in revising and approving final reports.

It is often necessary to precede a table of numerical data with an explanation of the headings of the columns. This should be done whenever there seems to be a chance that the headings will not be clear.

It is also advisable to put at the beginning of the subdivision on "Experimental Details" a description of the general procedure followed, such as the method and order of mixing the ingredients used, the method of working up or purifying the crude product, the method of heating, etc.

Discussion of Results

The tables of numerical data should be followed by as full a discussion of the results as is considered necessary, covering such points as the reasons for the selection of a certain procedure, the proper grade of materials to be used, recommendations for plant equipment, causes of poor results in unsuccessful experiments, etc. This section should, in general, include any discussion, explanation or statement of theory necessary to connect the "Summary and Conclusions" and "Experimental" sections.

Estimate of Materials Costs

This subdivision should include, in detail, figures on which the estimated materials costs given in the "Summary and Conclusions" section are based. These estimates should, of course, be made as accurate as possible, and it may be necessary in some cases to obtain figures from the main office. In any case, the source and data of the figures used should be given.

For the sake of uniformity, the estimates of cost should be arranged in a table under the following headings:

Materials Required	Weight Required Per Pound of Product	Materials Cost Per Pound	Total
Aniline	Pounds	$0.11	$0.109
H$_2$SO$_4$, 94%	0.987	0.008	0.019
etc.	2.350		

The totals of the fourth column will then give the total costs of materials required for the preparation of one pound of product. If the process involves the recovery of valuable materials, a second set of columns should be given under the following headings:

Materials Recovered	Weight Recovered Per Pound of Product	Recovered Material Value Per Pound	Total Value
. . . .	. . . .	. . . .	. . . . .

By subtracting the totals of the fourth column of this second set from the totals of the corresponding column of the first set, the net materials costs per pound will be clearly shown.

It is believed that an estimate presented in this way is the most easily accessible for any recalculations made necessary by changes in the market.

Literature

The section on "Literature" is probably the most elastic part of a formal report. In some cases, literature may be wholly lacking. In other cases, the investigation may have been preceded by a careful review of the literature which has been submitted to the Chemical Director as a separate report or memorandum. In the latter case, it is often necessary only to refer to this review and to give the date and file of the letter of transmittal. In most cases, this should, however, be followed by a list of the references, or at least of the most important references. In cases where the experiments have been based on special information received in the form of a letter or report, a statement should be made as to where this information may be found. If information has been obtained from an article or patent not easily available in our libraries or files, a brief abstract of the reference should be given. In general, this section should contain all information necessary for a complete review of the subject under investigation, or if a complete review of the literature has not been made, such information as will serve as a starting point for a complete review.

Index

A